Cost Planning of Buildings

Douglas J. Ferry, PhD, FRICS, AAIQS, MBCS
and
Peter S. Brandon, MSc, FRICS, MACostE

Fifth Edition

BSP PROFESSIONAL BOOKS

OXFORD LONDON EDINBURGH

BOSTON PALO ALTO MELBOURNE

First published in Great Britain by Crosby Lockwood & Sons Ltd 1964
Second edition (metric) 1970
Third edition 1972
Reprinted 1974
Fourth edition 1980 by Granada Publishing
Reprinted 1981, 1983
Fifth edition 1984 by Granada Publishing
Reprinted by Collins Professional and Technical Books 1986, 1987
Reprinted by BSP Professional Books, 1988

British Library
Cataloguing in Publication Data

Ferry, Douglas J.
Cost planning of buildings. —5th ed.
  1. Building—Estimates—Great Britain
  I. Title   II. Brandon, Peter S.
  690'.068'1   TH437

ISBN 0-632-02403-8

BSP Professional Books
A division of Blackwell Scientific
  Publications Ltd
Editorial Offices:
Osney Mead, Oxford OX2 0EL
  (Orders: Tel. 0865 240201)
8 John Street, London WC1N 2ES
23 Ainslie Place, Edinburgh EH3 6AJ
3 Cambridge Center, Suite 208,
  Cambridge, MA 02142, USA
667 Lytton Avenue, Palo Alto, California
  94301, USA
107 Barry Street, Carlton, Victoria 3053
  Australia

Printed and bound in Great Britain

Cost Planning of Buildings

Contents

Publisher's note
Some of the techniques described in this book have been
programmed for a microcomputer and can be found in *Computer
Programs for Building Cost Appraisal* by Peter S. Brandon,
R. Geoffrey Moore and Phillip Main.

Preface to Fifth Edition

In the current edition the structure of the Fourth Edition has been retained, and most changes involve either the updating of information or the further development of sections relating to areas where new initiatives are currently taking place.

The major alterations concern the impact of micro-computers, which both replace manual processes and make available a number of techniques (particularly of trial-and-error and iteration) which were not practicable without them, and a new chapter on Models for Optimisation. The book now assumes the use of the micro-computer, although it does not attempt to deal with the techniques of such use for which the reader is referred to *Microcomputers in Building Appraisal*, P. S. Brandon with R. G. Moore, Granada. Together with the universal availability of the cheap hand-held calculator, the computer renders the exhaustive mathematical tables which were included in previous editions unnecessary, and emphasis is now placed upon the formulae from which such tables were devised.

The book seeks to provide an essential groundwork in all aspects of the discipline whilst containing ample material as a basis for seminar work, discussion and class development. However, it cannot claim to give full coverage to each of the many topics which are dealt with in principle, and a reader who wishes to explore any of these in greater depth will need to refer to specialist works.

Sydney NSW   Douglas J. Ferry
Portsmouth   Peter S. Brandon
1984

Chapter 1
Introduction

From the earliest times people have needed some idea of what a new building was going to cost before they started work on it. The New English Bible says "Would any of you think of building a tower without first sitting down and calculating the cost, to see whether he could afford to finish it? Otherwise, if he has laid its foundations and then is not able to complete it, all the onlookers will laugh at him. 'There is the man' they will say 'who started to build and could not finish.'" (St Luke Ch. 14.)

Forecasting the cost of a building, however, is not the same thing as planning the cost, any more than a weather forecaster on television can be said to be planning the weather—in both cases things may turn out very differently from what was expected for reasons quite outside the forecaster's control. Nevertheless, until the early nineteenth century rough-and-ready forecasting satisfied the need fairly adequately. Most major building was undertaken either as an act of religious faith or by the very rich for their own pleasure and gratification and in both cases the necessary resources were likely to be forthcoming in the end. The building process itself comprised a series of fairly autonomous craft activities of which the costs had become established and known over a lengthy period of time. Even so miscalculations occurred—the building of Blenheim Palace almost bankrupted the Duke of Marlborough, and it was not at all unknown for prospective owners of buildings to suffer the fate of the man in the Bible. Readers of Robert Louis Stevenson's *Kidnapped* will remember the unfinished House of Shaws which provided such an exciting start to the tale.

With the advent of the Industrial Revolution, however, something better was clearly needed for three reasons. Firstly, the people commissioning large building projects were increasingly cost-conscious, being either industrialists concerned with profitability, government bodies concerned with accountability, or joint stock companies concerned with both. Secondly, the projects themselves were of an increasing technological complexity. Thirdly, the traditional settled economic and social order was turning into something more sophisticated and dynamic.

In order to deal with the needs of this new situation the price-in-advance system was developed, where responsibility for the execution of the whole project was handed over to a "general contractor" at a previously agreed price. The building owner and his architect had thus got rid of many of the problems of organisation, and secured a firm cost commitment before starting work, by a single ingenious move.

For over a century this system worked very well indeed, and it is still in widespread use today although much of the simplicity of the original concept has been lost in recent years. However, it did place one additional burden upon the architect—complete drawings and specification of the work had to be prepared before prices could be sought.

Prices were normally obtained by competitive tender; the documents would be sent to a number of general contractors who would submit sealed offers to be opened by the architect at a time and date set in advance. The job would then usually be given to the firm whose tender was the lowest.

In order for the firms to prepare their tenders it was necessary for them to calculate the quantities of labour and material which would be required to build the project. This was done by measurement off the drawings, and since the figures should be the same for all the firms tendering (unless a mistake were made) it was obviously more economic for this task to be undertaken by one person on behalf of them all. This was the origin of the quantity surveyor, whose task was the preparation of a "Bill of Quantities" setting out the labour and material requirements expressed in terms of the quantity of finished work to be produced. His fee was paid by the successful tenderer.

A difficulty immediately arose. The success of the tendering system depended upon there being true competition, and there was always a danger that the tenderers might get together secretly in order to agree on an inflated price and a suitable division of the proceeds. The architectural profession was worried that if the tenderers had to meet in order to agree the appointment of a quantity surveyor they might seize the opportunity to make some other less desirable arrangements at the same time. The custom soon arose of the architect sending out a Bill of Quantities with the drawings and specification, so depriving the tenderers of an excuse to consort together, although the successful builder was still at that time responsible for paying the quantity surveyor whom the architect had appointed. From this point, quantity surveying developed in the United Kingdom (and many of its overseas dependencies) into a fully recognised profession.

Although the system of firm price competitive tendering gave the prospective building owner a firm budget prior to committing him to actual expenditure on building, he had already committed himself to a good deal of other expenditure by this stage which could not be recovered if he found he was unable to go ahead because costs were too high. The architect and other design consultants would have completed most of their work and would require a substantial proportion of their fees, as would the quantity surveyor, irrespective of whether the job went ahead or not. (The only people who would have worked without charge would have been the builders, who would not have expected to be able to recover their tendering costs—a sore point with many of them.) In addition, the client would probably have bought the land for the project and this money would now be locked up in an unproductive asset, in addition to which he might have made plans for the use of the building which would have to be abandoned with consequent loss. An alternative to abandonment, of course, would be complete redesign on a more modest scale and the seeking of fresh tenders but this would involve a further loss of time and would not relieve the client of the abortive expenditure on the first scheme. It was therefore important that the client should have a good idea of what the building was likely to cost before he had committed himself very far, and this was done by means of an "approximate estimate".

This was an attempt to forecast the cost of a building at some stage prior to the completion of the Bill of Quantities or the obtaining of a tender. Once the Bill of Quantities was available, of course, quite an accurate estimate could be prepared by the quantity surveyor pricing it out in detail as if he were a builder, but this would be far too late in the process to be of much use and would involve an additional fee. (It was sometimes done for a quite different reason however, as a check on the reasonableness of the builders' prices.)

Because the client was anxious to have some idea of his commitments as early as possible, and because the architect wanted to know whether his design was financially possible before he had gone too far with it, the approximate estimate would be prepared at a fairly early stage when even the basic drawings would be rudimentary and there would be little or no supporting documentation.

Although the usual terms of appointment of the architect required him to prepare this estimate, it was in practice usually done by the quantity surveyor on his behalf, the latter having both a greater expertise and a wider range of available cost data. It was not a lengthy task and was normally done free of charge as a piece of goodwill to the architect, who was usually responsible for nominating the quantity surveyor to the client.

The techniques for preparing an estimate of cost in these circumstances will in fact be dealt with later in this book, since they are still valid today in some circumstances as part of a comprehensive system of cost planning and control. These traditional methods are basically "single-price-rate" estimates; the size of the building is calculated in square or cubic measure and the result multiplied by a single price-rate to give the estimated cost.

However well such an estimate was prepared (and this called for a good deal of experience, skill, and judgement) it suffered from a vital defect; it was not possible to relate the cost of the work shown on the detailed drawings to the estimate during the progress of the design. The quantity surveyor might feel, as he prepared his Bills of Quantities, that these drawings were showing something rather grander and more extravagant than he had in mind when he produced the estimate, but it was not possible to prove this contention to the architect or client except by preparing and pricing "approximate quantities". These are a simplified version of a formal Bill of Quantities; major items are grouped together, minor items are ignored in measurement and dealt with by loading the prices of major items.

The disadvantages of such a course are obvious. The task would require extra time and the cost would be too great to be covered by "goodwill" and would involve an additional fee, the drawings had to be fairly complete and the whole of the building had to be dealt with; even if the approximate quantities when prepared showed a far higher total than the original estimate, the discrepancy could not be easily traced. It still could not be seen whether any particular part of the building was extravagantly designed and there was nothing to show where the cost could be cut most economically. All that could be done was to cut the more high-class parts of the specification and substitute lower quality, which was not the same thing at all. At this late stage the architect would obviously resist any major redesign.

As a rule, therefore, approximate quantities would not be prepared but the job sent out to tender by the architect, who would just hope for the best. If the tenders came in too high the same course would have to be followed of cutting the cost where it was most convenient rather than most efficient to do so (without having to alter too many drawings), and the result was likely to be a lot of wasted work and an unsatisfactory and unbalanced design.

During the unsettled years following the second world war the art of accurate single-price-rate estimating became increasingly difficult to practise. Both for this reason and because of a demand by public authorities in particular for value in building, a system of cost planning and control during design stage came into vogue. This system was called "Elemental Cost Planning" and enabled the cost of the scheme to be monitored during design development as well as facilitating the rational allocation of costs amongst the various elements of the building structure, finishes, and services. The technique is widely used for these purposes today and two chapters of this book are devoted to it exclusively.

Unfortunately, no sooner had success been achieved in rationalising the economic approach to the obtaining of tenders than the price-in-advance system itself began to deteriorate. There were two reasons for this, the first being that the British system of tendering upon sophisticated Bills of Quantities enabled tenders to be obtained upon a basis which was theoretically that of a completed and worked-out design, but in practice was little more than a hypothetical construct, so that an enormous number of changes both great and small would occur during the construction stage. The contractor would thus find it difficult to organise the work properly but would have ample excuse to charge a price which differed substantially from his original offer. The second reason, very much compounded by the first, was the changed social, economic, and moral climate which made it very difficult for a general contractor to quote a firm price for a major project in competition, which would adequately allow for all the risks involved. Such symptoms as rampant inflation, industrial action, social legislation, and financial irresponsibility showed clearly that society was very different from that in which the Victorian concept of price-in-advance, and the consequent abrogation of management responsibility by the client and architect, had developed.

In these circumstances alternative methods of building procurement have come into favour, in some of which there is no place for formal Bills of Quantities and in which there may be no such concept as a "tender price". Quantity surveyors, by virtue of their cost planning experience in the traditional situation, have been well placed to act as building economists in a wider sense. In the UK the quantity surveyor has become the acknowledged source of expertise and advice on costs and their manipulation, and is often engaged for this purpose on many projects where Bills of Quantities are not required. However, the importance of cost planning and control is such that members of the architecture, engineering and building professions need to have a working knowledge of the principles, and some of them may come to specialise in this aspect of their work and see themselves as cost planners. The development of integrated computer systems which manipulate cost as one of a number of design parameters will tend to assist this process, as will the undertaking of work overseas.

Today's cost planner therefore needs to be able to do much more than merely use techniques to obtain an acceptable tender price, important though this task may often be. He needs to work with his client from the very inception of a scheme (or even earlier in the devising of an investment or development programme of which the project may one day form part) to the time when the scheme is eventually completed and handed over. To do this a flexibility of approach is essential—the client will need to know the best way of going about the project in the particular socio-economic situation that exists at the time and in the place concerned. There is thus no single tailor-made set of standard procedures that can be learnt and applied without much thought; what is required is a thorough understanding of the issues involved and the solutions available. We have tended to avoid using the terms "optimum" or "optimisation" in this book; anybody who achieves satisfactory results in practice will have done quite well enough.

The role of the cost planner is now so important that he must be prepared to take his full share of social responsibility in the advice which he gives and the work which he does. Whilst there may be occasions where the image of the ruthless cost-cutter is the right one, he must be able to see when this is so and when it is not. In particular, he must be able to understand the needs and points of view of the client, the architect, and the community in relation to the project and balance them as far as is possible within his brief. His concern should be value rather than minimum cost, and value often goes far beyond those things that can be easily quantified in money terms. A broad education and a wide range of social and cultural interests are necessary for him to do his job really well, in addition to common sense and a feeling for practical probabilities.

The advent of silicon-chip technology is going to provide not only cost planners but also designers, clients, and builders with ever-increasing opportunities for data collection and manipulation. In this situation it will be most important that the cost planner's special expertise in interpreting and using this material should be recognised and sought; the blind processing of figures by people who neither understand where they have come from nor exactly what they represent will be a great source of danger in this situation.

This book is arranged in a manner which should help towards a wide understanding of the subject. The first five chapters set the scene in which building development is carried out, whilst the next five chapters explain the design process and the basic tools available to the cost planner. When all this has been assimilated, the techniques to be used in various circumstances are dealt with at greater length. Finally the last chapter continues the theme of this introduction in looking into the future.

In conclusion, a word of apology is due to women readers. In the interests of clarity and because the majority of cost planners are male we have used the male pronoun in referring to cost planners rather than adopting some form of circumlocution. We do hope that this device will not prevent women readers from identifying themselves with the person described.

Chapter 2
Developer's Motivation and Needs

The carrying out of building work is often termed "development", and the person or organisation responsible is the "developer". More often in the building industry he is called the "client" or "building owner", or in some parts of the world the "proprietor". In popular usage the term "developer" is restricted to those who build for profit, but this is not correct and those who build for their own use or for social purposes are equally developers.

All development arises from a consumer demand. It may be a direct demand (for housing, for offices, for a town hall or library), or may be an indirect demand; that is a demand for something else which will require building development in order to satisfy it (such as a demand for TV sets which will necessitate a factory to produce them). But the demand must always be an economic one, there must be someone willing to foot the bill or who can be induced to do so. Where the development is likely to be profitable such a person should not be hard to find.

The client, whether an individual or a corporate body, will be building either for direct profit or for use; in the first case his approach to cost will be governed by the terms in which his income will be received and in the second by the units of accommodation which he requires.

A factor which makes building development quite different from other entrepreneurial activities is that there can be no building without a plot of available land. This has all sorts of economic consequences, because the supply of land is largely fixed ("Buy now!" said a recent estate agent's advertisement, "They have stopped making it!").

No developer can start work until he has acquired an interest in the land on which his building is to stand.

Total building cost

When any type of building development, private or public, takes place the total expenditure on the development will be much higher than the net cost of the building fabric, and will comprise:

(a) Cost of land.
(b) Legal, etc., costs of acquiring and preparing the site.
(c) Demolition or other physical preparation of the site.
(d) Building cost.
(e) Professional fees in connection with last.
(f) Furnishings, fittings, machinery, etc.
(g) Costs in connection with disposal (sale, letting, etc.) where the building is to be disposed of at completion.
(h) Cost of financing the project (this principally represents interest, etc., on the moneys expended before any return is obtained either by way of income or of use).
(i) Cost of management, running, and maintenance where the building is to be retained by the client for use or only partially disposed of, or where the building is let to a tenant but the owner has made himself responsible for some or all of these costs.

It is important to realise that "building cost" is only one of nine items of total cost which is incurred by the client, and that in the end it is the total which counts. It may be thought, therefore, that many cost planning exercises, including some in this book, are unduly obsessed with this one item rather than with optimising the whole package. There is certainly some truth in this allegation, which probably has its roots in the fact that so many of the techniques were developed in the public service where total costs were rarely considered. We must always be on our guard to avoid this trap unless it is forced on us, and even then we should be ready to query its validity.

For instance, the cost of the land may be such an important factor in the costing exercise that everything else has to be fitted round it and the problem then is to get the maximum amount of permissible accommodation almost regardless of building cost. The effect of land costs on the developer's budget is further considered in Chapter 5.

It sometimes happens that the building is only a small part of the total project, as in the setting up of a main TV transmitter station where the mast, electronic equipment, and cable-laying dominate the project and the transmitter building is of minor importance. In such circumstances it would be a mistake to consider the cost of the building in isolation—it is much more important that it should phase in with the general programme and that its completion should not be a source of worry to the engineer in charge. It may not be necessary to indulge in cost planning of the building at all.

Cost targets for profit development and social development

In considering cost targets we may differentiate between the private and public sectors of the economy, and also between buildings which are to be economically viable (i.e. self-supporting in the sense that receipts from the use of the buildings will more than cover costs) and those which are not.

Economic viability is not exclusive to private development (local authorities or government boards often undertake profitable development) neither is private development always aimed at making a profit (for instance, churches or charitable buildings). Some development may be partially self-supporting, such as local authority housing schemes paid for partly by rents and partly by rates and subsidies.

Because the calculations involved in budgeting for both the above types of development are similar it is easy to forget that the basic situations are very different.

1. *Profit development*

The setting of budget targets for profit development (e.g. office blocks for letting, housing for letting or sale) must be related to free-enterprise economics; the sole purpose of the development is to make a profit and setting a target is straightforward. A calculation by the developer will soon show how much he can afford to spend under the heading of "building costs" for his scheme to be profitable after the other factors in the list have been taken into account. There is a certain amount of flexibility here because the standard of building will partly determine the rents or selling price that can be asked, although this income is often dictated within fairly close limits by the environment and by the cost of the land. It would obviously be unwise to erect a high-cost luxury building for sale or rent in an unpopular neighbourhood, just as it would not be economic to try a low-cost, low-income development in a fashionable district where land costs are high and there is a good income potential.

Once a final decision has been made on income levels the cost will have been determined and must not be exceeded; from this point onwards tight cost planning and control will be vital and if any item goes up in cost the money must be saved elsewhere. Otherwise the anticipated profit will not be made by the developer, and from his point of view the project will be a failure, however pleasant or useful the resulting buildings may be. There is no room for "hard luck stories", allowances for abnormals, or anything of this kind, but on the other hand there is the challenge of working in a situation where, for instance, time means money. Early completion of a department store may involve substantial extra profits, late completion (e.g. after Christmas instead of before Christmas) can be financially disastrous.

In the early stages of considering alternative ways of developing a site the probable receipts must be compared with the probable costs, and a misjudgement of either figure will have exactly the same effect on the profitability of the scheme; neither is more important than the other, and no amount of detailed cost planning is going to rescue a scheme based on unsound investment assumptions.

The valuation surveyor is an expert on the value of buildings for investment and the income which various types of development can be expected to produce, but as a rule his knowledge of construction costs (and particularly of the sort of factors which we will be discussing in this book) is far more limited. Just as it would be unwise for the client to ask his quantity surveyor to estimate the likely income from a development in order to arrive at a conclusion on feasibility, so it would be foolish for him to rely upon his valuer's ideas of relative construction costs.

In conclusion, however complicated the situation may become, with grants, subsidies, taxation reliefs and so on to be taken into account, the basic exercise remains delightfully straightforward because profit (the main reason for the building) is quantifiable. Even if some non-quantifiable element, like preserving the environment, has to be taken into account it will have to be assessed against its effect on profit. If an adequate profit cannot be foreseen the building will not be built.

2. *Social development*

In social development, however, the main object of the exercise is the actual provision of the buildings, and it becomes very difficult to set realistic cost targets since there is no definite limit at which the building ceases to be possible. The only limit is what can be afforded, or what can be raised, and while this may be a very real factor in some private non-profit building it can hardly apply in most public development where it is usually possible (though not always expedient) to raise whatever sum of money may be required for the purpose. Any constraint is usually at a higher level than the individual project, for example, the proportion of the national budget which is allocated to education may determine the amount to be spent on school building as a whole.

Therefore, in order to determine a reasonable cost for this type of development it used to be common to set artificial limits, based upon the cost of similar buildings erected elsewhere. The gross floor area was too crude as a basis for the purposes of this comparison and so various targets based upon user requirements were set up, often by the ministries responsible so as to ensure a nation-wide standard. In the case of schools the unit of cost was the number of "cost places" (a fictitious number of pupils calculated from the teaching space), while for hospitals the number of beds was once the basic yardstick.

These cost targets were usually determined by a set of artificial standards which had to be adhered to; these although tight in some ways usually made exceptions for technical difficulties associated with a particular project. But here we are not in the world of simple profit economics; the early completion of a school would usually be a financial burden to the Education Committee, however welcome it might be in other ways.

The cost planning of social development projects, therefore, may resemble the playing of a board-game, where one tries to win according to a set of rules which have little validity in the real world outside. Sometimes the rules may be very crude indeed, such as a rule that money cannot be transferred from one fund to another (so that it is useless trying to save money on furnishings or running costs by spending extra on the building), or that money cannot be spent outside the financial year in which it is allocated, or that no major contract can be let except by competitive tendering on a firm Bill of Quantities with no allowance for cost fluctuations.

In these circumstances the skill in cost planning may consist of "loophole" designing, to take advantage of the regulations in the same way that a clever accountant takes advantage of the tax laws. An example of this, from outside the UK, occurred when a national system for cost control of flat-building at one time gave a greater cost allowance for balconies than the actual cost of providing them. The blocks of flats built during this period can be identified by their lavish provision of unnecessary balconies.

It is recognised by the government that unrealistic cost rules lead to bad design, and many far-sighted efforts have been made to do away with the cruder kinds of inconsistency, by allowing money saved in one direction to be spent in another, by trying to bring the assessment of running costs into the cost comparisons, or by working out very complex cost criteria for such buildings as hospitals instead of "so much per bed". This is a very commendable attempt to get nearer to reality, but while it has undoubtedly led to some improvement it also tends to make the "game" more complicated, and the loophole-finding more of a challenge to the experts. It becomes increasingly difficult to avoid the "balcony" type of inconsistency mentioned above.

The consequence of all this is that everybody can become so preoccupied with trying to meet tight cost targets by clever application of the rules, that they lose sight of the social purpose of the whole exercise. The cost is not a clear-cut measurement of the effectiveness of the project (as it is with profit development); the benefits of a hospital, clinic, school, or police-station are largely unquantifiable.

Although cost planning is essential to meeting cost targets, and cost analysis of past projects will have played its part in setting the targets, nobody really knows whether they ought to be spending twice as much money (or half as much) on buildings of this kind, and no amount of cost planning is going to give them the answer. The most it can do is to help them to use the total allocated funds more effectively within the current framework of rules, and accept that the basic values will be decided for political reasons.

Cost-benefit analysis and option appraisal

In order to overcome some of the difficulties just outlined, and to justify the spending of money on public projects, the techniques of cost-benefit analysis were developed. Such analyses were attempts to quantify all factors including the various social benefits and disadvantages, and were widely used in connection with traffic and airport schemes and with hospital building. Cost-benefit analysis might be applied, for instance, to a proposal to carry out works to remove a sharp curve and speed restriction from an inter-city railway. The cost of the work could be set against the saving in brake blocks, fuel, and wear and tear on equipment; however it is possible that on these grounds alone it might not quite be worthwhile. On the other hand, if the curve is removed it might save two minutes each on a million passenger journeys a year—thirty thousand man-hours are worth something, and if they are priced and included among the benefits the scheme is now justifiable in relation to the national economy.

This is all very well, but one is soon faced with problems of attaching money values to things which cannot be quantified. As an illustration of the problem, what value should one attach to a human life? One could work this out on the basis of the contribution which the individual person makes to the economic life of the community measured in terms of salary, so that a surgeon might be worth tens of thousands of pounds while an unemployed labourer might have a negative value. Even on practical grounds this is obviously unacceptable; if you attempted a cost-benefit analysis of a geriatric hospital on this basis you would find that it would be cheaper to let people die and build a mortuary instead! Or, as another less extreme example, you could justify a ring road which saved a few minutes for "important" people while wasting the time of humble pedestrians.

It was therefore customary to take a notional figure representing the worth of an "average" person. There was little wrong with this except that such figures, being notional, were conjured out of thin air and could be used in practice to "prove" that a politically desired result was the right one. As an example, suppose a traffic improvement scheme was going to cost £100,000 a year and was estimated to reduce road accident deaths by three per year. If you cost a life at £50,000 the scheme was obviously worthwhile; if you cost a life at £20,000 it wasn't. If you remember that the reduced number of deaths was a guess anyhow, you can see that this sort of exercise was not really worth very much, and the more complicated it got and the more social benefits that were quantified, the more questionable was the result.

Cost-benefit analysis in its extreme form is now largely discredited, but its successor in the public domain, option appraisal, draws upon its techniques. Option appraisal can be applied to any proposal for public investment, and involves the appraisal of all possible options (including the "do-nothing" option). CBA is used to evaluate those aspects which have a clear money value, both of a capital and recurrent nature, but intangibles are merely assessed and shown separately. It is left to the administrators to make the subjective decisions, knowing the financial outcome of the more tangible parts of each option.

The client's needs

Every building client will have a set of needs, some of which are more important to him than others. We have to look at these rather carefully, because it is common to be told, for instance, that a low cost is required, or that time is important, without these very basic requirements being defined in more detail—and it is the detail that decides the best way of tackling the project. We can now look at the main time and money requirements which the client may have, and the different forms which each may take, remembering that some clients may have more than one of the requirements under each heading. The bracketed letters refer to the more suitable contractual arrangements amongst those set out on pages 17–21.

Time requirements

(1) *No critical time requirements.* This is quite common, especially in social development. [A, B]
(2) *Shortest overall time, from the inception of the idea to "turning the key".* This is likely to be the requirement on a simple profit development. [A, B(b)(ii)/(iii)/(iv), B(d)]
(3) *Shortest contract period from the time the contractor is appointed.* This by itself is not often relevant to the client's needs, but it is surprising how often it is asked for. [B(a), B(b)(i)/(iii)/(iv), B(d)]
(4) *Shortest contract period from the time the contractor starts on site.* This is a reasonable requirement where, for example, there is a delay in acquiring the property, or where people have to be moved out of property on the site before demolition can take place, or where the building work will cause inconvenience or disruption. [A(e), B(a), B(b)(i)/(iii)/(iv), B(d)]
(5) *Early start on site.* This may be required where the payment of a grant or subsidy depends upon work having been started by a certain date. It is also asked for sometimes by a dilatory archi-

tect to give the client the impression that something is happening at last. [A(a)–(d), B(b)(ii)/(iii)/(iv), B(c), B(d)]

(6) *Reliable guaranteed completion date stated by contractor.* This may be wanted so that firm arrangements can be made well in advance for commissioning the building. [A, B(a), B(b)(iii), B(d)]

(7) *Reliable guaranteed completion date stated by client.* This may apply where the client is under notice to quit existing premises or where there is a particular event that the building must be open for, such as the beginning of the summer season for a hotel. [A, B(a), B(b)(iii), B(d)]

(8) *Early completion unwelcome.* It is often assumed that if the client says that time is critical then he will be even more pleased if he gets the building early. This is not necessarily the case; if, as in (6) or (7), he is making all his arrangements on the basis of a particular date, early completion simply means that he has got to waste money watching and maintaining an empty building and also that he has to pay for the building earlier than he need, so upsetting his cash flow position. [A, B(a), B(b)(iii), B(d)]

(9) *Phased programme to fit in with plant installation.* This is especially important in the case of sophisticated projects such as TV transmitters or chemical works where the actual building work is only a small part of the total scheme. [A, B(b)(ii)/(iii), B(c)]

(10) *Handing over in sections.* This is often very important in alteration works or in rebuilding, where people or processes from one section have to be rehoused elsewhere before work can be carried out in that section. [A, B(a), B(b)(iii), B(c), B(d)]

Cost requirements

(11) *No critical cost requirements.* Today this is not very common. [A(a), A(c), A(d), B(b)(iii)/(iv), B(c)]

(12) *Low total cost of whole project.* By contrast, this is usually said to be the main priority. However, we also need to see whether any of the following points are also important. [A(c), A(d), B(a), B(b)(i)/(ii)]

(13) *Low cost in relation to units of accommodation.* This is a most usual cost requirement, in both the profit and social sectors. [B(a), B(b)]

(14) *Good budgetary control of whole project.* In many cases it is important that all the initial cost forecasts should be accurate, even if this does not mean the lowest cost that the market might

possibly produce at the time the orders are placed. [B(b)(iii)/(iv)]

(15) *Low total cost of building contract.* This is not unlike (12), but the concern here is to keep the building cost to the minimum, even if this does not minimise administration and supervisory costs, or costs of furnishing and maintenance. It is often required on public projects where these things come out of different funds. [B(b)(i)/(ii)]

(16) *Good budgetary control of building contract.* Similar to (14), in the circumstances outlined in (15). [B(b)(iii)/(iv)]

(17) *Good forecast of cost at contractual commitment.* This is required by a client who wants an accurate forecast of final cost before committing himself contractually. [B(a), B(b)(iii)/(iv), B(c), B(d)]

(18) *Best combination of capital and maintenance costs.* One would like to think that this was more common than it is—there are all sorts of reasons like taxation, cost yardsticks, etc., which tend to prevent these two things from being weighted equally. [A(e), B(b)]

(19) *Low capital cost.* The more usual requirement, especially if the building is going to be sold, or if running costs come out of a different fund. [B(b), B(d)]

(20) *Low maintenance cost.* Less usual, but may be required if maintenance is going to be inconvenient, for example by putting the building out of commission while it is going on. [A, B(b)]

(21) *Timing of cash flow.* This may be required in order to optimise the cost on a DCF basis (see Chapter 4) or else to phase in with the availability of the client's funds. [A(a)–(d), B(b)(iii)/(iv), B(d)]

(22) *Minimum capital commitment.* This would be required if the client wanted the contractor to bear most of the cost until the building was handed over. [B(b)(iii), B(d)]

(23) *Share in risk of development.* A variation on the last, where the contractor is paid by a share in the profits; this has been used on large speculative developments. [B(b)(iii), B(d)]

Meeting the client's needs

The client, of course, may wish to combine three or four or more requirements from the above list; as a result there are many different sets of possibilities, and the way in which he goes about the project should reflect his individual combination of needs. He should not adopt a standard solution simply because it is the usual one—it may be quite unfitted to his needs—but whatever he eventually decides to do he is likely to require the services of the construction industry.

Unless the client happens to be an employer of building labour (which is unusual) he will have to enter into contractual relationships with one or more people or organisations inside the industry in order to get the work carried out. Since the nature and terms of these contracts will materially affect the cost control of the project we must now consider the options which are open.

Basic forms of building contract

Although there are many different forms of contract they are basically of two different kinds:

(1) *Cost reimbursement.* The contractor agrees that all his expenditure on labour, materials, etc., will be met by the client, on top of which he will charge a fee on an agreed basis (e.g. "I will redecorate your drawing room for the cost of the paint plus £10 per hour for my time.").

(2) *Price in advance.* The contractor agrees to carry out his obligations for a sum of money agreed in advance (e.g. "I will redecorate your drawing room for two hundred pounds.").

The two types of contract are illustrated with "homely" examples because they are rarely used in their pure form on large projects. The lump sum "price in advance" contract involves too great a risk to the contractor (the building may need deeper foundations than he bargained for, or inflation may send wages rocketing), while the cost reimbursement contract encourages waste and extravagant working by the contractor, who has not got to pay for anything that he uses. In fact, in its most primitive form where his profit is a percentage of the cost, he has a positive incentive to waste as much money as possible.

From the point of view of cost planning, however, there is rather an interesting paradox. The "price in advance" contract gives the client almost no control over the details of methods, programming, or expenditure, but gives him a perfect forecast of his total cost. The "cost reimbursement" contract, on the other hand, allows him to give orders about the tempo or methods or work, and he can obtain detailed allocations of actual site costs, but he can never forecast the total cost with the same degree of certainty.

It should also be noted at this stage that the type of building contract which is chosen will have some effect on the type and scale of professional advice which is employed; for example, in the case of a large "cost reimbursement" contract it would almost certainly be necessary to employ a quantity surveyor to check all the invoices and wage payments.

Building contracts in detail

We can now look at the various contractual methods of building, trying as far as possible to match them against the time and cost criteria which have just been set out. While this list may be used to suggest the best approach to the individual problem it must be remembered, firstly, that no form of contract is proof against things going wrong and that, conversely, a keen combination of design team and building team will make a good job of things whatever the contractual arrangements. However, all other things being equal, a suitable form of contract will help. In the following list the time and cost requirements which are especially catered for by each of the contract types are shown as references to the numbered paragraphs on pages 13–15.

A. Cost reimbursement

(a) *Cost plus percentage* (1, 2, 5, 6, 7, 8, 9, 10, 11, 20, 21). In many ways the most convenient contractual basis of all; the contractor can be selected, the contract placed and work started before the scheme has been finalised and without any estimates or quantities needing to be prepared. Further, the contractor's management methods, in theory at any rate, can be used for the direct benefit of the client. The client also knows that the contractor will not make an exorbitant profit. The disadvantages of such a contract have already been mentioned; there are the usual cost reimbursement drawbacks of poor cost forecasting facilities, and low productivity arising from the fact that people are not "working to a price" so can afford to do things properly (or slowly and extravagantly). In addition to these usual drawbacks, however, there is a positive incentive towards wastefulness because the contractor is being rewarded with a percentage of everything that is spent, so it is not surprising that this method of contracting has a bad cost reputation.

However, because of the virtues which have been mentioned it is a widely used method for such projects as:

(i) Emergency first-aid and repair work.
(ii) Alterations and repairs to old buildings where the exten of the works cannot be foreseen until the contract has started.
(iii) Contracts where very high quality work is required.
(iv) Contracts where cost is not important but where the client wants control over the method of working.

(b) *Cost plus fixed fee* (1, 2, 5, 6, 7, 8, 9, 10, 20, 21). An attempt to mitigate the worst feature of the above contract by paying the contractor a fee based on the estimated cost of the project instead of a percentage of the actual cost, so reducing the incentive for wastefulness. Unfortunately, this means that a fairly detailed scheme and an estimate have to be prepared before work can start, so losing some of the advantage of the "cost plus" system; it is also likely in practice that the so-called fixed fee will have to be re-negotiated at the end of the job because of the major variations which are sure to arise in projects of the type for which such a contract would be used.

(c) *Direct labour* (1, 2, 5, 6, 7, 8, 9, 10, 11, 12, 20, 21). This is not, strictly speaking, a "contract" at all, because the client employs labour, buys materials, and engages sub-contractors in a series of minor contracts, doing all the organising and bearing all the risk himself. It is not often used except by clients who normally maintain a building department, such as major industrial concerns and public authorities. As far as the client for a one-off building is concerned, his main difficulty would be in getting together an efficient management team on such a short term basis; it has been suggested that in the future his professional advisers (because they have a longer term interest in building management) might be able to organise this, but little has been done by such methods at the present date. Direct labour has the usual cost reimbursement advantages and disadvantages, although it is sometimes possible to set up a "model system" of tendering and cost control. In the public sector it suffers from being the subject of strong party political controversy.

(d) *Management contract* (1, 2, 5, 6, 7, 8, 9, 10, 11, 12, 20, 21). A recent development designed to give the ordinary client the benefits of direct labour, whereby a management team organises the project on the client's behalf, for a fee. This method has been used with success on major industrial projects where time and integration with complex engineering contracts are vital; it is now increasingly used for more general projects. The usual cost reimbursement advantages and disadvantages apply, although the management team may let out part of the work to sub-traders on a "price in advance" basis. Where a construction management division of a building contracting firm is acting as the management team there is often not much difference between this and the "cost plus fixed fee" contract (Type b).

(e) *Target cost* (1, 2, 4, 6, 7, 8, 9, 10, 18, 20). An attempt to get the benefits of cost reimbursement without the disadvantages. A Bill of Quantities is prepared and priced by negotiation to arrive at a target cost; the contractor then carries out the work on an actual cost basis. There are various methods of arriving at the final price; if the actual cost is lower than the target cost the contractor and client usually split the difference between them, while if the actual cost is higher than target the contractor has to be content with his actual costs plus a small overhead percentage. The contractor therefore has an incentive to do the job as cheaply as possible and the client gets a direct benefit if he does so; the main disadvantages are that the target cost is subject to revision in respect of the many likely variations (so that one might as well have an ordinary lump sum or remeasurement contract), and the quantity surveyor's fees are likely to be high because there is dual documentation (cost reimbursement accounts to be checked and Bill of Quantities to be prepared, priced, agreed, and updated).

This system however retains some of the benefits of cost reimbursement, especially the ability of the contractor and client to work closely together in the management of the project, and it has been used with particular success on a "continuation" basis where the client has a succession of projects in which the same contractor can participate.

B. Price in advance

One of the difficulties about "price in advance" contracts is, as we have seen, inflation. Because large building contracts will last for a year or more it is unreasonable to ask a builder to bear the total risk of inflation during this period, and most of the contract methods set out hereafter have two versions—one for use on small projects where the contractor bears the inflation risk, and another (for larger projects) where the risk is borne in whole or in part by the client. It should be noted that while the former gives the client a firm cost forecast the latter may well be the cheaper, even on short term jobs; builders do not like this risk and tend to over-price it if they are given a choice of tendering on the two methods (we will see from the cash flows in Chapter 4 why the contractor is in a worse position than the client to take even a modest degree of extra risk).

(a) *Lump sum* (1, 3, 4, 6, 7, 8, 10, 12, 13, 17, 19). In a lump sum contract the builder commits himself to a price on the basis of the work shown on the drawings and in the specification. Although commonly used abroad, it is difficult to obtain prices in competition on this type of contract in the UK, except for very small schemes. A quantity surveyor is not usually employed and Bills of Quantities are not used; this means that preliminary cost forecasting, budgeting, and valuing of changes in the scheme may be unsatisfactory. But where the client's requirements are firm, and the drawings and specification are good, this is a very simple and effective contractual basis.

(b) *Contract based on Bills of Quantities.* This is the normal mode
   for carrying out major building work in the UK and for this
   reason will have to be considered in most detail. Wide usage has
   developed a number of variations on the basic theme, as
   follows:
   (i) *Competitive tender—Standard Form of Contract* (1, 3, 4,
       12, 13, 15, 18, 19, 20). Most major work in the UK is
       undertaken on this basis. The scheme is designed, and a
       number of contractors are asked to submit lump sum
       tenders based upon the pricing and totalling of a Bill of
       Quantities prepared on behalf of the client. The success-
       ful contractor's Bill then becomes the instrument for
       financial administration of the project, so that the one
       document provides a simple means of contractor selec-
       tion, price commitment, and contract management. This
       method of contract probably gives the lowest price of
       any, under UK conditions; although superior to any of
       the previous methods in regard to cost forecasting and
       budgeting it has a number of disadvantages in this re-
       spect which are set out in Chapter 12. However, it is this
       type of contract, with its competitive Bill of Quantities
       rates, which provides most of the raw data for elemental
       cost analysis, and indeed acts as a control against which
       the cost of buildings erected under less competitive
       arrangements can be judged. It should be noted that, in
       practice, the provisions of the JCT Standard Form of
       Contract make the total price and time commitments
       rather less firm than they appear to be in theory.
   (ii) *As (i), but Bill of Approximate Quantities* (1, 2, 5, 9, 12,
        13, 15, 18, 19, 20). Used as an alternative where the
        scheme has not been fully designed, the Bill of Quanti-
        ties being only a notional representation of the finished
        project. The work is measured as executed, and a final
        price agreed using the items and rates in the Bill
        of Quantities as far as possible. This method has the
        advantage of permitting an earlier start to be made, but
        control, both of time and money, is much weaker than
        in the previous case. A contractor who has under-
        estimated the cost of his commitments under such a
        nebulous arrangement as this is sure to be able to find
        some way of recouping his actual costs.
   (iii) *Negotiated tender* (1, 2, 3, 4, 5, 6, 7, 8, 9, 10, 11, 13, 14,
         16, 17, 18, 19, 20, 21, 22, 23). A contractor is selected
         early in the design stage, either with a pin or else by
         means of a simple tender document in which he states his

management costs, on-costs, and labour charges. The contract Bill of Quantities is then prepared and priced jointly with him as the design develops (he will usually be involved in the detailed design also). This assists cost forecasting and budgeting, as there is some contractual commitment to the cost assumptions made during design. An early start can also be made on site, and, because everything is negotiated, the contract terms and the arrangement of the Bill of Quantities can be tailor-made to suit the actual requirements of the parties. This method of contracting is very suitable for use on a "continuation" basis, where the same client, professional advisers, and contractor can establish a good working *rapport;* however, it probably does not produce rock-bottom prices and requires some degree of special expertise on both sides to obtain the best results. Partly for this last reason, the quantity surveyor may well be the most influential member of the professional team and may be appointed first.

(iv) *Serial contracting* (1, 2, 3, 4, 5, 11, 13, 14, 16, 17, 18, 19, 20, 21). This method is only open to clients with a continuing work programme; contractors are asked to price, in competition, a typical Bill of Quantities, on which basis they agree to carry out any similar work which the client may require over a fixed period of two or three years. Usually the contractor is asked to take the rough with the smooth, and to quote average rates which will apply on both difficult and straightforward projects. Some local authorities use this system, which obviously relies rather heavily on the integrity and fair play of the client. It does not usually produce rock-bottom prices but gives superb cost forecasting control, as contractually binding detailed prices are available for the future schemes before they are designed.

(c) *Schedules of prices* (1, 5, 9, 10, 11, 17). Used almost entirely for repair and maintenance work, particularly by government departments. It has something in common with the serial contract, as the contractor binds himself to a "price list" at which he will undertake work as required for a period of years. Sometimes used as a matter of convenience for small new works which arise during its currency of operation.

(d) *Package deal* (1, 2, 3, 4, 5, 6, 7, 8, 10, 17, 19, 21, 22, 23). Sometimes more correctly called "design-and build"; under this system the contractor acts directly for the client, filling the roles of both the professional design team and builder. The big advantage is that the contractor is willing to commit himself firmly to a price and completion date at an early stage, because he has total responsibility for working out the scheme without interference from others. Disadvantages are the lack of competition and the drawbacks of production-oriented design; because of the first factor the client usually appoints a quantity surveyor to keep an eye on costs, and he may ask a consultant architect to advise on design—however, the latter role is so limited and frustrating that not every architect is keen to take it on. The contractor may have his own in-house design team or he may employ outside consultants; as these latter are responsible to him and not to the client this is not much more than a domestic detail.

Summing-up

There are a variety of client requirements, and many contractual methods of satisfying them. The method of contracting for a particular project or group of projects should be chosen with the individual client's need in mind, not just on the "the usual basis"; it is, for instance, pointless to prepare a Bill of Quantities for a client who is concerned not with money but with convenience. We must also remember that the client may not really need a building at all—perhaps he should be changing his distribution methods instead of building a new warehouse. It may therefore be important that he should not go initially to somebody who has a vested interest in putting up buildings.

Chapter 3

How Building Costs are Incurred

We have seen that the developer will normally need to involve himself with the Building Industry in order to get his building work undertaken.

The Building Industry and the Civil Engineering Industry together are often spoken of as the Construction Industry, and many firms (certainly most of the large ones) operate in both sectors, even though their staff and organisations may be largely separate. It is, however, very difficult to separate the two halves statistically, because of the overlap which occurs. For instance, the construction of foundations of very large buildings could almost be classed as civil engineering (and you will find it so referenced in your library, if this operates the Dewey or UDC system), and there may be quite a lot of building work on some civil engineering projects.

The Construction Industry in the UK consists mainly of small firms, although the bulk of its turnover is carried out by comparatively large organisations—for instance in 1970 the 0.1% of firms with more than 1,200 employees undertook nearly 25% of the work. (Figure 3.1 shows this distribution of firms in graphic form, with over 20,000 firms employing less than 5 people, and 33,000 employing between 5 and 10. Only 443 firms employed more than 110 people.)

The industry is quite large, manufacturing as it does approximately 50% of the fixed capital formation (i.e. plant, ships, aeroplanes, etc.) of the UK and about 6½% of the gross national product. Much of its output will be paid for directly or indirectly by government bodies such as the local authorities, central government departments, the nationalised industries, etc. This means of course that the actions of the government have a considerable impact on the well-being of the industry. It has been suggested that the British government uses construction as a regulating mechanism for the economy as a whole, although there is very little evidence to show that building faired worse than any other industry until perhaps the early 1970s. In 1973, however, when the government urgently needed to deflate the economy they announced a massive cut-back in public expenditure of which approximately 80% was in the building programme. The depression

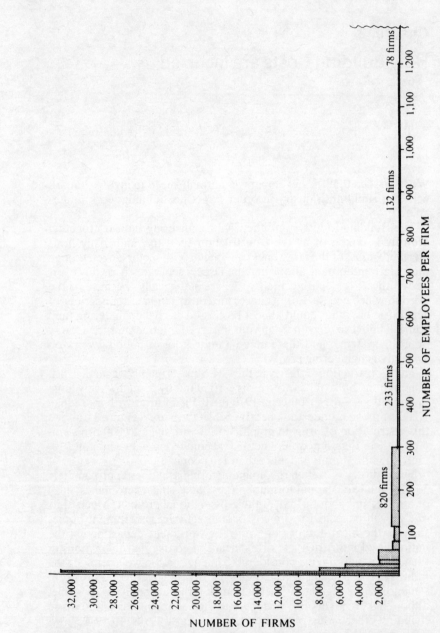

FIG. 3.1. *Distribution of firms in the Construction Industry by size of firm (taken from Annual Bulletin of Construction Statistics 1970, by kind permission of the Department of the Environment)*

that ensued from this and other constraints relating to financial control had a devastating effect on the demand for building. For many years the industry has suffered from a series of "stop-go" periods in the economy which has resulted in the series of fluctuations which can be seen in Fig. 3.2, but the severe cutbacks of 1973 can be clearly seen as having an enormous impact on orders received by various sectors of the industry, the professions, and the total output.

The graph is an interesting one, as it attempts to combine three possible measures of the *capacity* of the industry with recorded orders and output. Capacity is the ability of the industry to meet the demands placed upon it; when the economy is overheated and demand exceeds the ability of the industry to cope, then these measures respond accordingly. The three measures chosen are: (i) ratio of bricklayers' vacancies to numbers of bricklayers unemployed, (ii) construction bankruptcies, and (iii) brick stocks.

In the 1972/73 period demand increased through an easing of financial controls (in an attempt to boost the economy), and the building industry which had been run down over a series of years suddenly found it could not supply according to the new demand. The result was that the ratio of bricklayers' vacancies to employed rose to new heights, construction bankruptcies reduced considerably, and brick stocks were small. The deflation of the economy had the reverse effect and this is clearly seen in the rapid decline after the peak of 1973. The graph is well worth a few minutes study, paying particular attention to the time lags between various movements.

Some of the impact of the post-1973 depression can be seen in Fig. 3.3 showing an index of cost trends of resources related to tender prices, as measured by the BCIS Tender Price Index. In looking at the widening gap it should be remembered that of course the various indicators do not start from a point of equilibrium in 1974 as might be falsely inferred from the index level of 100 applied to all of them in this year. In fact, as will be seen subsequently, tender prices were high in relation to resource costs at that time, and the early stages of the chart represent a return to equilibrium.

It is clear that from the end of 1973 contractors were able to absorb the increase in cost of materials and labour until 1977 when this was no longer possible and the various indices began to rise in parallel. Since 1980 the recession has really begun to bite and this is shown by the stabilisation of the Tender Price Index. How long this can continue is of some concern to the industry.

An understanding of the effect of government decision on the industry is essential for a client and his professional advisers both in forecasting future costs and returns and in determining at which point in time it is preferable to build. These matters should be borne in mind when using the techniques and when following the discussion in the remaining chapters.

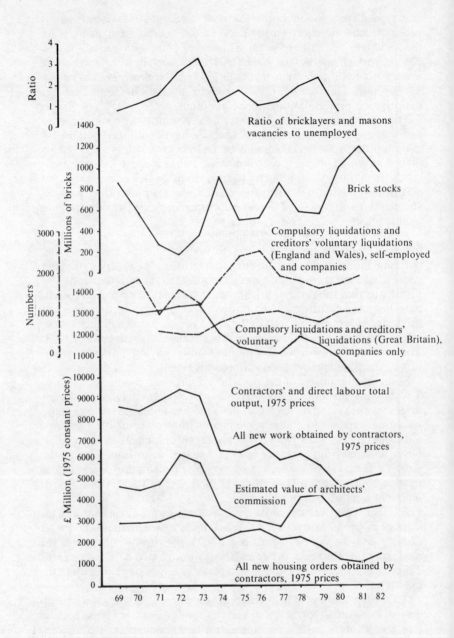

FIG. 3.2. *Examples of fluctuation in construction (reproduced by kind permission of the Controller of Her Majesty's Stationery Office)*

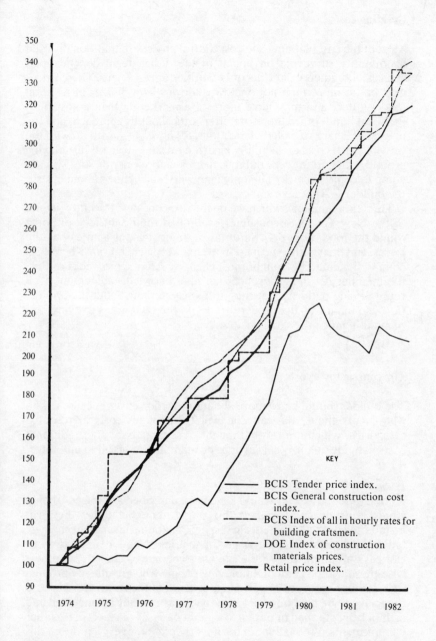

KEY

BCIS Tender price index.
BCIS General construction cost index.
BCIS Index of all in hourly rates for building craftsmen.
DOE Index of construction materials prices.
Retail price index.

FIG. 3.3. *Cost trends. 1st quarter* 1974 = 100. *(Reproduced by kind permission of the Building Cost Information Service)*

Building costs

Most of the cost planning and cost control procedure traditionally used by quantity surveyors on behalf of the design team depend upon "prices" obtained from Bills of Quantities or elsewhere. These prices may be no more than notional breakdowns by a builder of his total tender offer, and may have more of a marketing than a cost bias. Practical builders are therefore often critical of this approach, and say in effect "These so-called elemental rates have nothing to do with the way in which costs are actually incurred on site—you are just playing around with a lot of very dubious figures, and sooner or later you are going to come unstuck. The only man who really knows about costs is the builder." Are they right?

There is an analogy which we might also consider. Recently, in one of the New Towns, a consumer group had the bright idea of going round the food shops on a Saturday morning, making a note of all the prices, and then putting up a list in the market place showing where each commodity could be bought most cheaply. After some weeks of this, the members of the group became quite knowledgeable about local retail pricing patterns, but they still knew nothing about the production economics of the grocery trade. Is the quanitity-surveying cost planner in much the same position?

The contractor's costs

The builder should know more about production costs, because it is he who incurs them. Basically he will think of his costs in resource categories, which are rarely thought of separately by the traditional cost-planning quantity surveyor as he manipulates his all-in unit rates.

1. *Site labour*

At one time these costs would have been described as "wages", being almost entirely composed of this single item, but today they will include substantial payments in respect of national insurance schemes, holiday schemes, etc.; the wages or salaries of junior supervisory or clerical staff employed on the site are sometimes included, but otherwise these will be costs of employing people who are directly productive. Labour costs are of particular concern to the contractor because they have to be paid out weekly in ready cash as they are incurred and cannot be postponed or put on to a credit basis, as can most of his other commitments. We shall see in the next chapter how very important this is. It is convenient to also consider "labour only" sub-contractors under this heading, as they will usually require weekly cash.

2. *Materials and sub-contractors*

The amounts comprising these costs will usually be paid by means of monthly credit accounts, payment being due at the end of the month following that in which the materials are delivered or the work carried out (so that materials delivered in January are paid for at the end of February). Such settlement usually entitles the builder to a "cash discount", 2½% being the most common figure although 5% may sometimes be allowed.

It is not unusual for a builder to delay payment beyond the "cash" settlement date, sometimes for a further one or two months. Since he may well lose his 2½% or 5% for the sake of a few weeks credit this is an expensive way of borrowing money compared to bank overdraft, but it has the advantages of being ready and convenient and of not requiring collateral security. Within reason, builder's merchants are not averse to acting as financiers to the industry in this way; if the contractor owes a substantial amount it is difficult for him to withdraw his custom, or even to reduce his level of buying substantially, as immediate settlement of overdue accounts might then be called for.

"Nominated" suppliers and sub-contractors are also paid by credit account, but as they are in a position to complain to the architect if settlement is delayed, and since such a complaint casts doubts upon the contractor's solvency, he will make efforts to pay them promptly.

In most cases the contractor will have been paid by the client for the materials or work before settling with his merchants and sub-contractors. We will see the importance of this also in the next chapter, and it must be remembered that because of the increasing tendency to buy-in fabricated components instead of making things on site a higher and higher proportion of the total project expenditure falls into this category.

3. *Plant*

Large items of mechanical plant may be dealt with in two ways; either they may be charged to the job when brought on to the site and credited (less depreciation) when removed, or else an hourly or weekly hire charge will be made plus a charge for bringing the plant to the site and removing it. Most large contractors find it convenient to set up a subsidiary plant company, which will charge the equipment out to the sites on a hire basis, while plant hired from outside will be similarly dealt with and paid for by credit account. Lorry transport is usually arranged in a like manner.

It is unusual for a building contractor to own large items of plant, except through a subsidiary company. There are substantial advantages in hire purchase through a finance company, since the interest charges (less tax) will be lower than the return which the contractor expects to make on the working capital which he employs; it would therefore be uneconomic for him to invest this capital in plant purchase.

4. *Establishment charges*

These represent costs incurred in running the company as a whole, and which cannot be attributed to any particular contract—head office expenses, builder's yard, salaries of supervisory and office staff and directors.

Allocation of resource costs to building work

Keeping an accurate record of costs in the above four categories, and allocating them to the right contracts, is comparatively easy, but the lump sums obtained do not really contribute very much to the understanding of how costs are incurred. A detailed site costing system is much more difficult to arrange.

In theory it might be possible to cost each contract in terms of finished work, attaching costs to the measured items (or groups of items) in the Bills of Quantities. One disadvantage of trying to do this is the difficulty and expense of keeping records of time and material for a multiplicity of items and subsequently processing them, but more important is the fact that many costs are not directly related to specific quantities of work. We can identify four types of cost, as follows:

(a) *Quantity related.* These are the costs which bear a straight relationship to quantity of finished work—many material costs fall into this category as do some components of labour cost. With this type of cost, twice the quantity of work costs twice as much.

(b) *Occurrence related.* These costs are related to a particular event, or occurrence, such as the bringing of excavation plant to the site, or the moving of a plasterer's equipment from room to room. While the scale of the occurrence is obviously affected by the scale of the work which is anticipated, its cost will not vary in proportion to actual quantity of work executed.

(c) *Time related.* Some costs (such as the hire of a major item of plant) are related to a length of time, and not to the amount of work done in that time.

(d) *Value related.* Fire insurance, for instance, will be related to the value of the project; establishment charges are also often allocated on a basis of project value and can be included under this heading.

In addition to these four types of cost, it must be remembered that some of the work done will relate to temporary items (such as erection of site huts and conveniences) which do not form part of the permanent works. On many projects the shuttering of concrete work is a very large item in this category.

Identification of differing variable costs

It is all very well to make these rather academic distinctions between different types of cost, but in practice they may be difficult to separate. For instance, the plasterers are unlikely to keep separate the time involved in moving from room to room, and the charge for a major item of plant may well incorporate several cost types, e.g.

Quantity related	Fuel, and part of hire charge.
Occurrence related	Bringing to site and removal, moving, assembling and dismantling.
Time related	Part of hire charge.

However, even an arbitrary division into these different types will be better than trying to allocate total cost pro rata to quantity of finished work, and would form a more suitable basis for using cost information for estimating or cost planning purposes. Recent revisions of the *Standard Method of Measurement* have taken a step towards identifying costs under these various categories.

Costing by "operations"

In practice, costs are rarely kept to any lower level than an "operation", which has been defined by the Building Research Station as "a piece of work that can be completed by one man, or a gang of men, without interruption by others". A typical operation might be the whole of the brickwork to one floor level, or the whole of the first fixings of joinery. It is comparatively simple to record costs on site for such overall parcels of work, and to allocate materials to them, and it is much more meaningful to attach the time-related and occurrence-related costs to total operations than to try to split them up among quantities of measured work to which they bear little relation. If the contractor's estimate can be similarly sub-divided he will be able to compare cost with estimate at each stage of the job.

Use of the builder's cost information for design cost planning

The builder would appear to be in a much better position than the quantity surveyor as far as real cost information is concerned, yet he would be ill-advised to use the actual costs from a particular project for cost planning another quite different one. There are two reasons for this:

(i) Many of the factors which affect site costs on a particular project have nothing to do with the design of the building and will not repeat from job to job. These include the weather, industrial and personal relations, the skill with which the work was organised, accidents, late delivery of materials, defective work, failure by sub-contractors.

(ii) Although the "operation" is an excellent concept for collecting costs it is very difficult to re-use the information arising from it because each operation is unique; the only way in which first fixing of joinery on one project can be compared with another quite different one is by looking at the quantities of the different types of work involved, and the whole essence of operational costing is that the costs are not broken down in this way. If they were, we would be back to costing work items from the Bill of Quantities, and, as explained, this is impracticable. In some instances, the operation may embrace more than one cost planning element.

However, the contractor's operationally based estimate has neither of these disadvantages when considered as a cost planning data base. Firstly, it should be based upon an assessment of "average" costs, and as such will have a closer relationship to future tender prices than ascertained costs from a particular project. Secondly, it will break down each operation into a set of measurable characteristics for pricing purposes (the estimated costs of which may be based either upon experience or work study methods) and these can be used for the purposes of design cost analysis.

In so far as the builder has access to this kind of estimate, and the quantity surveyor has not, he may be said to have an advantage in cost knowledge. Against this the average quantity surveyor is much more experienced than the average builder in translating project cost data into terms which are relevant at early design stage, and this expertise is essential to cost planning and control—the quantity surveyor's need is for a Bill of Quantities which reflects more closely the way in which operational estimates are built up. For instance, if the "Preliminaries" section of the Bill of Quantities were always priced in a consistently itemised way (like the other sections of the Bill) the quantity surveyor could analyse and manipulate this important part of the cost in detail instead of as a "percentage of the measured work". It must be remembered that the proportion of project cost represented by the execution of the measured builder's work is steadily declining, and the proportion represented by specialist work, fixed charges, and management costs is increasing.

The topic of resource-based cost planning is dealt with in greater detail in Chapter 14.

System building, prefabrication, and cost

No discussion of building costs would be complete if it did not deal with the effect of system building and prefabrication on costs. System building involves varying degrees of discipline; in its most simple form it may only be a standardised form of more-or-less traditional building, saving time and money by the familiarity of the standard construction and detailing, the repetitive use of formwork units, standard components, and so on. It is difficult to obtain competitive tenders for this sort of work, because if prices are given by two or more firms each firm will quote for its own patent system and it will be almost impossible to compare the value of the tenders without a considerable amount of work. In these circumstances cost comparisons based on cost modelling techniques of the type described in this book may provide a truer picture than an attempt to check detailed quantities and prices, even where these are provided.

However, in its more highly developed forms system building may involve the delivery of the whole building in the form of a kit of parts ready to fit together in a few days (in the case of a house) or in a few weeks in the case of a larger building. The economics of this practice are not easy to evaluate, partly because of the advertising and hard selling which often go with it and partly because the economics are in fact much more complicated than the more usual building costs.

The cost advantages which the prefabricator possesses are, at first sight, considerable. He has the benefit of planned mass production under factory conditions, safe from the weather hold-ups which affect site output and free from the difficulties of supervision and quality control which occur when men are working all over a scattered site. He can employ expensive but money-saving plant which would be too cumbersome, valuable, or delicate for site use and which in any case could not find full employment for its output on a single site. He can take advantage of modern methods of transport and handling to bring his large fabricated units direct from his factory to the position on site where they are required. In fact we might tend to accept the common view that the lack of development of factory-building techniques simply shows that the construction industry is hopelessly old-fashioned.

However, there are very sound reasons why prefabrication has had a much smaller impact upon the industry than was at one time expected. The purpose of this book has not been to explore the aesthetic and technological problems associated with factory-produced buildings, except perhaps to comment that these might be more acceptable if there really was a strong economic justification for them. In fact the economic gains have proved to be very disappointing indeed. What are the reasons for this?

First are the obvious reasons in favour of site production, although these were always known about and it was hoped that they would be more than offset by the above-mentioned advantages. The site builder has none of the heavy overheads of factory production (he will not have to pay rent for his site workshops and probably will not even have to pay rates); many of the cheap techniques (such as bricks-and-mortar) which he uses are not suitable for off-site production, and the crude handling methods which he can use with his small and rough components are cheaper than the tackle required for handling large units carefully. He is also able to provide a "made to measure" building instead of one "off the peg".

With greater experience other economic problems have come to light. A broken brick is simply a broken brick, but if the corner of some special component is damaged another one will have to be ordered. The cost of replacement is the least part of the difficulty, the disruption to programme caused by the resultant delay can be far more serious.

It has also become apparent that the disadvantage caused by the fact that only the building superstructure can be prefabricated and the infrastructure has to be produced on site is much greater than was supposed. On low-rise projects, such as housing and hospitals, the site preparation, levelling, foundations, drainage and site services, roads, paths, car parks, fencing, landscaping, etc., involve so much work on site and so much site organisation that the prefabrication of the basic superstructure (particularly if it does not include all finishings and services) is only dealing with a part of the problem, and not always the most significant part. Also, on a low-rise development of any size, and particularly on an undulating site, there is usually a certain amount of site building to be done in linking up the various prefabricated units. This work is so "bitty" and fragmented that its cost has sometimes represented a substantial part of the whole superstructure cost, and it really would have been cheaper in such circumstances to build the superstructure properly on site.

The more important and less obvious handicap which faces the prefabricating firm is the large capital investment which has to be made in developing and testing the system, establishing and equipping the factory, and most of all, stock-piling the components until they are bought by the customer. There is little opportunity to obtain the very high rate of return on capital invested which the site builder is able to obtain on his much more limited investment (as will be explained in the next chapter), and contractors have not found this to be a worthwhile field for deploying their resources of capital.

Even where it is possible to produce a scheme for prefabrication which shows at any rate a reasonable return on capital, there are still two further difficulties to contend with. The first is the actuarial risk of some major snag developing in the system once it is tried out in the harsh conditions of the real world, involving both the costs of putting things right and the possible loss of custom resulting from publicity; it is not really practicable to make adequate allowance for this in a pricing structure.

The second difficulty is the one which is most often quoted by firms who have been unsuccessful in this field, but it is nevertheless quite true. Factory-produced buildings need a large and assured market in order to be competitive in cost, as do all factory products which involve a heavy capital expenditure on plant, tooling and design, and preferably demand should not fluctuate too wildly year by year. These conditions are not met by the construction sector which is notoriously subject to boom and slump as a result of economic forces or, more often, government policy and we have just been looking at some of the effects of this. The site-organised building industry has enough trouble as a result of "stop-go", but it is absolutely fatal to a capital-intensive factory production of buildings. Those firms from outside the building industry who moved into this field have therefore largely abandoned it.

The only sector where prefabrication seems to have succeeded in establishing the right conditions for its survival is in the field of temporary and light industrial buildings (sheds, garages, temporary classrooms, church halls, etc.) where the prefabricated building dominates the market. However, in many ways the production, distribution, and erection of these light units does not involve the same difficulties that occur with larger and heavier components.

A further justification for prefabrication is that the industry may be unable to cope with the volume of work required at busy times because of a shortage of qualified tradesmen to work on site. As we have seen, this unfortunately cannot be the answer to short-term "boom" problems of this nature. The long-term answer as to which way we are going is more likely to be found in sociology rather than building economics—whether for example in future people are going to prefer working in factories to an open-air life.

Meanwhile the prospective building owner would be advised to be careful in accepting the claims made for new building systems, particularly in advertisements or "sponsored" articles. The results, both in time and in cost, which are obtained on a pilot scheme are not always maintained in the rougher conditions of general use. Apart from this, it should always be made very clear what is included in the advertised or quoted cost; whether the price is for a complete building or whether it is just a superstructure shell and excludes foundations, floor slabs, decorations, services, etc. Phrases like "comparable with" or "competitive with" traditional cost should always be suspect, the manufacturer who is actually offering a cheaper-than-traditional building will have no hesitation in saying so quite clearly.

In any cost comparison between different forms of patent construction or between patent and traditional building, it will be necessary to consider economic life and maintenance costs as well as first cost, and this may be more difficult than usual because these factors will be pure guesswork so far as new materials or finishes are concerned. The prudent architect or surveyor will need to be a little less optimisitic than the salesman when assessing the probabilities. The very expensive maintenance which has proved necessary with some systems because of difficulties at the joints between components was quite unforeseen at the time when the systems were evaluated.

A point of importance is that prefabrication often gives quicker completion, and in subsequent chapters we will see that this feature can sometimes (although not always) be worth quite a lot of money.

Effect of job organisation on costs

It has already been pointed out that many major costs on building projects are not directly related to the quantity of work produced, but are concerned with time and with occurrences of various kinds. The main quantity-related resource is material, so that given prudent buying and no unreasonable wastage, there should be little variation in the cost of this part of the work whichever contractor is appointed and however he organises the work. The real scope for saving (or wasting) money lies in the non-quantity-related items and depends on the way in which the job is planned and managed. This is where the real competition between contractors takes place.

A well-managed job is one where both the plant and the men have clear uninterrupted flows of work. Money is not spent on removing or returning either men or plant from the site, or on unproductive time waiting on site because of gaps in the work flow, or on moving them unnecessarily about the site. It is not merely a question of the actual time spent hanging around—people work much more productively when they can see a clear task in front of them and where they feel that they are taking part in an efficient operation. Again we are getting into the realms of sociology.

Engineering services

If you were to ask a cost planner what was his biggest headache, he would be almost certain to answer "Services costs!". The reason for the headache is not merely that this part of the work is difficult to cost plan, but also that it forms an ever-increasing proportion of the cost of the building (often over 50%). It is therefore no use forgetting about it and hoping that it will go away.

The difficulty exists both in the establishment of suitable element sub-divisions and the obtaining of cost data, and is compounded by a certain amount of professional rivalry. Of the two areas of difficulty it is the obtaining of detailed cost data which is of most concern, as it is no use working on the other problem unless one has the capability of attaching costs to the chosen sub-divisions.

By engineering services we mean all the plumbing, hot water, heating, air-conditioning, electrical, gas, oil, and similar installations, complete with all their pipes, wiring, motors, and appliances. Some modern buildings are really not much more than an envelope for these installations. Few builders are in a position to undertake work of this sort, except perhaps simple plumbing on a domestic scale, and large specialist industries exist for the purpose. These industries are often rooted in engineering practices rather than the practices of the building industry.

When an architect is designing a building there are basically two ways in which he can deal with the engineering installations, bearing in mind that he is not capable of designing them himself. He can either call in a specialist engineering contractor to undertake the design and submit a tender for the work, or he can employ, on the client's behalf, for a fee, a firm of professional consulting engineers to do the design work, prepare contract documentation, and seek competitive tenders from a number of specialist contractors. The latter method is obviously less open to abuse and is more normally used, especially on public work. (It is quite usual to employ a separate firm of consultants for the electrical work.) The quantity surveyor is rarely involved in this exercise and is usually informed of the amounts of the successful tenders for the various services for inclusion as p.c. sums in the Bills of Quantities.

Traditionally, the consulting engineer undertakes a "scheme" design only—he decides the type, size, and position of appliances and the size and type of pipes, cables, fittings, etc., but the final details of the installation are worked out by the tenderers. No Bill of Quantities is provided, and tenderers normally quote a lump sum price.

It is, of course, possible for the consulting engineer to design the scheme in full detail and for Bills of Quantities to be prepared; the drawbacks are that the engineer will charge a higher fee for the additional design work, the Bills of Quantities will have to be paid for, and as these procedures are not traditional in this field and are disliked by many, there is no guarantee of a more favourable price as a result. These additional costs may therefore be a complete extra as far as the client is concerned, and will be difficult to justify to him. It may, however, be possible to obtain some sort of crude price breakdown without having to resort to full Bills of Quantities.

An important matter, and one which causes the most controversy, is whether the quantity surveyor or the consulting engineer should be responsible for preparing any Bills of Quantities for this type of work, and for cost analysis and cost planning. The engineer feels that as he has the total responsibility for the installation he must also control the costs, and that he alone has the expertise to understand this specialist field. The quantity surveyor, on the other hand, feels that he has responsibility for total cost and so therefore must control this part of it, and that he can employ assistant surveyors who will specialise in, and understand, this work. At the present time the bulk of neither profession is fully equipped for this task.

A vital point, however, is that if the engineering consultants are going to be responsible to the client for cost planning the engineering services, and the quantity surveyor for cost planning the rest of the building, somebody will have to co-ordinate their efforts in order to optimise the client's total project costs. Who is going to do this? The architect is not qualified to do it—he has accepted the cost control of his own work by the quantity surveyor for this very reason—and it would be absurd to appoint a cost control "overlord" for the purpose, who would probably turn out to be another quantity surveyor anyway. For this reason alone, it would seem likely that the project quantity surveyor will become far more expert, and involved, in engineering services than at present.

As a final consolation to the quantity surveyor, this is a field where the average builder knows even less about costs than he does.

Chapter 4
Money, Time, and Investment

If you were asked "Would you rather be given £1,000 now, or in five years time?" you would almost certainly say "Now", particularly if inflation was rampant, but even if you were living in a time of zero inflation you would still be right to prefer to have the money right away. After all, you might be dead in five years' time, or there might be a revolution or world war before you had the opportunity to collect. Alternatively, the man who was going to pay you might have died, or disappeared, or gone bankrupt, or forgotten his promise. Even if you were not going to need the money for five years you would still do better to have it now and place it in a savings bank where it could accumulate interest.

We can therefore see that a sum of money in the future will always be worth less than the same amount of money today, and the difference will depend upon the length of time involved and the probable interest rate. In doing the calculations one might assume an interest rate that would reflect likely inflation and any special risks rather than a rate which might actually be obtainable at the time.

Just as a future lump sum is worth less than its equivalent today so are future recurrent expenses or receipts. If you had to put a sum of money aside to pay somebody £1,000 a year for ten years the amount required would be much less than £10,000, because the unexpended balance of the sum would be earning interest each year and in the early years in particular this would be quite a lot of money. (In fact if interest rates were as high as 10% the £10,000 would provide £1,000 a year for ever and ever, not just for ten years.) The actual sum which would be needed to provide £1,000 a year for 10 years is an amount which, with all its interest earnings, would be exactly used up at the end of ten years when the last £1,000 had been paid out. Its actual worth would depend upon current interest rates.

Until mid-century it was common practice for quantity surveyors to consider the cost of the building as a lump sum of money, and when interest rates were only 2 or 3%, and construction times were quick, this was possibly good enough.

However, it seems likely that interest rates will continue to be high

for some years (especially during expansionary periods when large programmes of building work are being undertaken), and with the increasing
complexity of large buildings it is not uncommon for some years to elapse
from the start of expenditure on the project to the time when an income is
produced. Under these circumstances it is necessary to consider the phasing
of the project finance very carefully; an apparently low total cost may not
be much of a bargain if it involves a long-drawn-out contract with high
early expenditure on which interest charges are piling up.

It may be asked "Does this apply to all development, or only where
profit is involved?" Basically it applies to all development, because the
money is either being borrowed (and attracting interest charges), or
else it is the developer's own money, which being spent on the development is not available for investing elsewhere (and is not accumulating
interest).

Strangely enough, although most quantity surveyors are aware of
this factor, some clients' accounting systems do not recognise it and so
in practice one is not always able to demonstrate any benefit from
optimising payment in relation to time. However, private developers
in particular are certainly aware of the importance of the timing of
income and expenditure, and building contractors have always recognised its significance even if they have not always been able to
formalise their methods of dealing with it.

Methodology

In considering development finance we have three kinds of expendi-
ture/income which we need to compare with each other:
  (a) Lump sums today.
  (b) Lump sums in the future.
  (c) Sums of money occurring at regular intervals during the period
      under consideration (wages, rents, etc.)

We cannot compare these, one with the other, unless we modify
them in some way in order to put them on a common basis. There are
two basic methods, and as usual they are just different ways of expressing the same thing:
  (1) Present-day value.
  (2) Annual equivalent.

1. *Present-day value*

All expenditure is expressed in terms of the capital sum which would
have to be set aside today in order to meet present commitments and
also to provide for future lump sums and future regular payments.
These future payments are "discounted" to allow for accumulation of
interest. Income is similarly treated; future income is discounted to the
present day in the same way.

2. *Annual equivalent*

All items of lump sum expenditure are expressed in terms of the annual payments which would be required to pay them off over the term of years in question (rather like paying off house purchase through a building society). These payments are usually shown in two parts.

(a) The interest on the capital cost:
(b) A "sinking fund"—an amount of money put away annually to repay the capital cost at the end of the period.

To these amounts are added the amounts of any regular annual payments, such as wages, rents, etc. Income is similarly treated.

Which of these two methods is used is largely a matter of convenience and depends upon whether one is thinking mainly in terms of capital finance or in terms of annual income and expenditure.

Calculations

It is usual these days to undertake the necessary calculations for these comparisons with the aid of a computer or even a pocket calculator rather than by looking up the values in compendious books of tables. The formulae are set out in Appendix D, but are repeated here; short tables showing a few principal rates of interest are also included in Appendix D to assist those who do not have a suitable calculator available.

In the following formulae n represents the number of periods and i the interest rate expressed as a decimal fraction of the principal, e.g. $5\% = 0.05$.

Calculations are often required that involve monthly, or even weekly, payments and in such circumstances annual interest rates are not of much use. Such calculations should use an equivalent rate for the period, dividing the annual rate by 12 or 52. Strictly speaking this is not correct, as it ignores the effect of weekly or monthly compounding. The exact annual equivalent of a monthly interest rate i is not $12i$ but $(1 + i)^{12} - 1$. The yearly equivalent of 1% per month is therefore 12.68%, and conversely the monthly equivalent of 12% per annum is 0.94888%. Where comparisons between two or more alternatives are being considered this difference is rarely of much significance, but it should be allowed for if specific annual interest rates are an important factor.

Formula 1—Compound interest $(1 + i)^n$

If a sum of money is invested for a number of years it will have earned some interest at the end of the first year. Compound interest assumes that this earned money is immediately added to the principal and re-invested on the same terms, this process being repeated annually. Many forms of actual investment provide for doing this automatically, but it is in any case the correct method to use when making investment calculations, since it should not be assumed that money would be allowed to lie idle.

EXAMPLE

What will be the value of £5,500 invested at 9% compound interest for five years?
Formula $(1 + i)^n = (1.09)^5$ and shows that £1 so invested will grow to £1.54. £5,500 will therefore grow to $5,500 \times £1.54 = £8,470$.
Note that this formula is also useful for extrapolating inflation rates over a period of years.

Formula 2 — Future value of £1 invested at regular intervals $[(1 + i)^n - 1]/i$
Instead of a single lump sum being invested we might put away a regular annual amount on the same basis. At the end of each year the total in the fund would comprise all previous investments, plus the compound interest earned on them, and to this would then be added the next annual contribution.

EXAMPLE

If £150 is invested annually at a rate of 11% compound interest for six consecutive years what would the fund be worth at the end of the sixth year?
Formula $[(1.11)^6 - 1]/0.11$ shows that £1 annually so invested will grow to £7.91, assuming that the investment is made at the *end* of each year
If the investment is regularly made at an earlier part of the year then 11% p.a. interest will require to be added to £7.91 for the additional part of the year involved. If the investment was always made at the *beginning* of each year then a whole year's interest would have to be added, that is, 11% of £7.91 = £0.87. The total per £1 at the end of the sixth year would therefore be

$$£7.91 + £0.87 = £8.78.$$

The example concerned a figure of £150 annually and the result for £1 must therefore be multiplied by 150 in each case.
The answer is therefore £1,186.50 if the money is deposited at the end of the year and £1,317 if it is deposited at the beginning.

Formula 3—Present value of £1 $1/(1 + i)^n$
In the compound interest example it will be remembered that £5.500 invested for 5 years at 9% compound interest grew to £8,470. The converse of this is that the *present* value of £8,470 in five years time at 9% interest is £5,500, i.e. that is the amount which would grow to that sum at the end of five years.
To avoid having to work out present values backwards in this fashion we use the reciprocal of the compound interest formula. One pound in five years time at 9% will therefore have a present value of $1/(1.09)^5 = 65.0$p, so £8,470 would have a value of $8,470 \times 65$p = £5,505. (The small error of £5 is due to the value being taken to the nearest tenth of a penny only. We shall discover later that the calculations for which

these formulae are used are so conjectural that such an "error" is of no real significance.)

What is the present value of £1,200 in 35 years time discounted at 15% per annum?

By use of the formula the present value of £1 in such circumstances is 0.8p. The present value of £1,200 is therefore 1,200 × 0.8p = £9.60. We can understand why there is little point in having 60 year tables when interest rates are high.

Formula 4—Present value of £1 payable at regular intervals
$$[(1 + i)^n -1]/[i(1 + i)^n]$$
Just as the previous formula showed the present value of future lump sums this shows the present value of future regular periodic payments or receipts over a limited term of 40 years (or other periods). It is, therefore, very useful for assessing the capital equivalent of things like running costs, wages, or rents.

EXAMPLE

What is the present value of £1,200 payable annually for ten years assuming an interest rate of 8% per annum?

We see from the formula that the present value of £1 paid annually in such circumstances is £6.71. The present value of £1,200 annually is therefore 1,200 × £6.71 = £8,052. This is the sum which would have to be invested today at 8% compound interest in order to discharge such an obligation and leave nothing over at the end.

It is interesting to see what difference would result if the money were to be paid in quarterly instalments of £300 instead of at the end of each year. Eight per cent per annum is equivalent to 2% per quarter, and (according to the formula) the present value of £1 over 10 × 4 = 40 periods at 2% is £27.36. The present value of £300 paid quarterly for ten years is therefore

$$300 \times £27.36 = £8,208,$$

compared to £8,052 for the yearly payments of £1,200.

The present value of £1,200 payable for ten years is sometimes referred to as "Ten year's purchase of £1,200". There is little point in using this old-fashioned land-agents' jargon, but you might come across it somewhere.

Formula 5—Annuity purchased by £1 $[i(1 + i)^n]/[(1 + i)^n-1]$
This is the reciprocal of the previous formula, and gives the annuity (or regular annual payment) purchased by a lump sum payment of £1. At the end of the given number of years the money will be exhausted. It is therefore useful for calculating the annual equivalent of a given present-day lump sum (whereas Formula 4 calculated the present-day lump-sum equivalent of a given annual amount).

EXAMPLE

What annual saving in maintenance costs over a period of ten years would justify an increase in capital costs of £90,000, assuming an interest rate of 8%?

The annual equivalent of £1 by the formula in these circumstances is 14.9p. The annual equivalent of £90,000 is therefore 90,000 × 14.9p = £13,410; if the saving in maintenance costs exceeds this amount then the additional capital investment of £90,000 would be justified.

Formula 6—Sinking fund $i/[(1 + i)^n - 1]$

It will be remembered that Formula 2 showed the lump sum which would result in the future from investing a fixed sum of money each year (or other periodic interval). However, sometimes you want the same information a different way round; you want to know how much you must invest each year to accumulate a certain sum in a certain number of years (for example to provide for replacing some worn-out piece of equipment). The formula for calculating this is the reciprocal of Formula 2 (Future value of £1).

EXAMPLE

How much must be invested at the end of each year at 7% per annum to amount to £20,000 at the end of 12 years?

We see from the formula that 5.6p has to be invested each year to produce £1 in such circumstances. For £20,000 the figure is therefore

$$20,000 \times 5.6p = £1,120.$$

In practice, money is rarely put away into a sinking fund. However, it is a valuable economic concept.

A worked example

We can now proceed to work out a very simple cost-benefit analysis to demonstrate the use of the formulae. As the example involves a comparison between recurrent expenditure and capital costs, both the "present-day value" and the "annual equivalent" method are equally appropriate, and it is worked out both ways to show that the two methods obtain the same result.

EXAMPLE

Comparison of cost of providing a mechanical stoker for a boiler with the cost of employing a fireman, assuming the life of the installation is twenty years and the interest rate is 8% per annum.

1. *Present day value*
    (a) Fireman's wages etc. say £8,000 p.a.
        3 men (three shifts per day) = £24,000 p.a.
        £1 for twenty years at 8% = £9.82 (Table 4)

                                 24,000 × £9.82   £235,680

(b) Cost of mechanical firing equipment, together with con-
sequent alterations to boiler house.   £200,000

Total saving by using mechanical firing   £35,680

2. *Annual equivalent*
(a) Firemen's wages etc. (as above)   £24,000
(b) 8% interest on cost of mechanical firing
equipment, etc. (£200,000)   £16,000
(c) Sinking fund to repay capital cost of the
equipment at the end of twenty years.
(Taken at 8% although it is common
practice to adopt a lower interest rate for
this purpose)
£200,000 at 2.2p   £4,400
                                                   £20,400
                                                                                         £20,400

Annual saving by use of mechanical firing   £3,600
⎰ Note: Table 5 can be used to combine stages (b) and (c)

3. *Check*
£3,600 for twenty years at 8% (Table 4)   £35,352
                                                               approximately
                                                          the same as the capital
                                                              saving of £35,680

Note that in order to keep the example simple, various extra factors
(like maintenance, different type of fuel, etc.) have been ignored.

It is important that the principle of these techniques should be
understood, as they have to be used extensively in cost studies and are
referred to and developed throughout the rest of the book.

Cash flow

We have seen that project planning needs to take into account not just
the total lump sum involved but the timing of the various payments and
receipts. This is the concept of "cash flow"; there is a positive flow
when money is received into an organisation and a negative flow when
money is paid out.

Cash flow is a valuable concept because it enables us to look at the
financing of a project in a different light. We shall first look at its uses in
connection with the finance of a project by a building contractor,
because it is here that its influence is most dramatic, although it is
equally applicable to the client's finances, as we shall see in due course.

Cash flow and the building contractor

As an example a simple contract for a £410,000 building, to be erected in 30 weeks, has been chosen. The prime cost to the contractor is £400,000, leaving £10,000 profit. This represents 2½% on turnover, which is fairly usual, but the real profit percentage may be very different to this miserable figure which is so often quoted as an example of the poor financial returns of the building industry.

In Table 1 is shown the weekly outlay on labour, plant hire and overheads, the weekly value of material deliveries, and the sub-contractors' accounts which are received monthly. The table also shows the total prime cost at the end of each month together with the surveyor's valuation.

In this particular example it is assumed that 10% of the value of the work is withheld by the client each month as "retention" until the total of the retention fund amounts to £25,000, after which remaining work is paid for in full. This arrangement would be less generous to the contractor than the current requirements of the British JCT Standard Form of Building Contract, and if this Form was being used the contractor would have rather more cash in hand than is shown in the examples.

It will be seen from Table 1 on page 47 that as usual the job gets into its stride slowly, following the normal "S-curve" of expenditure

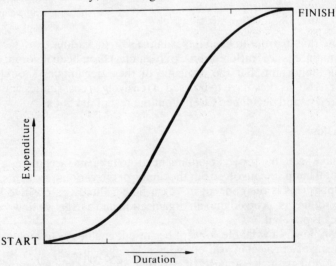

FIG. 4.1. *Typical S-curve of project expenditure plotted against duration*

plotted against time (Fig. 4.1), and because much of the early expenditure is in any case related to setting-up rather than producing finished work the first surveyor's valuation does not meet the full cost. By the time the job is halfway through it is showing a handsome profit (perhaps the "loading" of Bill rates for the early trades may have helped) although the finishing-off, again as usual, is not very profitable.

TABLE 1

Week No.	Wages, plant hire and overheads	Materials delivered	Sub-contractors accounts received	Total prime cost and overheads	QS valuation	Valuation less retention
	£	£	£	£	£	£
March 1	1,000	2,000				
2	1,500	1,000				
3	1,500	1,000				
4	2,000	3,000		13,000	10,000	9,000
April 5	3,000	10,000				
6	3,000	10,000				
7	3,000	6,000				
8	4,000	6,000	10,000	68,000	70,000	63,000
May 9	4,000	10,000				
10	4,000	3,000				
11	5,000	20,000				
12	5,000	10,000				
13	5,000	10,000	10,000	154,000	170,000	153,000
June 14	5,000	17,000				
15	6,000	15,000				
16	6,000	10,000				
17	5,000	5,000	10,000	233,000	250,000	225,000 (max retention now withheld)
July 18	5,000	5,000				
19	5,000	10,000				
20	4,000	5,000				
21	3,000	3,000	30,000	303,000	325,000	300,000
Aug. 22	3,000	2,000				
23	3,000	—				
24	2,000	5,000				
25	2,000	—				
26	2,000	5,000	30,000	357,000	375,000	350,000
Sept. 27	4,000	10,000				
28	4,000	—				
29	3,000	—				
30	2,000	—	20,000	400,000	410,000	385,000
Total	106,000	184,000	110,000	400,000	410,000	385,000
					retention	25,000
						£410,000

TABLE 2. PAYMENTS AND RECEIPTS BASED ON TABLE 1

	Week No.	Payments			Total	Amounts received	Cumulative cash flow
		Wages etc.	Materials	Sub-contractors			
		£	£	£	£	£	£
March	1	1,000			1,000		−1,000
	2	1,500			1,500		−2,500
	3	1,500			1,500		−4,000
	4	2,000			2,000		−6,000
April	5	3,000			3,000		−9,000
	6	3,000			3,000	9,000	−3,000
	7	3,000			3,000		−6,000
	8	4,000	7,000 (March)		11,000		−17,000
May	9	4,000			4,000		−21,000
	10	4,000		9,000	13,000	54,000	+20,000
	11	5,000			5,000		+15,000
	12	5,000			5,000		+10,000
	13	5,000	32,000 (April)		37,000		−27,000
June	14	5,000			5,000		−32,000
	15	6,000		9,000	15,000	90,000	+43,000
	16	6,000			6,000		+37,000
	17	5,000	53,000 (May)		58,000		−21,000
July	18	5,000			5,000		−26,000
	19	5,000		9,000	14,000	72,000	+32,000
	20	4,000			4,000		+28,000
	21	3,000	47,000 (June)		50,000		−22,000
August	22	3,000			3,000		−25,000
	23	3,000		27,000	30,000	75,000	+20,000
	24	2,000			2,000		+18,000
	25	2,000			2,000		+16,000
	26	2,000	23,000 (July)		25,000		−9,000
Sept.	27	4,000			4,000		−13,000
	28	4,000		27,000	31,000	50,000	+6,000
	29	3,000			3,000		+3,000
	30	2,000	12,000 (August)		14,000		−11,000
October	32			18,000	18,000	35,000	+13,000
		Release of retention		5,500	5,500	12,500	
	34		10,000 (September)		10,000		+3,000
April	60	Release of retention		5,500	5,500	12,500	+10,000
	Total	106,000	184,000	110,000	400,000	410,000	(10,000)

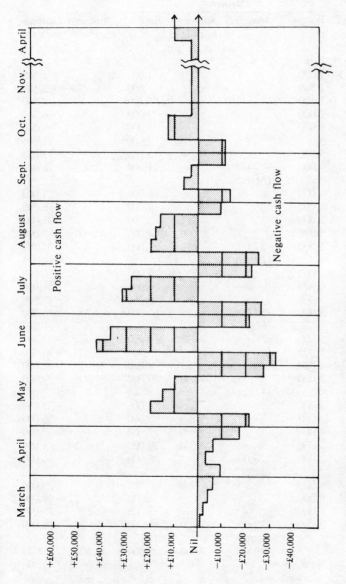

Positive cash flow

Negative cash flow

Fig. 4.2. *Diagram showing cumulative cash flow as Table 2*

TABLE 3. AS TABLE 2 BUT WITH LATE AND UNDERESTIMATED PAYMENTS BY CLIENT

	Week No.	Payments Wages etc.	Payments Materials	Payments Sub-contractors	Total	Amounts received	Cumulative cash flow
		£	£	£	£	£	£
March	1	1,000			1,000		−1,000
	2	1,500			1,500		−2,500
	3	1,500			1,500		−4,000
	4	2,000			2,000		−6,000
April	5	3,000			3,000		−9,000
	6	3,000			3,000		−12,000
	7	3,000			3,000		−15,000
	8	4,000	7,000 (March)		11,000	8,000	−18,000
May	9	4,000			4,000		−22,000
	10	4,000			4,000		−26,000
	11	5,000			5,000		−31,000
	12	5,000		9,000	14,000	52,000	+7,000
	13	5,000	32,000 (April)		37,000		−30,000
June	14	5,000			5,000		−35,000
	15	6,000			6,000		−41,000
	16	6,000			6,000		−47,000
	17	5,000	53,000 (May)	9,000	67,000	88,000	−26,000
July	18	5,000			5,000		−31,000
	19	5,000			5,000		−36,000
	20	4,000			4,000		−40,000
	21	3,000	47,000 (June)	9,000	59,000	70,000	−29,000
Aug.	22	3,000			3,000		−32,000
	23	3,000			3,000		−35,000
	24	2,000			2,000		−37,000
	25	2,000		27,000	29,000	75,000	+9,000
	26	2,000	23,000 (July)		25,000		−16,000
Sept.	27	4,000			4,000		−20,000
	28	4,000			4,000		−24,000
	29	3,000			3,000		−27,000
	30	2,000	12,000 (August)	27,000	41,000	48,000	−20,000
Oct.	34		10,000 (Sept.)	18,000	28,000	34,000	
		Release of retention		5,500	5,500	12,500	−7,000
May	64	Release of retention		5,500	5,500	22,500	+10,000
	Total	106,000	184,000	110,000	400,000	410,000	(10,000)

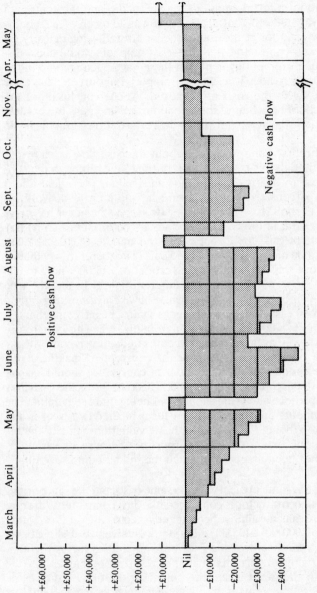

Fig. 4.3. *Diagram showing cumulative cash flow as Table 3*

Table 2 illustrates the contractor's cash flow, on the assumption that everything goes as it should. The client pays the amounts of the valuations about a fortnight after they are made, and the contractor pays the nominated sub-contractors as soon as he receives the money. Materials are paid for at the end of the month following delivery (in practice the sub-contractors and materials suppliers would allow discounts for such prompt payment, but these have been ignored in the example in order to keep it reasonably simple). Labour, etc., has to be paid for weekly as the costs are incurred. At the conclusion of the project the client pays half of the retention sum and pays the balance six months later. The cash flow in Table 2 is also shown graphically in Fig. 4.2.

What is the first thing we notice about the cash flow as shown in Table 2? Although this is a £410,000 contract, and although the contractor is certainly bearing the risk (and undertaking the organisation) of a project of this size, such a figure has nothing to do with his financing of the job. Except for one or two weeks he never has more than £25,000 sunk in the contract and in fact he often has no money invested in it at all—for example, by the middle of June he has received £43,000 more than he has paid out. If we therefore say that he could carry out the job on a working capital of £25,000, his £10,000 profit is not 2½% but 40%, a very different figure! In fact the true situation is even better than this, because his *average* working capital (setting positive cash flows in some weeks against negative in others) is much less than £25,000, as can be seen from Fig. 4.2. This is therefore not a £410,000 job, as far as the contractor's budgeting is concerned.

Before we become too excited at the prospect of making 100% (or more) per annum profit as a matter of course, we should look at Table 3 and the accompanying Fig. 4.3. This represents the cash flow on the same project where the client is not being quite so helpful. The monthly payments are being delayed for a further two weeks, and the surveyor is being "prudent" with his valuations, finally under-certifying to the extent of £10,000 (possibly because of variations which have not been agreed), although the full amount is eventually paid over.

This is still the same project with the same costs and the same profit, but as far as the contractor is concerned it is on a completely different scale. He now has an almost permanently negative cash flow, often amounting to £30,000–£40,000; this job will involve two or three times the capital commitment of the previous one and as far as the contractor's financing is concerned it is a project of more than double the size, although the profit is still the same. On the other hand, if the contractor were to complain the client might wonder what all the fuss was about; as Fig. 4.4 shows, the effect of the different payment pattern on his own cash flow is proportionately very small. Many

FIG. 4.4. *Diagram showing client's cash flow as Tables 2 and 3*

TABLE 4. As TABLE 3 BUT WITH ONE MONTH'S DELAY IN PAYMENTS TO MATERIALS SUPPLIERS

	Week No.	Wages etc.	Materials	Sub-contractors	Total	Amounts received	Cumulative cash flow
		£	£	£	£	£	£
March	1	1,000			1,000		−1,000
	2	1,500			1,500		−2,500
	3	1,500			1,500		−4,000
	4	2,000			2,000		−6,000
April	5	3,000			3,000		−9,000
	6	3,000			3,000		−12,000
	7	3,000			3,000		−15,000
	8	4,000			4,000	8,000	−11,000
May	9	4,000			4,000		−15,000
	10	4,000			4,000		−19,000
	11	5,000			5,000		−24,000
	12	5,000		9,000	14,000	52,000	+14,000
	13	5,000	7,000 (March)		12,000		+2,000
June	14	5,000			5,000		−3,000
	15	6,000			6,000		−9,000
	16	6,000			6,000		−15,000
	17	5,000	32,000 (April)	9,000	46,000	88,000	+27,000
July	18	5,000			5,000		+22,000
	19	5,000			5,000		+17,000
	20	4,000			4,000		+13,000
	21	3,000	53,000 (May)	9,000	65,000	70,000	+18,000
Aug.	22	3,000			3,000		+15,000
	23	3,000			3,000		+12,000
	24	2,000			2,000		+10,000
	25	2,000		27,000	29,000	75,000	+56,000
	26	2,000	47,000 (June)		49,000		+7,000
Sept.	27	4,000			4,000		+3,000
	28	4,000			4,000		−1,000
	29	3,000			3,000		−4,000
	30	2,000	23,000 (July)	27,000	52,000	48,000	−8,000
Oct.	34		12,000 (August)	18,000	30,000	34,000	}+3,000
		Release of retention		5,500	5,500	12,500	
Nov.	38		10,000 (Sept.)		10,000		−7,000
May	64	Release of retention		5,500	5,500	22,500	+10,000
	Total	106,000	184,000	110,000	400,000	410,000	(10,000)

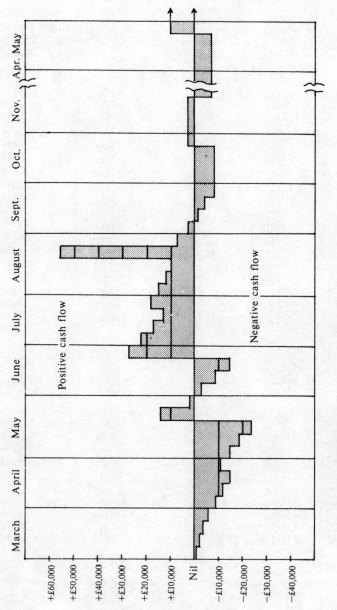

FIG. 4.5. *Diagram showing cumulative cash flow as Table* 4

TABLE 5. AS TABLE 2 BUT BUILDER'S WORK UNDERESTIMATED BY 10%, AND ONE MONTH'S DELAY IN PAYMENTS TO MATERIALS SUPPLIERS

	Week No.	Payments				Amounts received	Cumulative cash flow
		Wages etc.	Materials	Sub-contractors	Total		
		£	£	£	£	£	£
March	1	1,000			1,000		−1,000
	2	1,500			1,500		−2,500
	3	1,500			1,500		−4,000
	4	2,000			2,000		−6,000
April	5	3,000			3,000		−9,000
	6	3,000			3,000	8,100	−3,900
	7	3,000			3,000		−6,900
	8	4,000			4,000		−10,900
May	9	4,000			4,000		−14,900
	10	4,000		9,000	13,000	49,500	+21,600
	11	5,000			5,000		+16,600
	12	5,000			5,000		+11,600
	13	5,000	7,000 (March)		12,000		−400
June	14	5,000			5,000		−5,400
	15	6,000		9,000	15,000	81,900	+61,500
	16	6,000			6,000		+55,500
	17	5,000	32,000 (April)		37,000		+18,500
July	18	5,000			5,000		+13,500
	19	5,000		9,000	14,000	65,700	+65,200
	20	4,000			4,000		+61,200
	21	3,000	53,000 (May)		56,000		+5,200
Aug.	22	3,000			3,000		+2,200
	23	3,000		27,000	30,000	70,500	+42,700
	24	2,000			2,000		+40,700
	25	2,000			2,000		+38,700
	26	2,000	47,000 (June)		49,000		−10,300
Sept.	27	4,000			4,000		−14,300
	28	4,000		27,000	31,000	48,000	+2,700
	29	3,000			3,000		−300
	30	2,000	23,000 (July)		25,000		−25,300
Oct.	32			18,000	18,000	33,500 ⎫	⎫ −3,900
		Release of retention		5,500	5,500	11,400 ⎭	⎭
	34		12,000 (August)		12,000		−15,900
Nov.	38		10,000 (Sept.)		10,000		−25,900
April	60	Release of retention		5,500	5,500	11,400	−20,000
	Total	106,000	184,000	110,000	400,000	380,000	(−20,000)

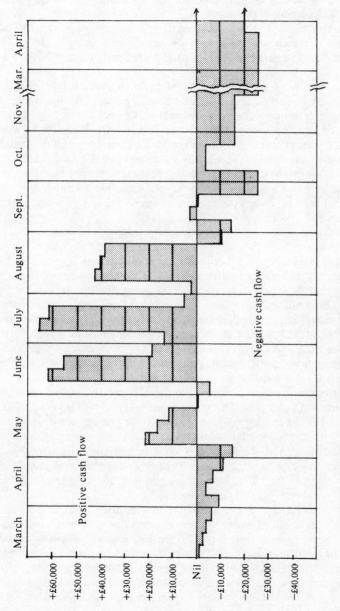

FIG. 4.6. *Diagram showing cumulative cash flow as Table 5*

contractors would confirm that this kind of situation is neither unusual nor does it be any means represent the worst that may befall them as regards deferring of payments.

The contractor's remedy is often to defer payment in turn to his own suppliers, which in the above example could more than restore the cash flow figures to their former satisfactory state (Table 4 and Fig. 4.5).

It is possible that delaying payment in this way might cause the contractor to forfeit some of the cash discounts which the materials suppliers give him. These are normally of the order of $2\frac{1}{2}\%$; in the event of all the suppliers refusing to give him the discount he would stand to lose a total of £4,600, although in practice it would be unlikely that more than a few would do so unless the delays became very serious. He might be prepared to accept the loss of a few cash discounts as a small price to pay for the benefit of cash flow so much improved that he could carry out the project without any capital commitment at all after the first 16 weeks.

Finally, however, a dreadful warning: suppose we have an exactly similar job, where the client pays punctually and fully (as in the first example) but where the contractor has underpriced his work by 10% and is therefore not going to make £10,000 profit but £20,000 loss; also, because of financial difficulties, he is paying his suppliers one month late. The resultant cash flow (Table 5 and Fig. 4.6) looks eminently satisfactory until the end of the project in September; it is in many ways better than that of the soundly managed contractor in Figs 4.2 and 4.5, and requires a working capital of about £10,000 for a few weeks only. However, instead of a handsome profit this contractor will finish by losing the whole of his working capital twice over. If he has several such jobs going on concurrently, so that the negative cash flows on one coincide with the positive flows on another, he will be able to keep trading for some time before the crash comes and meanwhile his cash flow figures may look fairly healthy.

It will be seen how difficult it is to distinguish the early symptoms of insolvency when looking at a contractor's accounts, and indeed it is quite possible that a badly managed contracting firm may not itself realise what is happening until it is too late.

When times are bad in the building industry it is common for contractors to submit very low tenders in order to obtain work and so keep their organisation employed, and they can then easily become short of cash. It is also not unknown for contractors who have already got into this position, either for the above reason or through bad management, to continue to quote absurdly low prices. This is because they urgently need the cash flow from new work in order to pay their past debts; if the contractor in the above example is receiving payments on another job by September he will be able to pay his suppliers and keep going (although the new job in turn will be getting into even worse difficulties in due course and will need an even more drastic dose of the same medicine). Quantity surveyors do well to be suspicious of a building company which is expanding its operations rapidly at prices which its competitors cannot match.

However, we can see from the earlier examples that even a soundly managed contractor will find it very tempting to get deeply into debt at the bank if he is able to get returns of more than 50% on money which he is borrowing at less than 15%.

So cash flow assessment of accounts must be used carefully, but these examples do demonstrate that quite small percentage differences in estimating can have a dramatic effect on profitability. This is in fact the principal weakness of the construction industry, that the difference between a substantial profit on capital and a substantial loss can lie inside the normal margin of error in estimating. A greater capital investment in a project on the part of contractors might lead to greater stability, as the required profit on turnover would then have to be much higher than 1% or 2%. If the contractor had to make 10% profit on turnover to get a reasonable return on capital, then estimating errors of 2% or so would have a proportionately smaller effect on his overall profit percentage and would not make the difference between "boom or bust". Any move to reduce "retentions" will have exactly the opposite effect.

Discounted cash flow

In the above examples we have forgotten about the time/money relationship. However, following from what was written earlier we realise that, for example, the £6,000 negative cash flow in the fourth week of Table 2 must be worth more than the £6,000 positive flow in the twenty-eighth week. If we therefore discount all the payments and receipts to a common date we shall be able to measure the true profitablity of the project. There are basically two ways in which this can be done.

Rate of return

This involves calculating the "rate of return" on the working capital, and could be used to show the profit as a percentage of average working capital in the kind of study we have been looking at in Tables 2–5. Unfortunately this cannot be done very easily without a computer, because it involves "trial-and-error" experiments with different discount rates until a rate is found which discounts the total receipts and the total expenditure to exactly the same present-day figure, but it is the only DCF method which shows the profit as a percentage on capital employed.

As a matter of interest, the rates of return on the contractor's working capital in two of the previous examples are as follows:

Table 2   270% per annum
Table 3   42% per annum

and as proof the figures in Table 3 are shown again in Table 6, discounted at 42% per annum, or 0.80% per week.

TABLE 6. AS TABLE 3, DISCOUNTED TO BEGINNING OF WEEK 1 AT 42% P.A.
(0.8% PER WEEK)

		Actual cash flow		Discounted cash flow	
	Week No.	Negative	Positive	Negative	Positive
March	1	1,000		990	
	2	1,500		1,480	
	3	1,500		1,470	
	4	2,000		1,940	
April	5	3,000		2,880	
	6	3,000		2,860	
	7	3,000		2,840	
	8	11,000	8,000	10,320	7,510
May	9	4,000		3,720	
	10	4,000		3,690	
	11	5,000		4,580	
	12	14,000	52,000	12,720	47,260
	13	37,000		33,360	
June	14	5,000		4,470	
	15	6,000		5,320	
	16	6,000		5,280	
	17	67,000	88,000	58,510	76,850
July	18	5,000		4,330	
	19	5,000		4,300	
	20	4,000		3,410	
	21	59,000	70,000	49,910	59,220
August	22	3,000		2,520	
	23	3,000		2,500	
	24	2,000		1,650	
	25	29,000	75,000	23,760	61,450
	26	25,000		20,320	
September	27	4,000		3,230	
	28	4,000		3,200	
	29	3,000		2,380	
	30	41,000	48,000	32,280	37,800
October	34	33,500	46,500	25,550	35,470
May	64	5,500	22,500	3,300	13,510
	Total	400,000	410,000	339,070	339,070

Now that we have figures, the enormous difference in return between the Table 2 and Table 3 situation can be seen, caused purely by slightly late and "conservative" payment by the client.

Very high returns, such as the 270%, would be dependent upon the contractor having other projects in progress on which the surplus funds arising from this contract (e.g. the £43,000 in Week 15) could be profitably but temporarily employed at the same rate. It is unlikely that the cash flows of several projects can be perfectly matched, but much the same result could be obtained by ironing out the worst peaks and troughs in the cash flow diagram, for example by delaying payment to some merchants for a week or two and making up for it by paying them early in a month when funds are plentiful.

In cases such as this (where there are large positive cash flows quite early in the time scale of the project) the "rate of return" method can be most misleading. It would, for instance, show an annual rate of return of over 200% when applied to Table 5; this money-losing project would therefore appear to be most lucrative *provided* that the contractor was able to earn 200% on the positive cash flow elsewhere in his business. Such projects would better be dealt with by the "NPV at criterion rate of return" method which is next to be described; alternatively the "rate of return" method could be used ignoring any short-term positive cash flows on the basis that it would be difficult to obtain any return on these.

Note that the "rate of return" method cannot be used for calculations where there are no receipts to set against expenditure.

NPV at criterion rate of return

This is a much easier calculation, and will probably be more often used by surveyors in assessing the viability of development. It involves the selection of a "criterion" rate of return, which would be either the rate at which money can be borrowed to finance the project, or else a minimum acceptable profit, depending on the circumstances of the case. The income and expenditure are both discounted at this rate and the difference found; this is the NPV or Net Present Value of the project. If the discounted income exceeds the discounted expenditure then the NPV is positive and represents a profit over and above the criterion rate; if, on the other hand, the discounted expenditure is larger than the discounted income then the NPV will be negative and the project would not service its loan or pay the minimum acceptable profit and is unlikely to be carried out.

It will be realised that this method can be used for two different purposes:

(1) To assess whether a project is worth carrying out.

(2) To see which of two or more alternative solutions is the best from the point of view of cost. (The example on page 44 concerning the mechanical stoker used a criterion rate of return of 8%.) When used in this way there may not be any income to set against expenditure, but unlike the "rate of return" method the "criterion rate" method will work in these conditions; it will of course always show a negative balance, and the scheme with the smallest negative balance will be the best choice.

Examples of "criterion rate" calculations

A simplified investment problem has been chosen as an example. A plot of land is being bought for £400,000, a block of flats is to be erected and the whole development disposed of for £1,350,000.

TABLE 7

End of month:		Case A £	Case B £	
	1	− 400,000	− 400,000	(land purchase)
	3	—	− 20,000	
	4	− 20,000	—	(professional fees)
	5	—	− 20,000	
	6	—	− 30,000	
	7	—	− 50,000	
	8	− 20,000	− 70,000	
	9	—	− 90,000	
	10	− 20,000	− 110,000	
	11	− 30,000	− 90,000	
	12	− 30,000	− 80,000	
	13	− 30,000	− 70,000	
	14	− 40,000	− 60,000	(payments to
	15	− 40,000	− 50,000	builder
	16	− 50,000	—	and professional
	17	− 50,000	—	fees)
	18	− 60,000	—	
	19	− 70,000	—	
	20	− 60,000	—	
	21	− 40,000	—	
	22	− 40,000	—	
	23	− 30,000	—	
	24	− 30,000	—	
		− 1,060,000	− 1,140,000	
Sale		1,350,000 (month 24)	1,350,000 (month 15)	
Profit		£290,000	£210,000	

In "Case A" full drawings and Bill of Quantities are to be prepared and tenders invited for a building contract of 15 months duration at a cost (including professional fees) of £660,000.

In "Case B" the project is to be started before full documentation has been prepared and the building programme will be compressed into 10 months. However, the result of this rush will be a cost (including fees) of £740,000.

It is required to examine these two programmes to see which would be the more profitable. The cash flows are set out in Table 7.

Suppose that a criterion rate of 12% p.a. is chosen. This will be equivalent to 1% per monthly period and so the two alternatives can be discounted using the 1% DCF tables (Appendix D—Table 3).

TABLE 8

End month:	Case A			Case B		
1	$- 400,000 \times 99.0p =$	$- 396,040$		$- 400,000 \times 99.0p =$	$- 396.040$	
3				$- 20,000 \times 98.0p =$	$- 19,410$	
4	$- 20,000 \times 96.1p =$	$- 19,220$				
5				$- 20,000 \times 95.1p =$	$- 19,030$	
6				$- 30,000 \times 94.2p =$	$- 28,260$	
7				$- 50,000 \times 93.3p =$	$- 46,630$	
8	$- 20,000 \times 92.3p =$	$- 18,470$		$- 70,000 \times 92.3p =$	$- 64,640$	
9				$- 90,000 \times 91.4p =$	$- 82,290$	
10	$- 20,000 \times 90.5p =$	$- 18,110$		$- 110,000 \times 90.5p =$	$- 99,580$	
11	$- 30,000 \times 89.6p =$	$- 26,890$		$- 90,000 \times 89.6p =$	$- 80,670$	
12	$- 30,000 \times 88.7p =$	$- 26,620$		$- 80,000 \times 88.7p =$	$- 71,000$	
13	$- 30,000 \times 87.9p =$	$- 26,360$		$- 70,000 \times 87.9p =$	$- 61,510$	
14	$- 40,000 \times 87.0p =$	$- 34,800$		$- 60,000 \times 87.0p =$	$- 52,200$	
15	$- 40,000 \times 86.1p =$	$- 34,450$		$+ 1,300,000 \times 86.1p =$	$+1,119,750$	
16	$- 50,000 \times 85.3p =$	$- 42,640$		NPV =	£98,490	
17	$- 50,000 \times 84.4p =$	$- 42,220$				
18	$- 60,000 \times 83.6p =$	$- 50,160$				
19	$- 70,000 \times 82.8p =$	$- 57,940$				
20	$- 60,000 \times 82.0p =$	$- 49,170$				
21	$- 40,000 \times 81.1p =$	$- 32,460$				
22	$- 40,000 \times 80.3p =$	$- 32,140$				
23	$- 30,000 \times 79.5p =$	$- 23,860$				
24	$2+1,320,000 \times 78.8p =$	$+1,039,590$				
	NPV	£108,040				

It will be seen from Table 8 that both schemes would be profitable assuming 12% per annum as a criterion rate of return, although the profit of Case A would have a present value of £108,040 while the profit of Case B would be slightly lower at £98,490. In these circumstances it would appear to be more profitable to go for the longer and less expensive contract arrangements.

If, however, the criterion rate of return was 15%, the NPV's would be reduced to £70,160 (Case A) and £73,770 (Case B). Both schemes are still profitable, but with higher interest rates the shorter and more expensive scheme now shows the better profit.

In Fig. 4.7 the NPV and rate of return for the two schemes is shown graphically. It will be seen that Case A is much the more profitable at low interest rates, that both schemes show an equal NPV of about £82,000 at 14%, and that Case B becomes relatively more and more attractive as the required rates of return rise above this point. Case A ceases to be profitable if a rate of more than 21% is required, and Case B at 25%.

This demonstrates the point that if a high rate of return is required it is usually worthwhile to compress the design/building period even if this results in a less efficient building process and higher cost.

Care required with DCF techniques

These discounting techniques are very useful in enabling a project to be looked at from the point of view of profitablity. By themselves, however, they only tell part of the story and it is vital that the cash flow situation should be considered as a whole before a decision is made. For this purpose the undiscounted figures for each period should also be looked at, either in tabular form as Table 7 or, better still, in diagram form as in Figs 4.2, 4.3, etc.

In looking at Table 7, for instance, we can see that Case B not only requires a higher capital commitment, but also requires it over a much shorter period. By the end of the first year Case A requires an investment of £520,000 whereas Case B requires no less than £960,000, and the client may not be able to raise this amount of money in the time available. From this point of view Case A might suit a client who was committed to a number of developments in progress simultaneously, while a client who liked to finish one development at a time and then go on to the next might prefer Case B. This question of keeping capital expenditure to a minimum, or of phasing payments, might be more important than a small difference in NPV.

A further factor which could offset any advantage which Case B might have over Case A would be the inflation of property prices. Since the price of houses and flats in many parts of the country has been increasing more rapidly than the general rate of inflation it is possible that the flats which would sell for £1,350,000 at the end of 15 months might sell for £1,500,000 at the end of 24 months, so destroying the previous calculations and giving an advantage to Case A.

It is worthwhile remembering that undiscounted cash flow statements and diagrams can be very useful in the social development field, where the funding of capital expenditure may be done on a quarterly or yearly basis, and it is useful to be able to plan which period the expenditure will fall into. This topic is developed in greater detail in Chapter 13.

FIG. 4.7. *Diagram showing NPV at different rates of return for Cases A and B*

While DCF appraisals are useful, they must be used with discretion. In any case, DCF assessment of investment can only really work if there are quantifiable receipts to set against expenditure; otherwise it merely proves that the less that is done, and the slower it is done, and the longer it can be put off, the better. Unlike straightforward cash flow statements, it therefore has little place in programming a purely social development, although it can be used for cost comparisons of alternative solutions within a given time scale.

Chapter 5
Development Budgets

A feature of all cost planning and control procedures is the setting of a budget, and the subsequent budgetary control which is exercised to make sure that the client's financial resources are not overspent. At the root of any budget for a specific design is the allowance made by the developer for the building in the overall costs of the project, which as we have already seen will include such items as the cost of land, legal fees, design fees, external works, loan charges, interest on money expended during development, and advertising costs as well as the building cost itself. In commercial development there is a very close relationship between how much the project will produce in revenue and its commercial value, the latter being largely the capitalised value of the former, and the total costs of the scheme must not exceed this commercial value. In social development this relationship may be expressed in cost-benefit terms, by quantifying what are considered to be social benefits, but the issue is never so clear cut and other criteria may be more important in assessing the amount that can be spent on the scheme. As we have seen, one of the most important items on any developers balance sheet is the cost of the land and we must now consider this aspect.

Land values and development

This is really the specialist province of the valuation surveyor, but anybody who is involved in cost planning of buildings needs to have some knowledge of the factors affecting the costs of land for development.

Like the prices of other commodities, land values are affected by the laws of supply and demand. However, unlike, say, sugar, the amount of land available in any one area is finite and cannot be increased at times of high demand by manufacturing at a higher rate, or bringing some in from outside. This means that if there is a high demand in a particular area the prices of land in the locality will rise very steeply, even though similar land may still be cheap fifty miles away.

Building development of any kind requires a plot of land on which it can take place, and which, once used, will no longer be available for any other development, unless the first one is either demolished or converted. The "development value" of a piece of land is the difference between the cost of erecting or converting buildings on it and the market price of the finished development (including the land). Nobody can commission building operations on a piece of land unless they have an interest in it; if possible they would wish to own it, so as to obtain the full benefit of the "development value", although in some areas where land is in very short supply they may have to lease it.

The development value of land will be determined by:

(1) Its position—both its geographical region and its local position in that region in regard to amenities, communications, etc.

(2) Restrictions on its use, either imposed by the vendors in the form of covenants, or by the community in the form of planning restrictions.

(3) Any "easements" which go with the land, such as right of way across it.

(4) The physical state of the land—whether it is level or very hilly, and whether there are buildings on it which need to be demolished.

(5) The current state of the economy.

To illustrate how the value may be determined by position, we can do a simple cost-benefit analysis showing the cost effect of a family house in an inner London suburb compared to a similar house in the outer commuter area, from the point of view of somebody employed in London.

Annual cost	£	£
London house, building society repayments		
(after tax rebate)	3,500	
Annual season ticket to City	250	
Travelling time say 1½ hours per day		
200 days per annum = 300 hours at £5	1,500	
	£5,250	5,250
Similar outer area house, building society repayments		
(after tax rebate)	1,500	
Annual season ticket to City	500	
Travelling time say 3 hours per day		
200 days per annum = 600 hours at £5	3,000	
	£5,000	5,000
Annual saving of outer area house		£250

The annual costs of the two alternatives are fairly equal, and it is this calculation which helps to explain the different prices of two quite similar houses whose actual building costs would be identical.

Effect of building cost on land value

We can express the value of land for development as an equation:

Value of development
= Price of undeveloped land + Building Costs + Profit.

As we have seen, the value of the development in a free market is its worth to the consumer (as compared to other alternatives), and this in turn largely fixes the price of the undeveloped land—the equation can therefore be better expressed as:

Price of undeveloped land
= Value of development − (Building Costs + Profit).

The people selling the undeveloped land should be just as capable of doing this calculation as the developer is, and will fix their selling price accordingly. It is therefore not really correct to say that the cost of land is pushing up the price of housing or other accommodation; in fact it is the other way around—the market price of development pushes up the cost of land.

In conditions where there is a shortage of suitable building land and a constant rise in development values, as in the south-east of England, fluctuations in building costs will have little effect on land prices. However, if the situation were reversed (as it is in some parts of the country) and development values remained constant, then an increase in building costs would have the effect of reducing undeveloped land values. It is usually the price of "undeveloped land" which is the result of the equation, when the other figures have been filled in.

Social considerations

Most people agree that a completely free market in land for development is socially undesirable, and the setting of limits on the scale and nature of development under Town and Country Planning legislation brings a measure of public control to the process. Even so, there is a strong body of opinion that wants to see the public obtain much of the benefit of any increased development value of private land, and this would certainly make it much easier to undertake social development in urban areas.

The more radical members of this group dislike the whole idea of anybody making money which they have not actually earned, but the moderate elements base their arguments upon the loss of green land or other pleasant environment to the community as a whole when development is undertaken for profit, the fact that public expenditure on infrastructure (roads, services, transport systems, etc.) has often contributed to the rise in value, and the way in which decisions taken by the planning authorities are handing windfalls to some lucky land-owners and withholding them from others, thus providing strong incentives for undesirable (or even improper) influence upon those decisions.

Several unsuccessful attempts have been made by British governments to deal with the problem, including the Town and Country Planning Act of 1947 and the Community Land Act of 1975. These Acts tended to inhibit development of any kind, as landowners had little incentive to allow their land to be built on, and preferred to wait until a fresh government repealed the legislation. However, so that the community does not actually lose money over private development, the developer may often be asked to contribute towards infrastructure costs as a condition of the granting of planning approval. The agreement of these costs is obviously an area where the cost advisers on both sides should be involved. An interesting technique has been used in recent years in Hong Kong, where the new underground railway system has been largely financed from the increase in development values in the areas around its suburban stations.

Effect of land values on cost planning techniques

It is possible to try and optimise building costs by looking at such factors as low wall/floor ratios, the avoidance of multi-storey construction, the centralisation of services, and so on, in isolation from land costs. Where land prices are relatively low this may be a perfectly valid way of looking at the problem.

However, where development values and land prices are high the picture alters somewhat. Suppose that the current price of flats in a fashionable urban area is 20% building cost and 80% land cost (and profit) and a piece of land has been bought at a price which assumes that 20 flats can be built on it. If it should prove possible to build more than 20 flats on the same piece of land, the building cost of these extra flats would be only 20% of their market value, leaving 80% profit. It would therefore be worthwhile to accept a less efficient building configuration to provide these extra flats—even if this increased the building cost slightly there would still be a handsome profit.

In these circumstances cost planning may develop into an exercise to secure the maximum number of accommodation units on a given site, at the same time optimising the design from the point of view of grants and subsidies (if there are any of these to be had). Unfortunately for the developer, a scheme which squeezes the utmost in hard cash out of the site is rarely acceptable to the planning authorities, who have more regard for the amenities and appearance of the neighbourhood. Their veto on a scheme is final, apart from the possibility of a lengthy and time-consuming appeal to the central government (which has the same general motivation).

On such projects the costing and income appraisal of many alternative schemes will be required, and this will be the main cost planning contribution. Once a scheme has been approved by the authorities speed may be vital (because of the need to recover a massive investment as soon as possible), and the surveyor will be required to advise on a suitable contractual system to achieve speed with an appropriate measure of cost control.

However, not all private development is of this speculative kind. The client may be wishing to erect a building for his own use—as offices, warehouse, store, etc. In this case the effect of high land costs on the cost planning exercise should be to cause an examination of the economics of possible alternatives—perhaps carrying out the development in a less expensive area, or possibly changing the client's requirements for a building by solving his problem in another way. An example of the latter might be to avoid the cost of branch warehouses by a system of daily distribution from the factory. It might be thought that there would be an advantage in building in a high cost area because the firm would always have the value of the site on its books, but there are many disadvantages in having too many of a firm's assets tied up in site values.

Grants, subsidies, and taxation concessions

Whilst action under Town and Country Planning legislation can prevent undesirable development it cannot cause socially desirable development to be undertaken. It can certainly earmark a certain area for a particular type of development, but unless the development itself is to be carried out by a public agency, or unless it is obviously going to be highly profitable, the matter will rest there. In order to make such development attractive to a private investor the government may therefore offer special financial inducements. They are usually offered on a sector basis (e.g. for hotel or other tourist building) or on a regional basis, or both (e.g. for factories in an area of high unemployment). These incentives will need to be taken into account in preparing budgets for the type of development concerned, and may be of crucial importance in deciding between alternative sites. The extent to which incentives of this kind may be nothing more than compensation for straightforward commercial disadvantages, such as high transport costs, will certainly emerge from such calculations.

The incentives may be of several different kinds:

(a) *Low rent or rates.* Land (or even completed buildings) may be made available by a public body at a very low rent or with substantial relief from local authority rates, or both. This concession usually runs for a limited period of years, after which more normal conditions will apply, so that some kind of DCF analysis will probably be necessary.

(b) *Grant towards capital costs.* The Department of Industry provides grants towards the cost of factory building and plant located in "areas for expansion", and an increasing number of authorities provide partial funding for new development, rehabilitation, or improvement in the fields of tourism, leisure, conservation, etc. The situation is always changing over the years as different political priorities come into play. A most important factor in assessing the value of such a grant is its timing in relation to the developer's expenditure, particularly whether it is a reimbursement or an advance.

(c) *Taxation relief.* Taxation relief may be given under some circumstances on development and plant costs. The main disadvantage of taxation relief compared to a grant is that there must be a tax liability against which the relief can be set. It is therefore necessary to make a profit before the benefit can be obtained.

It should be noted that other forms of financial encouragement, such as a subsidy paid for each person employed, may need to be taken into account in a development budget even though strictly speaking it is not a grant towards the development itself. It is also worth pointing out that it is possible for the government to impose financial disincentives for types of development of which it does not approve. The lack of grants for industrial building in some regions can be seen as such; a more extreme example has been the long-term discouragement of private rental housing development by fixing rents at uneconomic levels.

Social development

In the past the costs of site acquisition have usually been ignored in cost planning social development, at any rate as far as the quantity surveyor is concerned. It has already been explained that one cannot prepare a profit-investment appraisal for such projects, and the cost of the land is just one of the many items on the expenditure side with which no comparison with income can be made. However, there is an increasing tendency to use the profit-development type of calculation on social projects, such as housing, where there is a real or hypothetical income.

Cost of financing the project

This is the intangible component of total building cost; all the other things like buying land, paying professional fees, etc., involve paying money to somebody else in exchange for something.

As soon as this tangible expenditure starts, however, the developer will be laying out his money, and there will be nothing to show for it in terms of income (or use) until the building is ready for occupation or can be disposed of. Hence the cost of lending this money to the development for a period of possibly several years becomes part of the cost of the development itself. When interest rates are high this financing cost can be considerable, so that the project should be planned to avoid unnecessarily early expenditure on any part of it.

Where the money comes from

The capital for the development may come from a number of alternative sources.

Private development

(a) Bank overdraft. This is rarely available as a means of financing a whole development, but may be useful for short term bridging purposes; the money is lent on the security of the development.

(b) Loan from merchant bank or insurance company. This is similar to the last, except that it is possible to obtain longer term finance from these sources. Interest rates are usually somewhat higher.

(c) Capital account. Where the development is being undertaken for a firm's own use—such as a factory, warehouse, etc.—the capital for the development can be regarded as part of the general capital expenditure of the firm.

(d) Trading funds. Property companies will have funds for carrying on their business.

(e) Shares in the development. Speculative development is sometimes financed by paying the contractor with shares instead of cash.

(f) Finance by the intended occupier. It may be possible to persuade the intended occupier to pay part of the sale price during the erection of the building—this is often the case with houses which are built for sale.

Public (social) development

(g) Government funds. These will be available either as direct finance for government building (e.g. defence works) or as a grant or subsidy for local authority building.

(h) Loans from government funds. These are usually available at a lower rate of interest than money raised on the open market, but are very restricted as to eligibility and amount.

(i) Issue of stock. Local authorities and public boards are empowered to issue fixed-interest loan stock on the Stock Exchange. Full market rates of interest have to be paid, and there is a long term commitment to these which can prove very expensive if interest rates subsequently fall.

(j) Local authority mortgages. These are a useful way of raising money, as there is a firm commitment by both sides, but for a short period of three to five years only. Interest rates are usually a little higher than current yield on gilt-edged securities.

(k) Loans from other funds. A public authority can borrow from its other funds (if it has any) for development purposes.

(l) Rates. It is common for a local authority to raise money for development from the rates—this has the advantage that the money does not have to be paid back!

(m) Private developer. In large-scale urban redevelopment a private developer can be required to undertake some social development in exchange for being allowed to participate in the scheme.

The quantity surveyor and the budget

Many years ago a quantity surveyor was often not appointed until the architect had prepared his working drawings of the final scheme, or, if he were appointed earlier, he would play no part in things until this stage was reached and he could start work on the Bill of Quantities. Things have changed since those days, and now the quantity surveyor is sometimes appointed before any other professional adviser and takes over total responsibility for the client's financial interests in the scheme. However, most appointments fall between these two extremes.

When the quantity surveyor is appointed there are a number of questions which will have a bearing on his concern with the budget, and which need to be answered:

(1) *Who is responsible for his appointment?* If he has been appointed on the recommendation of the client's architect his relations with the client will tend to be conducted through the architect, whereas if his appointment has been made by the client as a result of previous experience or outside recommendation his relationship will usually be more direct. Apart from any other factor, a client who decides to appoint a quantity surveyor directly will probably have an above-average interest in costs,

which will therefore play a predominant part in the scheme design.

(2) *What is his role to be?* This may well be established by the nature of the appointment, as above, but it is important to establish whether the quantity surveyor will be concerned with the total budgeting of the project or whether he will be limited to particular areas, such as capital expenditure, or building and furnishing costs, or net building costs, or indeed whether he will be expected to do anything more than merely prepare a Bill of Quantities.

(3) *Who else has been appointed?* If other appointments have not been made, the quantity surveyor could assist the cost-oriented client in setting up his team of advisers, and this would obviously be of assistance in the context of total cost control.

(4) *What decisions have been made, or steps taken?* Any decisions which have already been taken, or implemented, will obviously constrain any cost optimisation programme which the quantity surveyor may produce. However, he should be very careful about questioning any of these unless his advice is definitely being sought or unless he feels that they are so fundamentally wrong as to make it impossible for him to carry out the task for which he has been appointed. In particular it would only be in the most extraordinary circumstances, and where he was in a very strong position, that he would cast doubts on specialist professional advice which the client had already received from valuers, accountants, lawyers, etc.

(5) *Is cost control to continue until the completion of the project?* In the past it was not unusual for the quantity surveyor's cost control role to finish at the point where a contract was signed with a contractor. In view of the many major problems which can occur subsequently this is a very short-sighted policy, as will be explained in Chapter 13.

It will therefore be seen that the extent to which the surveyor will be able to use the various techniques described in this book depends not only upon the priorities of his client but also upon the terms and circumstances of his appointment. One point which must be remembered is that where the quantity surveyor has been entrusted with the overall cost management of a project he must resist the temptation to make firm proposals to his client based upon his own elementary knowledge of property values, investment, taxation, etc. He is not an expert in these fields (although a large quantity surveying firm might possibly employ such experts) and the purpose of his education in this area is to make him aware of circumstances in which these matters may be important, and to help him in briefing specialists and assessing their advice.

Let us now look at two simple budget examples. These are in no sense "typical", in that every project has its own particular problems and priorities, but they give an idea of the type of basic calculation which is involved. The method of arriving at the various estimated costs has not been shown, as the concern here is how to manipulate the answers.

A budget for a profit-development for sale (24 town houses)

		£	
(a)	Cost of land	500,000	
(b)	Legal and professional cost of acquiring land, obtaining planning permission, etc.	50,000	
(c)	Demolition of existing property	10,000	
(d)	Building cost, and professional fees in connection	480,000	
(e)	Site layout, ditto	20,000	
(f)	Agent's charges for selling	10,000	
		£1,070,000	£1,070,000

		£	
(g)	Cost of finance (1½% per month compound interest—criterion rate of return)		
	Items (a), (b), (c) £560,000 for 12 months =	172,000	
	Item (d), (e) £500,000 for 4 months (av) =	30,000	
	Item (f) is paid after sale, no finance charge =	—	
		£202,000	£202,000
			£1,272,000

Minimum economic selling price = £1,272,000 ÷ 24 = £53,333 say £54,000 per house. Anything less than this will not produce the criterion rate of return, and if there is any doubt about obtaining such a figure then the development should not go ahead in this form.

It will be seen that instead of discounting all expenditure and receipts to the commencing date of the scheme, they have been carried forward to the end of the scheme and compound interest added. This has the same effect—it is easier to do it this way in this instance as it is the future selling price which we are interested in and not its present day value.

A budget for a profit-development (for rental offices)	£	
(a) Cost of land	250,000	
(b) Legal and professional cost of acquiring land, obtaining planning permission, compensation, etc.	85,000	
(c) Demolition	10,000	
(d) Building cost and professional fees in connection	350,000	
	£695,000	£695,000
(e) Cost of finance (1½% per month compound interest—criterion rate of return)		
Items (a), (b) £335,000 for 36 months =	237,850	
Item (c) £10,000 for 18 months =	3,100	
Item (d) £350,000 for 10 months (av) =	56,000	
	£296,950	£296,950
Total capital cost at completion		£991,950
say		£1,000,000
Annual income from rents (figure given by valuer)		£270,000
Less		
Allowance for vacant tenancies (voids)	25,000	
Maintenance, repairs, and redecorations (excluding tenant's responsibilities)	15,000	
Cleaning, heating, lighting, and rates on public part of building (staircases, entrance halls)	25,000	
Management expenses, including caretaker, arranging lettings, and collecting rents	9,000	
Sinking fund to replace capital at end of 40 years at 2½% p.a. £1,000,000 less cost of land (which will still be there when the building is demolished) = £750,000 at 1.5p =	11,250	
	£85,250	£85,250
Net annual income		£184,750

This gives a return of 18½% on the capital of £1,000,000. An alternative way of setting out this budget would be the following, which starts with the current rental value of office accommodation as a criterion.

	£
Estimated annual income from rents	270,000
less expenses (excluding sinking fund)	74,000
	196,000

Note: The cost of the sinking fund cannot be accurately assessed at this stage, as the capital value of the buildings, etc., is not known. It could be approximated thus:

Capitalised value of income at 18½% is approximately £1,040,000. Say 25% of this represents residual land value.

Sinking fund to replace £760,000 at 40 years at 2½% (at 1.5p)	11,400
Estimated net income	£184,600
40 years purchase of £184,600 at 18% (criterion rate of return) at £5.40 =	996,840

This represents the capitalised value of income at the date of completion in 36 months time. Discounted to present value at 1½% per month at 58.5p = £583,151.

	£	£
Present value of income		583,151
Estimated legal and other costs of acquiring land	85,000	
Estimated cost of demolition of existing buildings (PV of £10,000 in 18 months time at 1½% per month = 76.5p per £)	7,650	
Estimated cost of building and professional fees (PV of £350,000 in (average) 26 months time at 1½% per month = 67.9p per £)	237,650	
	£330,300	£330,300
		£252,851
The maximum amount which can be paid for the land at the present time, to give required rate of return say		£250,000

At this stage the calculations would have to be based on the minimum amount of accommodation for which the client could expect to get planning permission, unless an outline scheme had already been approved. It should be noted that taxation provisions, which are constantly changing, have been ignored in these calculations but cannot be ignored in practice.

If budgets of this type are prepared by computer it is possible to examine the effect of changing the values of the variables either singly or in combination, and thus to identify those that are crucial to the calculations.

Social housing development

The ordinary cost planning techniques are as applicable to housing schemes as to any other type of building work. But there is an additional field for cost investigation on projects of this type, and that is in determining with what proportion of houses, low flats, and tall flats the site can most economically be developed at the given density.

Where land use is of no consequence the cheapest type of accommodation will be two-storey houses; the building costs of low flats are higher (per dwelling) and the costs of tall blocks of flats higher still. Unfortunately it is difficult to house more than 190–200 people to the hectare in traditional houses, and with the shortage of urban building land and the large number of people who need to be housed much higher densities than this are often required.

Using tall blocks of flats it would be possible to accommodate up to 600 people to the hectare, depending upon the size of the average family (obviously a large family requires less housing area *per person* than a small one). Since housing densities are normally much lower than this it would seem that the necessary accommodation could be provided in tall blocks. However this would be a very unsatisfactory as well as expensive solution, and it is necessary to calculate the most economical proportion of houses, low flats (or maisonettes), and tall flats for the particular requirements of the site. The overriding priority should be to build residences which are socially desirable and in recent years it has been recognised that high rise dwellings are generally unsuitable for families. Economic considerations cannot be ignored, unfortunately, and getting the right mix of dwellings is an important economic consideration.

The answer is not the obvious one of providing as much of the accommodation as possible in two-storey houses and the remainder in flats, as this will probably make it necessary to build tall flats in order to house the number of people left over when the largest possible number of two-storey houses has been fitted in. The difficulty is that each house sterilises much more land than a flat of the same size, so that on a site where everybody could have been accommodated in four-storey flats the building of any houses will reduce the land available for flats to a greater extent than it reduces the number of people to be housed in them.

The correct approach is first of all to ascertain the density at which the site is to be developed and the average size of the family units. The number of families and their size will enable the total area of accommodation to be roughly calculated.

The maximum number of square metres of accommodation which can be obtained per hectare of site in respect of houses, low flats, and tall flats can be calculated either from DOE publications or may be determined in accordance with the architect's and client's own ideas on the subject. The most economical development of the site will be one in which each type of accommodation is used to its maximum density and the use of algebra will enable the proportion of each type of housing to be quickly calculated. The following example is only intended to demonstrate the calculation, and the data therein should not necessarily be accepted.

EXAMPLE

Data

Area of site 1.80 hectares.

Density 300 persons per hectare (five-person dwellings).

Average habitable area of five-person dwelling say 90 m^2.

Permissible density of two-storey housing 4,000 m^2/hectare.

Permissible density of four-storey flats or maisonettes 6,000 m^2/hectare.

Permissible density of tall flats 11,000 m^2/hectare.

Working

Number of families per hectare $= \dfrac{300}{5} = 60$.

Required density $= 60 \times 90$ m^2/hectare $= 5,400$ m^2/hectare.

This development (lying between 4,000 and 6,000 m^2/hectare) will therefore be designed most economically as a combination of two-storey houses and four-storey flats.

Let $x =$ floor area of houses.

$y =$ floor area of flats.

Then $x + y = 5,400$.

But also $\dfrac{x}{4,000}$ hectares $+ \dfrac{y}{6,000}$ hectares will equal 1 hectare, so that we have a simultaneous equation, and x will be found to be 1,200, and y will be 4,200. Therefore for each hectare the most economical solution will be 1,200 m^2 of houses and 4,200 m^2 of flats, or for the whole 1.80 hectares 2,160 m^2 and 7,560 m^2 respectively. The answer is therefore 24 houses (2,160 ÷ 90) and 84 flats (7,560 ÷ 90).

It should be noted that it would be possible to house everybody in flats, though at a higher cost; but if it was decided to build more than 24 or 25 houses (and of course the figures obtained by such rough methods are fairly flexible) then it would be necessary to build taller blocks of flats. We have seen that the cost of flats rises sharply above three or four storeys because lifts must be provided, so that this also will be a more expensive solution.

It must also be stressed again that there may be social or other reasons why the most economical solution cannot be adopted, but again any decisions can be reached with full knowledge of the cost consequences.

Cost yardsticks

At one time for most public building, "cost yardsticks" were published by the relevant government departments, setting out the rules for calculating cost targets. Recent government policy has been to abolish most of these rather inflexible cost limits and to replace them by "block allocations" of money for building programmes where theoretically the local authority is allowed more discretion. The major yardsticks shown below are, however, of interest from a historical point of view and there is a possibility that a similar framework could be revived by a future administration.

Housing Cost Yardstick (DOE) which gave local authorities freedom in deciding what type of accommodation to build (houses, low-rise flats, etc.) within a rather tight cost target. If the scheme did not comply with the yardstick then loan sanction would not be granted to the authority.

The major criteria for setting the target cost were:

(a) Average number of persons (i.e. bed-spaces) per dwelling.
(b) Density of persons per hectare.
(c) Allowance for car accommodation.
(d) Regional cost variation.
(e) Extra allowance if old people's dwellings and small developments.

The Yardstick contained tables for the various values.

The government now requires authorities to justify the proposed scheme in terms of its market value when completed.

Education Cost Limits (DES) set prices per "cost place" for many different types of school; the number of cost places was based upon the minimum teaching area. Different figures were used according to whether the school had a kitchen, or whether (in the case of a primary school) it had a second hall.

Hospital Cost Limits (DHSS). The yardstick is still operational and the procedures are relatively complex (reflecting the complex nature of such buildings compared to housing or schools); a basic cost for each type of accommodation area in each type of hospital is set out. In addition to this, the method and cost of running the buildings and departments is taken into account, as is the necessarily higher cost of high-rise building if this latter can be justified. Such a thorough evaluation can only be carried out on projects such as hospitals, which are relatively few and expensive. It would be difficult to apply such a thorough analysis to the schools programme, for instance.

Other government departments require schemes to be justified in terms of cost but do not necessarily publish cost tables containing rigid limits. There is a feeling that fixed limits are hard to implement with justice in every part of the country and the trend as demonstrated by recent government policy is to allow a more flexible approach to setting economic targets.

Chapter 6
Design Method and Cost Advice

The building design process is a complex interaction of skills, judgement, knowledge, information, and time which has as its objective the satisfaction of the client's demands for shelter, within the overall needs of society. Ultimate satisfaction is obtained when the "best" solution has been discovered within the constraints imposed by such factors as statutory obligations, technical feasibility, environmental standards, site conditions, and cost. (Optimisation is developed in more detail in Chapter 17.) Problems arise, however, in establishing which of the alternative options available is the "best", as some factors such as personal comfort or visual delight are difficult to measure. Neither is it easy to translate all attributes into a common unit or value, for example excessive noise levels compared with higher initial cost. In practice, compromises in the client's demands are nearly always necessary to get within the constraints. The role of the design economist is to provide information with regard to initial and future costs so that the design team can make decisions knowing the cost implications of those decisions. It is not usually the economist's responsibility to actually provide "value" as this must be the province of the team as a whole, of which, however, he should be a contributing member. In theory the team will pool their combined knowledge for the benefit of the client, whose representative should wherever possible be a member of the team and play his own part in the corporate decision-making process. As with any group activity the composition of the team should be carefully planned to avoid vociferous members unduly influencing the final decisions.

If the design economist is to be an effective member of the team he must have a clear idea of when the major decisions of cost significance are to be made so that he can provide information at the crucial time. In addition, he must have the techniques, knowledge, and experience to enable him to provide answers to questions of cost that will be posed as the design is refined.

It is, therefore, essential that he understands the manner in which the design team, and in particular the architect, thinks and operates— commonly referred to as the design method. Unfortunately each individual designer adopts a different approach, as there are many ways of solving the same problem. However, it is possible to identify some of the common techniques which are very often incorporated in a typical approach to the task of achieving good design. This knowledge can be used to select the form of cost advice most appropriate to a particular problem.

It is not possible to place all the responsibility for establishing a successful cost solution solely on the shoulders of the building economist, or quantity surveyor. The architect must of course co-operate in, and contribute to, the cost planning process, cost being one of the several constraints that he will face in varying degrees, depending on the type of project and the client's financial resources. In this respect he should have a reasonable grasp of the factors affecting the cost of the project and the options that are available to him within that constraint. This knowledge will very often be gained by experience, especially if his firm specialises in one particular type of contract, e.g. housing, factories, hospitals, etc. Even without this experience he should be aware of the very basic design and cost relationships shown below.

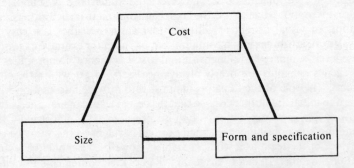

The advantage of illustrating this triangular set of relationships is that any two of the factors can be seen as functions of the remaining one. For example, if the size of the building is fixed, together with the form and specification, then a certain cost will be generated. Conversely, if the cost of the building is established together with its size (as is the case with some government yardsticks), then this constrains the form and specification that can be chosen. On the other hand if the shape and quality standard of the specification is declared together with an established sum of money, then the amount of accommodation is the design variable which is limited. Since one factor must be the resultant, it is never possible to declare all three in an initial brief.

This is an over-simplistic view of the cost system but it is a starting point in the understanding of the complex relationships which exist between design and cost. It is the skill of the design team in achieving the right balance between these factors that makes a project a success or a failure.

Recognition for this team approach to design is included in what has come to be known as the RIBA Plan of Work. This is a model procedure dealing with some basic steps in decision making for a medium sized project, and is included in the RIBA *Handbook of Architectural Practice and Management* (Volume 2). The responsibilities of each member of the design team at each stage of the design process are identified. A design-tender-construct procedure is envisaged and from the quantity surveyor's point of view it anticipates and incorporates some of the cost planning techniques described in later chapters. The pre-tender procedure includes the following stages:

Stage A	Inception	Appointment of design team and general approach defined.
Stage B	Feasibility	Testing to see whether client's requirements can be met in terms of planning, accommodation, costs, etc.
Stage C	Outline Proposals	General approach identified together with critical dimensions, main space locations and uses.
Stage D	Scheme Design	Basic form determined and cost plan (budget) determined.
Stage E	Detail Design	Design developed to the point where detailing is complete and the building "works". Cost checking against budget commences.
Stage F	Production Information	Working drawings prepared for the contract documents.
Stage G	Bill of Quantities	

It is of course recognised that a certain amount of overlap is bound to occur in practice. In recent years the RIBA Plan of Work has come under fire from a number of quarters because of the inherent inflexibility of its procedures, and because it tends to delay the letting of the contract which in times of rapid inflation can severely penalise some types of client. However, it was never intended as a rigid set of rules and the procedures adopted for any contract should be those which best suit the prevailing economic climate and the particular interests of the sponsor. The plan has been included at this point in order to give an overview of the complete design process, but the emphasis in the rest of the chapter will be on the very early design period, prior to sketch design, when the critical decisions affecting cost are usually taken.

Comparison of design and scientific method

To understand the concept of design it is useful to compare design method with the traditional approach of scientific method as shown in Fig. 6.1. To establish a scientific law an observation is made in nature and an inference drawn, e.g. light passing through a prism breaks down into several colours. A hypothesis is set up (e.g. white light is a combination of several colours) and tests are applied to establish whether the hypothesis is true. If the results of the tests conclude that the hypothesis and original inference are correct then a scientific law can be established based on the hypothesis. If not, a new solution must be set up and tested until the tests corroborate the hypothesis. Design can be said to follow a similar pattern. The brief is observed and some inference obtained. A hypothesis is set up in the form of a model (e.g. a drawing) and this is tested by evaluation to see whether it "works". A check is made to see whether it complies with the interpretation of the brief, and if it does then the design is accepted. There are, however, some very important differences. The design team cannot "loop" round the system producing new hypotheses (i.e. designs) *ad infinitum*. They work within the constraints of time and cost, and they must produce a final solution within the design period set by their client and within the fee structure by which they are paid. In addition, much of their creative work can only be evaluated in terms of social responses, such as aesthetic appeal, which at the present time do not have a satisfactory quantitative measure by which they can be tested.

Consequently, their objective tends to change from "what is the best solution for our client" to "how can we produce a design which satisfies as many of the demands of the brief in the time available". To arrive at a satisfactory solution, some kind of strategy, very often incorporating "rules of thumb" learned from previous experience, is used to narrow down on a particular range of alternatives. The responsibility of the design economist in this search for a satisfactory solution should be to indicate to the team where it should look in terms of form, quality, spatial standards, etc., to solve the cost problem. This will avoid wasting time on abortive designs which will not meet the cost criteria, and will thereby increase the chance of arriving at the "best" solution in the time available. In other words he should contribute to the overall design strategy.

A conceptual design model

A good deal of research work has been undertaken to establish a general pattern for design. The Building Performance Research Unit at Strathclyde University has put forward the following view, which is shared by several other writers.

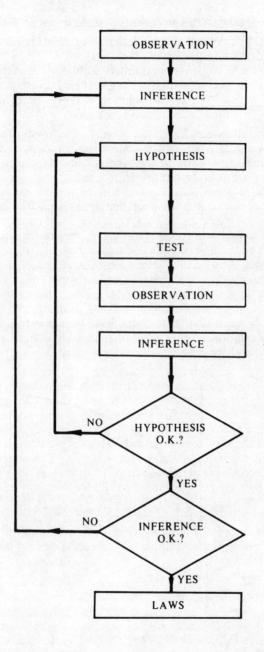

FIG. 6.1. *Scientific method*

They suggest that design consists of three stages as foilows:

(a) *Analysis.* Where the problem is researched in order to obtain an understanding of what is required.

(b) *Synthesis.* Where the information obtained in analysis is used to converge on a solution at the level being investigated.

(c) *Appraisal.* Where the solution is represented in some form which is then measured and evaluated.

Quantity surveyors have traditionally been involved almost exclusively in the latter part of the "Appraisal" process, and yet the real decision-making role is in the *Analysis* and *Synthesis* stages. New techniques are therefore required to enable the design economist to contribute to understanding and solving the design problem. It is assumed by the Strathclyde team that decision-making becomes more detailed and refined as time goes on (from, say, concepts of building form and spatial arrangement through to the eventual choice of ironmongery) and that at each stage different methods of problem-solving are adopted. Any cost technique must therefore follow a similar pattern, which may involve "coarse" measurement and evaluation in the very early stages and a more reliable measurement and cost application when more information becomes available. It is with these thoughts in mind that cost models have been constructed which can input information at each level of refinement. These are still being developed and are dealt with in later chapters.

Fig. 6.2.

One of the criticisms that can be made of traditional cost planning methods is that they do very little to contribute to the pre-sketch design dialogue, where all the major decisions of form and quality tend to be taken. Current research suggests that there is a heavy commitment of cost prior to a sketch design being formalised. This may amount to over 80% of the final potential building cost, leaving perhaps only 20% to actually "control". Figure 6.2 illustrates the point in a hypothetical diagrammatic form. With an improved understanding of design method it may be possible to input information prior to sketch design which will reduce the number of abortive design solutions needing to be produced.

Design techniques

It is not possible to describe the vast range of techniques applicable to design in a chapter or book of this nature. Those interested in developing their understanding of this area of study should consult other publications, such as *Design Methods* by Christopher Jones or *Design in Architecture* by Geoffrey Broadbent. It is possible to identify some decisions which form the basis of most design approaches. In very simple terms these can be illustrated by some general questions relating to matters of principle affecting the design. These include the following:

(1) "What are the constraints within which I have to work?"
The constraints on a project can be of three kinds, those imposed by physical factors, those imposed by external bodies and institutions, and lastly those imposed by the client and his advisers.

The physical factors very often relate to the site, and such things as the position of boundaries and easements, the method of access, the nearness to service supplies, any visual aspects and views and of course soil conditions and adjacent structures. In addition to the site, the physical performance of materials acts as a limitation and may exclude the use of a particular specification. These constraints are usually fixed and therefore provide very clear boundaries to the design problem.

Constraints imposed by external bodies, however, can often be the subject of negotiation. Planning requirements are usually the result of the policy of the local planning committee and are often open to interpretation—hence the facility for appeal when these interpretations conflict. Some building regulations can be waived if the appropriate authority can be convinced that an alternative construction form or arrangement is satisfactory. Resolving these problems can be a time-consuming business, and until they are settled the solution to the design problem has to remain flexible. However, once they are defined they again provide a clear boundary to the design problem.

Constraints imposed by the client and/or the design team tend to be far less stringent than the previous two categories, and can be compromised more easily. Even here some may be inflexible due to a specific demand which takes precedence over all other needs. An example may be the requirement to design a form which envelopes an expensive manufacturing process; because the plant is so expensive the form of the building must take second place. Another example is a cost limit which is subject to the financial standing of the client; this may however be imposed by an outside body such as a government department or finance company who will define the cost that it sees as being realistic. Most self-imposed constraints are able to be reconsidered in the light of experience and gradual evolution of the design solution.

Definition of the constraints is of enormous assistance in containing the design problem. They help in narrowing down the range of possible solutions, which are for practical purposes almost infinite without them. It is the responsiblity of the design economist to account for these controlling factors in his budget and, therefore, set a realistic strategy of cost. Ignorance of these issues will possibly result in abortive design effort and a less than satisfactory service to the client.

(II) "What are the priorities of the scheme?"
In a sense this is the question that sets the self-imposed constraints and whose solution should provide value for money. If priorities can be ranked and given their due importance in solving the design problem then it should be possible to spend the client's money in accordance with these requirements. This would be the ideal design and would provide the optimum solution. Unfortunately "ranking all the priorities" is an extremely difficult task. For example, should maintenance-free windows take priority over an improved reduction in noise levels between rooms in a commercial office block? It is difficult to compare the two, and it is even more difficult to award a satisfactory weighting. However, this kind of decision is at the root of good cost budgeting and, if possible, it should be made in conjunction with the designer. The theoretical aim should be to spend money in the same order and importance as the priorities.

Whether this can ever be achieved is a debatable point, as an item which is not given a high priority by the client may yet be essential, for example easy-to-clean windows on a multi-storey block. To provide this item may be more expensive than providing an item of greater ranked importance. This does not mean that the higher ranked item is of less value to the client but just that because of external economic forces and the nature of buildings he has to pay more to achieve his objective. This emphasises the difference between the two concepts of "value" put forward by the economist Adam Smith; value in exchange and value in use. In most buildings of a public or social nature it is value in use which is being considered, whereas in a speculative housing development it is value in exchange (which is much more dependent on scarcity factors) that is the major concern. There is, of course, a link between the two because the greater the degree of user satisfaction, the more likely it is that the client will be prepared to pay more for his building. Value for money is achieved when the priorities of the client, e.g. profit, symbolism, welfare, worship, etc. have been successfully balanced with the initial and future costs allowable for the development.

(III) "How much space is required?"

The purpose of building is usually to provide space for a particular activity within which the climate is modified so that the activity may function more efficiently. Other considerations such as the environmental and social impact of the building and its activity arise out of this prime need. It is therefore usual for the client's brief to give an indication of the usable area required, but even where this is stated there is considerable flexibility allowed; for example the circulation area (corridors, waiting, lifts, public areas, etc.) is not usually included in the list. In addition, the multiple use of space (e.g. assembly halls doubling up as dining halls in schools) may allow a more efficient use of a certain area and reduce the overall need. Part of the design problem is to discover the most efficient use of the spaces required to satisfy the client's brief and to arrange the areas in such a way that circulation is kept to a minimum.

As there is a strong correlation between the area of a building and its cost, the design economist should be an active participant in the discussion of areas and their spatial arrangement. Statutory requirements with regard to means of escape in cases of fire, health, and hygiene, etc., in conjunction with the client's requirements for efficient movement in the building will provide an indication of the minimum areas allowable for circulation and ancillary purposes. A careful study of these needs will provide the constraints for area and thereby indicate the balance between quantity and quality of building that can be achieved within a given cost limit.

(IV) "What arrangement of space is required?"

This question is heavily influenced by the amount of space needed. In answering it, a good designer can exercise his knowledge to enormous advantage. Indeed determinining spatial organisation has been recognised as one of the most fundamental of the architect's range of skills.

Despite the advent of computer programming techniques which attempt to optimise the positioning of space, the ability of the architect to take into account a large number of factors and bring them into a suitable relationship has not yet been surpassed.

A number of techniques have been developed to assist him in this important task, and perhaps the most common is the association matrix. In this design aid the relationship between spaces is identified in a table rather like a "mileage between towns" indicator in a road atlas. The figures in the table however will relate to the "cost of communication or movement" related to a unit of distance between spaces rather than measured distance. For example the salary cost of the managing director spending time in walking one metre may be five times that of his administrative clerk. It follows that his office should be given priority in being closer to the centres of communication. Problems arise in the technique when the subject has no direct wages cost, for example the casualty patient in a hospital who does not cost the hospital administration any salary. Without an artificial weighting factor, hospitals might be designed with the patient always taking the longest route!

The simplest form of the matrix is that in which a simple weighting system is used to define the ease of movement between spaces. To illustrate the use of such a table let us take the example of a new administration/accommodation wing added to the existing appliance garage of a fire station. The spaces required by the fire authority are as follows:

BLANKSTOWN: EXTENSION TO EXISTING FIRE STATION

Space	Area (m²)
(1) Administration area including watchroom	120
(2) Lecture room	80
(3) Firemen's dormitory	140
(4) Television room	25
(5) Recreation area	150
(6) Mess and officers' lounge	200
(7) Administration/visitors' toilet and wash room (male and female)	25
(8) Visitors' entrance	20
(9) Firemen's entrance	20
(10) Firemen's ablutions area	40
(11) Appliance garage (existing)	—
	820

The first step is to identify a suitable scale for the ease of movement required between spaces. The following may be considered reasonable:

Weighting	Degree of "ease of movement"
5	Essential
4	Desirable
3	Tolerable
2	Undesirable
1	Intolerable

By considering the relationship of each space to the other spaces an association matrix can be established using the above key.

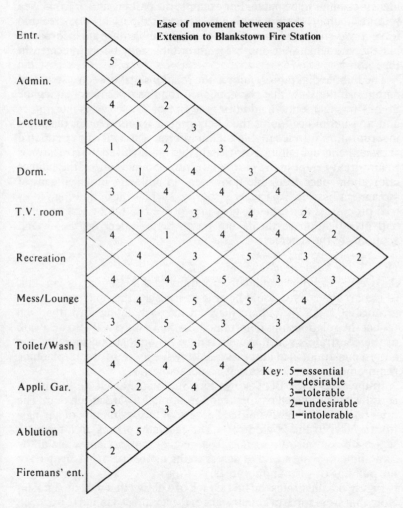

FIG. 6.3. *Design method association matrix*

It can be seen from the developed matrix (Fig. 6.3) that the crucial space is the existing appliance garage. This is fairly obvious as the efficiency of the station is centred around the ability of each fireman to reach his equipment quickly when an emergency call is received. The next step is to arrange the spaces in a diagrammatic form to show the desirable "clusters" of accommodation. This is usually shown by means of a "bubble" diagram identifying the spaces and their required links. In arranging the groups of spaces, consideration needs to be given to important constraints, such as the site, which may not allow ideal groupings to be made. For example the parking and practice area required behind the fire station may restrict the usable site area and force a two-storey solution. The resultant bubble diagram incorporating the site constraint and association table may be as indicated in Fig. 6.4.

The bubble diagrams reinforce the relationship between spaces and emphasise the view that the appliance room is the controlling factor in any arrangement. In addition, the size of the spaces is illustrated, and a visual indication of the likely room clusters is given ready for incorporation into a suitable building form. The efficiency of spatial arrangements in building is not a field that has involved the cost adviser to any great extent in the past, apart from commenting on the ratio of circulation space to usable floor area. In buildings in which ease of movement between spaces is a priority, such as those housing industrial processes, this area of study may prove fruitful for cost research and investigation as the layout has a major effect on the overall economy of the scheme.

(V) "What form should the building take?"

Answering this question involves another of the essential design skills of the architect. He should be able to translate the functional spatial arrangement of the bubble diagram into a building form that will reflect the relationships determined. In doing so he will also be aware of the constraints which usually reduce his options considerably, the largest constraint in many cases being the site itself. In others, planning requirements or cost limits may be paramount.

In the case of the Blankstown Fire Station the available site area is considerably reduced by the need for a practice yard at the rear. The orientation is also fairly limited because of the desirability of having a frontage on to the High Street. The resultant plan is an attempt to segregate administrative areas from recreation/work areas and at the same time provide speed of access to the appliances from any part of the building or surrounding areas.

Figure 6.5 illustrates the first sketch of a design that may be suitable. Note that from force of circumstances the architect has had to use open space in rooms for through access to the appliance garage. He has also

Extensions to Blankstown Fire Station
Note: Numbers of interconnecting lines shows strength of association

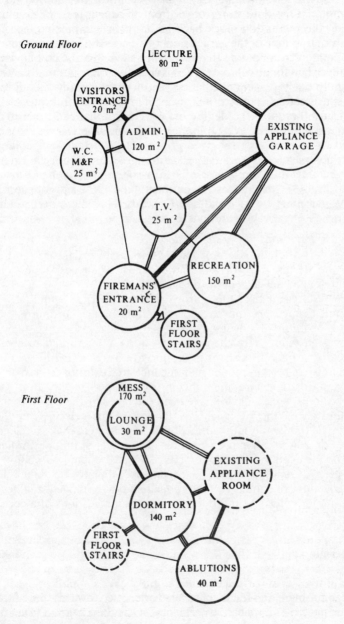

Fig. 6.4. *Bubble diagrams*

split the visitors/administration toilet facilities between ground and first floor to obtain male and female facilities. In addition he has attempted to isolate noisy areas from the quiet/rest areas and by setting the recreation block back he has provided passing motorists with a better view of the garage doors—very useful in an emergency.

It is interesting to note that it is at this stage that the cost adviser is usually asked for an estimate, yet it is clear that there is already a heavy commitment to space, circulation, and form standards. In addition, the specification standard will probably have been indicated in the brief and therefore the degree of cost control that can be exercised from this point on is severely limited. This reinforces the view that cost advice is most effective if given prior to the sketch design. In larger, more complex buildings a request to design a more compact form once the architect has already produced a solution is likely to involve considerable effort and also resentment. One of the aims of good cost budgeting must be to avoid abortive effort and therefore to advise where cost-acceptable solutions are likely to be found.

(VI) "What is the level of specification?"
This is very often the decision that has the least external constraint. It is also the design decision that suffers most when cost reduction is required at a late stage of the design process.

At the present time there are very few numerical techniques that attempt to measure quality. It is therefore a decision that is based largely on intuitive judgement arising out of the previous experience of the design team. The client's brief will have attempted to give an indication of need, perhaps in the form of a requirement for soft or hard finish in certain rooms, maintenance-free exterior, and so on.

Standards of environmental comfort and the need for prestigious public areas, etc., will also have been conveyed by the client. In these circumstances the designer has to narrow his selection to those materials that will fulfil the function required and to make a selection based on comparative performance. One aspect of that performance will be the economic considerations of installation and durability that will generate capital, maintenance, and operational costs. One role of the cost adviser should be the production of alternative estimates for each major solution, in order that the cost implications of a decision can be known.

Generally

The above series of questions is a gross over-simiplification of the design problem and the text has been orientated towards those factors which have cost implications. The object has been to give the student, in disciplines other than architecture, a grasp of the early stages of the

FIG. 6.5. *Sketch plans*

design problem and the potential for economic advice, and in particular to dispel the common misapprehension that the architect starts
work by sketching a building form neatly divided up into rectangular
rooms and passages.

However it should not be assumed that a linear chronological order has necessarily been implied by the sequence of the above questions. In some cases a linear sequence may be the method adopted for the solving of a particular problem, but in the vast majority of cases there will be a good deal of overlap. There may be simultaneous decisions covering all the points discussed and possibly reversal of the process. The above procedure has been largely a process of designing from the "inside-out"; from internal space requirements to external form. In buildings where external form is important or the site constraints are very tight then it may be necessary to design from the "outside-in". Each individual designer will develop his own methods and techniques which will suit his approach—not every architect, for example, will use numerical methods to assist in deciding on circulation priorities.

There are, of course, a large number of design decisions still to be made and these include the working and arrangement of the building services, the sizing and choice of the structure, the fixing of components, and the detailing of the specification and so on. Some of these decisions will be made in conjunction with those already outlined and in fact may depend upon those decisions and vice versa. Design cannot be neatly contained in water-tight compartments of sequential decisions, and this does make the input of information by other consultants more difficult.

An understanding of design method will, however, help the cost adviser to know when his advice is likely to be most helpful in its contribution to solving the design problem. It will also assist in determining the degree of refinement in cost advice that will match the stage of detail in the design process.

Recognition of design methods in cost information systems

It is generally recognised that any cost information system must be compatible with design method. However, unless cost is of paramount importance it should not dictate the approach the designer takes—if the financial tail wags the project dog this will not normally be conducive to satisfaction of all the client's requirements. The cost adviser should also be aware that striving to achieve optimisation in cost is only a part of the total objective. While all consultants would like to achieve optimisation in their own subsystem of activity it is the performance of all systems acting together that will determine the degree of client satisfaction.

Two examples will suffice to demonstrate recent attempts that have been made to marry cost advice to design method in the pre-sketch design stage, when the major cost-significant decisions are made. The systems are not yet fully developed but they give an indication of current trends.

Since these are the first of many cost control systems at different levels which we shall be encountering it is necessary to make a point which will be repeated on appropriate occasions. Systems such as the following represent overall strategies within which a cost control process operates. It is very rare, however, for the cost adviser to have sufficient resources available to be able to carry out every single step of the strategy in respect of every aspect of the design, and it is doubtful that this would be a very economical thing to do even if he had. Just as a general commanding an army cannot afford to attack all along a front but must concentrate his efforts at the most sensitive points, so the cost adviser must use his resources where they will do most good. Making a wise decision on this question is probably one of the most important and difficult parts of his job, and is one of the things which makes it a truly professional task.

1. *An evaluative system*

In this system the cost adviser attempts to evaluate the cost implications of design knowledge and decisions immediately they are postulated. Design is considered to be the arrangement of spaces into a building format. The procedure could be as follows:

(i)	Designer receives brief with room sizes given	Cost adviser evaluates cost of alternative finishes and room contents including service outlets.
(ii)	Designer organises rooms into groups and location in a building shape and form	The form generates a type of production method and site transportation which the cost adviser evaluates.
(iii)	Designer looks at the structure needed to support the chosen form	Cost adviser evaluates cost of alternative forms of support.
(iv)	Designer clads the structure	Cost adviser evaluates alternative specifications of external walls and roof.
(v)	Designer organises circulation and service runs etc.	Cost adviser evaluates alternative arrangements of lifts, service runs, and corridor space.

There are two problems with this method. Firstly, it assumes a "linear" design method, with each event occurring after the other, although in practice these decisions are very often taken simultaneously; secondly, it depends on the generation of information by the designer before evaluation can take place, and therefore gives no indication as to where to look for a good cost solution prior to a committed decision being made on building form. It is, however, a significant step forward in providing an evaluation of the decision-making process prior to sketch design.

2. A strategic cost information system

By use of this method the cost adviser attempts to explore a range of possible solutions available to the designer using a structured "search" process in which the designer is involved. The object is to identify a cost "strategy" which the designer can employ in his synthesis of building form and which will avoid abortive re-design at a later date. The procedure may take the following form:

(i) Design team receives brief with accommodation area and quality standard given	Cost adviser explores the cost of different components of the building according to changes in the major design variables (e.g. the area and shape of a bay in a structural frame).
(ii) Design team selects the specification and parameters for each component from the explorations undertaken	Cost adviser explores the use of these components and parameters in buildings of different shape and height according to a predetermined series of building descriptions, e.g. plan shape, number of storeys, density of partitions, etc. A cost table is produced of the feasible solutions available within the indentifiable constraints.
(iii) Design team identifies the lowest total cost from the table and uses it as the point of reference for selecting any other alternative.	Cost adviser contributes to the discussion of an alternative solution.
(iv) A solution is chosen from the table by the design team	Cost adviser provides a breakdown of the major component costs which is then adopted as the point of reference for the initial cost plan for use in traditional budgeting. The design variables incorporated in the selected solution are communicated to the designer.
(v) Designer uses the parameters and description as guidelines in the preparation of his design solution	Cost adviser uses traditional budgetary procedures to maintain control.

The descriptions conveyed to the architect for his design strategy should not be so rigid that a "strait-jacket" is imposed resulting in only one possible solution. Rather they are "coarse" measures which still allow the designer reasonable scope for using his skills of modelling and spatial organisation within the strategy adopted by the team as a whole. The choice of descriptors is important in making sure that the creativity of the designer is not stifled.

The advantage of this method is that it attempts to undertake a systematic search through possible solutions in order that the design team may know where the better cost propositions are likely to be. It identifies a "least cost" solution which can then form the point of reference for any alternative selection. It is, therefore, possible to obtain a gauge of value by comparing a specific choice with the lowest cost. The approach is developed further in Chapter 17.

There are however quite a number of problems. The setting up of "models" that will cope with the large number of components and design variables is an onerous task, even though the models need not be very refined at this stage of the design process. It is also extremely difficult to produce a satisfactory range of descriptors which will be simple enough for the design team to incorporate into their thinking and also comprehensive enough to allow a reasonable evaluation of the building as a whole.

Both the evaluative system and the strategic approach depend heavily on the use of computers to provide the information sufficiently quickly for decision-making purposes. The advent of micro-computer technology has meant that machines are now available, at less than the cost of one man-year, that will cope with these types of problems. The real expense is in writing the program to suit a particular type of building and it may mean that quantity surveyors of the future will need greater familiarity with computer techniques if they are to provide this improved service to the building client. Without the ability to re-use computer data and systems much cost advice is likely to be too expensive to be provided on any but the largest projects.

Summary

An understanding of design method enables the cost adviser to know:
  (i) The time when his advice will be most effective.
  (ii) The type of advice that needs to be given.
  (iii) The objectives of the design team additional to minimisation of cost.

It would appear that the earlier the advice is given the greater the chance of the advice being incorporated into the final design solution. The need is for techniques which contribute to the analytical understanding of the problem and assist in the convergence on the best solution in the shortest possible time. The development of cost models and computer techniques seems to show a possible way forward in achieving these objectives.

Chapter 7
Introduction to Cost Modelling

In the majority of cases in which an industrialist is about to manufacture a new product he first of all builds a prototype. He does this for a number of reasons, such as:

(i) To identify and solve three-dimensional problems that were not apparent in the drawings.

(ii) To identify the tools required for production.

(iii) To help estimate the cost of production.

(iv) To evaluate its functional performance (this may involve testing to destruction).

(v) To test the product's marketability.

(vi) To provide a sample for a customer as evidence of the quality standard to be achieved.

By building, manipulating, and testing the prototype he can iron out and avoid future problems when the product is actually manufactured, supplied, or sold. However, where the final product is large or costly it is not always feasible to build a prototype, especially with such products as a building where only one production model is to be built and the prototype costs cannot be written-off over a large production run. Most new structures are "one-off" designs of considerable capital and operational cost and are intended to be very durable, so that they would in any case need to be tested over a very long period of time to establish their efficiency. It would, therefore, be impracticable as well as uneconomic to build a prototype to test its functional and cost performance as a whole. It may be possible to build samples of major components (and this possibility may need to be taken into account in cost planning a building which is to incorporate some measure of innovation), but because of the time needed for construction, the great expense and the individual nature of buildings, it is just not realistic to construct the whole project a number of times to see whether or not it will work satisfactorily.

It might be interesting at this point to mention the Sydney Opera House, a building of great prestige and enormous innovation, where the construction and testing of prototypes and mock-ups was undertaken on an exceptional scale. The result of this was that very few problems were encountered in the use and maintenance of the building, considering the potential for trouble in a project of this nature, but of course a considerable penalty was paid in terms of construction time and cost.

If physical prototypes are not normally possible the design of a building must still be assessed in some way to try and ensure that the demands of the client are satisfied.

For the sake of expediency and cost it is, therefore, necessary to construct *models* that represent the real situation in another form, or to a smaller scale, so that a realistic appraisal of performance can be made. These models can be, for example, physical (as in a three-dimensional architect's balsa model); mathematical (as in a heat loss equation); or statistical (where some collected information indicates a certain trend). Cost is one of the measures of function and performance of a building and should therefore be capable of being "modelled" in order that a design can be evaluated. In recent years a considerable effort has been made to construct models that will help in the understanding and prediction of the cost effect of changing design variables.

Cost modelling may be defined as *the symbolic representation of a system, expressing the content of that system in terms of the factors which influence its cost.* In other words the model attempts to represent the significant cost items of a cash flow, building or component in a form which will allow analysis and prediction of cost to be undertaken according to changes in such factors as the design variables, construction methods, timing of events, etc. The idea is to simulate a current or future situation in such a way that the solutions posed in the simulation will generate results which may be analysed and used in the decision-making process of design. In terms of quantity surveying practice this usually means estimating the cost of a building design at an early stage to establish its feasibility.

Traditional cost models

If the above definition is understood it becomes clear that quantity surveyors have been using a form of modelling technique for a number of years. In their measurement for Bills of Quantities they have been representing the building in a form suitable for the contractor's estimator; and when prices are applied to the measured quantities the Bill becomes a representation (or model) of the cost of the building. By altering the quantity of the measured items or changing the price according to variations in specification it would be possible to evaluate the effect on cost of manipulating certain design variables.

The Bill is prepared at a very late stage of the design process however, and any information obtained from changing the quantities or price rates would come too late to avoid abortive design effort. An estimate obtained from a Bill would also be too late to give the client an indication of his likely cost commitment at the outset of the project or allow any cost control to be exercised. There is, therefore, an obvious need to use much simpler models at an earlier stage of design to overcome these problems. The complexity of the model will depend very largely on the amount of information the designer can give the cost adviser. It is not much use trying to take into account shape and layout of the building if all that has been determined is an idea of the approximate area of accommodation. Conversely, there is little point using an over-simplified costing technique when the building form and specification is known and sufficient time is available to do a more thorough job.

As in many instances in this world the choice of technique is a case of picking the right horse for the course. Figure 7.1 shows some of the more traditional models that have been developed over the years to suit various stages of the design process. The pyramid is an attempt to show that more detail is required in the structure of the model as we descend the list.

The first two model types are basically "single price-rate" methods of estimating cost as introduced in Chapter 1; the size of the building is measured in one form or other and the result is multiplied by a single price-rate to give the estimated cost. However, it will be remembered that such an estimate suffered from the defect that it was not possible to relate the cost of the work shown on the drawings to the estimate during the subsequent progress of the design. Attempts to deal with this problem at a later stage by a model based on "approximate quantities" (at level 4 of the pyramid) had other disadvantages: the quantity surveyor required extra time and a substantial additional fee for the work involved, the drawings had to be fairly complete and the whole of the building work had to be dealt with; even if the approximate quantities when priced by the surveyor showed a far higher total than the original estimate the discrepancy could not be traced, and rational measures to remedy the situation were, therefore, difficult. This particular model is therefore not structured in a suitable way to be compatible with the design process, nor is it sufficiently sensitive to allow for ease of adjustment.

What is obviously required is a technique whereby the original estimate can be prepared on the basis of a known and economic standard of construction and finish, and whereby this estimate can be constantly checked against the working drawings and any necessary adjustments made to one or the other. By the time the job goes out to tender the probable cost will, therefore, be known within close limits,

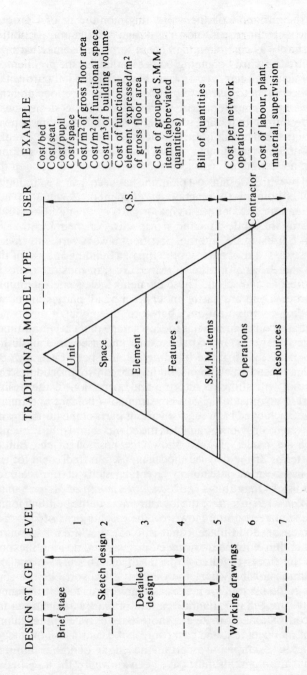

FIG. 7.1. *Traditional cost modelling*

DESIGN STAGE	LEVEL	TRADITIONAL MODEL TYPE	USER	EXAMPLE
Brief stage	1	Unit	Q.S.	Cost/bed Cost/seat Cost/pupil Cost/space
Sketch design	2	Space	Q.S.	Cost/m² of gross floor area Cost/m² of functional space Cost/m³ of building volume
Detailed design	3	Element	Q.S.	Cost of functional element expressed/m² of gross floor area
	4	Features	Q.S.	Cost of grouped S.M.M. items (abbreviated quantities)
Working drawings	5	S.M.M. items	Q.S.	Bill of quantities
	6	Operations	Contractor	Cost per network operation
	7	Resources	Contractor	Cost of labour, plant, material, supervision

and during the progress of the work this monitoring of cost can continue. Such a technique is known as design cost planning or sometimes more simply as cost planning. These terms are somewhat misleading because the word "planning" suggests that it is the *preliminary forecasting* which is all important, whereas the really vital part of the whole operation is the *control of cost* as the design develops and the building goes up. A better term therefore might be design-cost-planning-and-control, to remind us of this; it is too cumbersome a term to use in practice but we must remember that this is what we mean when we talk about cost planning. A cost plan without control is simply an "approximate estimate".

The model by which design cost planning has been achieved is that of dividing the building into functional "elements" (level 3 of our pyramid). Elements are defined as major parts of the building which always perform the same function irrespective of their location or specification. For example, internal partitions always vertically divide two internal spaces; a roof encloses the top of a building and keeps the weather out and the heat in; the sub-structure transmits the building load to the subsoil; and so on. These elements have some relation to the design process and are easily understood by all parties including the client, aiding communication. Therefore, the model of the cost of the building based on elements has the advantage that each major part of the design can be estimated separately and used as a basis for checking when that part of the building has just been designed. By setting a budget based on elements, budgetary control procedures can be adopted that will allow monitoring and correction of the design should it start to go outside the cost constraints. A balance in terms of cost can also be achieved between the various parts of the building and this is a first step to providing value for the client.

Level 5 of the model pyramid shows the position of the Bill of Quantities in terms of the detailed modelling used in traditional techniques. There has been an attempt in recent revisions of the rules for measuring Bills of Quantities (*The Standard Method of Measurement of Building Works*) to orientate the measurement of the building to the way costs are incurred on site. However, the vast majority of items are still largely measured "in-place"; that is to say they are measured as fixed in the building with no allowance for waste and no identification of the plant and tools required to instal them. This is to avoid the possible situation arising where the quantity surveyor tells the contractor "how to do his job" or makes assumptions as to his efficiency. Consequently, the Bill of Quantities is still primarily a document for obtaining a contractual estimate in a short space of time, rather than a document for management and cost control of construction on site. It is not possible, for example, to ascertain the lengths of timber required for roof joists (although this must have been known by the measurer), or the hoisting requirements for materials and components, just by looking at a Bill, unless it has been annotated for the purpose. However, it is probable that the rules will gradually be changed to more closely resemble the production process. The last two levels of 6 and 7 are indeed more closely related to construction. If a contractor prepares a "network", he outlines the activities or operations in the order that they will be undertaken on site. For example, external cavity wall brickwork, which may be one item in a Bill, will be broken down into floor levels and possibly into zones marked on the floor plan. This aids site management and the organisation of labour, plant, and material. These basic resources form the most detailed level of modelling as they are the ingredients of the production process. In fact all the other models used for forecasting cost entail the assumption that the resource requirements of the building have been considered, although in most cases the resource assessment is so distant that it is hardly recognisable. In the case of levels 1 to 4 on the pyramid the data used is actually based upon an analysis of the Bill of Quantities, which is somebody else's view (the estimator's) of what he intends to charge for the resources plus profit and overheads. Because of the large number of assumptions upon which a Bill price is based it is most unlikely that the real mix of resources for the project has been determined. The factor that allows each technique to work is the knowledge that the overall cost of the job, which has been analysed to provide data for the model, is the "going rate" for that building. If adjustment is made for current market conditions affecting price levels it should be possible to build an identical building on the same site for a similar price. This is the theory behind all estimating, but of course there are usually vast numbers of differences between one job and another and this is what makes forecasting very much a matter of professional judgement. The model is there to provide the structure or bare bones on which the cost adviser hangs his intuitive assessment. However, the major part of intuition is based on experience which in turn is based upon the amount of data passing through the adviser's hands. The sources and reliability of this data are the subject of Chapter 9 but it is sufficient to note here that its use requires considerable care. Forecasting is not just a "number crunching" excerise no matter how refined the model, and although the calculations based on the techniques outlined below are easy, their success depends on the interpretation of analysed price rates. It is in this latter area that the professional adviser earns his money.

Single price estimating models

The unit method
This technique is based on the fact that there is usually a close relation-

ship between the cost of a building and the number of functional units it accommodates. By functional units we mean those factors which express the intended use of the building better than any other. For example it may be number of pupils in a school, number of vehicle spaces in a car park, or number of theatre seats. Several cost yardsticks operated by government departments were based upon this relationship and provided a test of what was reasonable for a given scheme. Cost per person, or bed space, for housing development and cost per bed for hospital wards are further examples of this test of reasonableness. Assuming that the standard of the building compatible with the unit cost is "socially acceptable" (see Chapter 9) then this method of making sure that extravagant schemes are not foisted upon the tax- or rate-payer can provide a very good yardstick for the purposes of public accountability. After all, by costing a single functional unit instead of, say, floor area, the designer has greater flexibility in choosing between the quantity of building and its quality, and the funding organisation has the assurance that it has not paid beyond what is reasonable.

To take an example of the more general use of the technique, suppose a multi-storey car park for 500 cars had recently been constructed for the sum of £3,000,000. The cost per car space would obviously be:

$$\frac{£3,000,000}{500} = £6,000.$$

If a similar car park is to be built but for 400 cars then it might reasonably be assumed that the cost would be

$$400 \times £6,000 = £2,400,000$$

all other things being equal.

Unfortunately not all things are equal and consequently a number of judgements must be made about prevailing price levels (due to inflation and market conditions) at the proposed date of tender, site difficulties, specification changes, different circulation and access arrangements, etc. Once again as with all single price estimates these adjustments to the analysed figure are based on the cost adviser's judgement and are critical to success.

The cube method

This is a traditional method. All quantity surveyor's offices used to keep a "cube book". When a contract was signed the amount of the accepted tender was divided by the cubic content of the building and the resultant cost per cubic foot entered in the book. When an estimate was required for a new project the cubic footage would be calculated and an appropriate rate per foot taken from a previous job

FIG. 7.2. *RIBA pre-metric rules for cubing of buildings*

in the cube book. The method has largely died out as a result of a number of factors, the main one being that the cost of a building is usually more closely related to its floor area than its cubic capacity.

Even with a "blunt instrument" such as the cube, it was necessary to have common standards of measurement so that the rate obtained from one job might be fairly compared with another. The RIBA pre-metric set of rules was the one commonly accepted; these involved multiplying the plan area measured over the external walls by the height from the top of the concrete foundation to halfway up the roof if pitched, or to 2′ 0″ (0.60 m) above the roof if flat. (See Fig. 7.2.) Extra allowances were made for projections such as porches, bays, oriels, turrets and flèches, dormers, chimney stacks, and lantern lights.

This formula has little to recommend it except uniformity; the additional allowance for a pitched roof (which may well be cheaper than a flat roof) and the allowance for fluctuations in foundation depth are both very arbitrary.

The Standard Form of Cost Analysis (published by the Building Cost Information Service of the Royal Institution of Chartered Surveyors) still makes provision for cubing but uses a different set of rules.

The superficial area method

This is an alternative single-price-rate method in which the total floor area is calculated. The rule usually accepted is that the area of the building inside the external walls is taken at each floor level and is measured over partitions, stair wells, etc. In cases where columns to frames are situated inside the external walls these columns are ignored and the dimensions taken from the internal face of perimeter walls. Where there is no external wall at floor level (as in the case of freight sheds) the dimensions are taken from the external faces of columns.

More recent than the cube method, it first came into use for such projects as schools and local authority housing where the storey heights were reasonably constant. It has the virtue of being closer to the terms in which the client's requirements are expressed, as the accommodation is more likely to be related to floor area than to cubic displacement. Sometimes when a very early estimate is required the only data available may be the approximate floor area.

The storey enclosure method

This was a single-price-rate system which never achieved wide acceptance because it was quickly superseded by the elemental estimate. It is of interest for historical reasons as it was the first attempt to compensate for such factors as the height and shape of buildings.

In this method the areas of the various floors, roof, and containing walls are measured, each then being weighted by a different percentage and the resultant figures totalled to give the number of storey enclosure units. The rules are summarised below:

(1) Twice the area of the lowest floor, unless it is below ground level in which case it is multiplied by three. The area is measured between the internal faces of the external walls.
(2) The area of the roof measured flat on plan to the extremities of the eaves.
(3) Twice the area of the upper floors, plus the addition of a factor of 0.15 for the first floor, 0.30 for the second floor, 0.45 for the third floor and so on.
(4) The area of external walls. Any part of an enclosing wall below ground level is multiplied by two.

Note: It was recommended that lifts and other engineering services should be excluded from the calculation and worked out separately. This is common practice in single-price-rate estimating and applies equally to the cubic and superficial methods.

The paper presenting the method (in the early 1950s) claimed that it had performed far better than the other single price approaches but lack of use has meant that it has not been possible to verify this claim in practice. The system depends heavily on the "weightings" built into the rules, and these are unlikely to apply equally to every building. In addition the units tend to be abstract, not relating to the physical form of the building or the client's accommodation requirements, and therefore the technique suffers from deficiencies similar to those of the cube method.

Comparison of single price methods
Table 9 shows each of the above single price methods applied to a multi-storey office block. The actual cost of each building is known and the analysis of building A is used in each case to forecast building B. The buildings have exactly the same dimensions, except that A has seven storeys and B has eight storeys within the same envelope.

It can be seen that the cubic method has not taken into account the extra floor and there is, therefore, a shortfall of approximately 12% on the estimate. The superficial method on the other hand has over compensated for the extra floor by not taking into account the fact that the envelope remains the same but it has still produced a very reasonable figure. The storey-enclosure method by considering both envelope and floor has produced an even closer estimate well within acceptable limits for this kind of early exercise.

In each case a change in specification, site, or location would result in additional problems, and call for the skill of the cost adviser in using his judgement to compensate for the changes. In addition changes in plan shape and storey height would affect the cubic and superficial methods to a greater or lesser degree. These alterations, or variables, are enormously complex and difficult to assess. It is for this reason that single-price-rate methods tend to be rejected except for the very earliest estimates.

Elemental estimating
Although the storey-enclosure method could have brought increased accuracy it was still no more possible to relate the working drawings (when received) to the estimate than it had been with the earlier methods. The omnibus "rate" bore no definite relationship to the actual cost of any of the measured areas but was only a theoretical average of them all. In the discussion which followed the first presentation of the paper, James Nisbet (who subsequently became Chief Quantity Surveyor to the War Department) put his finger on the real weakness in the storey enclosure approach to the problem. He asked whether, if the walls, floors, and roofs were all going to be measured separately, it would not be simpler and more accurate to price each separately according to an assumed specification.

This basically is the "elemental" approach. The building is split up into a number of major components, or elements, which can be easily measured from sketch drawings and which are priced separately; these

TABLE 9. COMPARISON OF SINGLE PRICE ESTIMATING MODELS USING A COST ANALYSIS

Office A:		
Actual cost = £1,758,000	Storey height = 4.29 m	
Area = 5,024 m²	Foundation depth = 1.4 m	
Cube = 24,000 m³		
No. of storeys = 7		

Cubic metre	Square metre	
Office A analysis $\dfrac{£1,758,000}{24,000} = £73.25/m^3$	*Office A analysis* $\dfrac{£1,758,000}{5,024} = £349.92/m^2$	
Office B forecast £73.25 × 24,000 = £1,758,000	*Office B forecast* £349.92 × 5,742 = £2,009,000	
Error Underestimate of approximately 12%	*Error* Well within acceptable range	

elemental costs are then added together to give the total of the estimate. In its simplest form where no change of specification or location occurs the method merely involves adjusting for the revised "quantity" of the element. For example, supposing an external wall element costs £40,000 and the area of the wall is 1,000 m². The cost per square metre of wall (known as the elemental unit rate) is £40.00. If there are 1,500 m² of the same type of wall on the proposed project then the cost will be:

$$\frac{£40,000}{1,000} \times 1,500 = £60,000.$$

A cost index is then used to update the prevailing price levels to the proposed tender date and the new estimate for that part of the building has been established.

Having set out a series of estimates, one for each element (known as cost targets) it is then possible to consider each element in turn instead of trying to cope with the whole building. Costs can therefore be watched as design develops.

The initiative was immediately taken by several official departments in pressing for elemental estimating. The Ministry of Education had used elements in checking tenders for schools and in Hertfordshire the

OF OFFICE BLOCK "A" TO FORECAST OFFICE BLOCK "B"

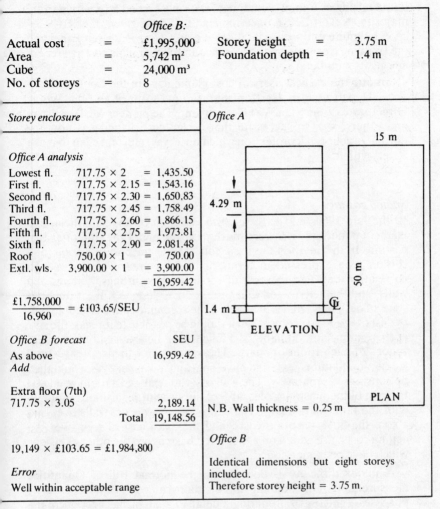

Office B:

Actual cost	=	£1,995,000	Storey height	=	3.75 m
Area	=	5,742 m²	Foundation depth	=	1.4 m
Cube	=	24,000 m³			
No. of storeys	=	8			

Storey enclosure

Office A

15 m

Office A analysis

Lowest fl.	717.75 × 2	=	1,435.50
First fl.	717.75 × 2.15	=	1,543.16
Second fl.	717.75 × 2.30	=	1,650.83
Third fl.	717.75 × 2.45	=	1,758.49
Fourth fl.	717.75 × 2.60	=	1,866.15
Fifth fl.	717.75 × 2.75	=	1,973.81
Sixth fl.	717.75 × 2.90	=	2,081.48
Roof	750.00 × 1	=	750.00
Extl. wls.	3,900.00 × 1	=	3,900.00
		=	16,959.42

4.29 m

$$\frac{£1,758,000}{16,960} = £103.65/SEU$$

Office B forecast	SEU
As above	16,959.42
Add	

Extra floor (7th)		
717.75 × 3.05		2,189.14
	Total	19,148.56

1.4 m   C L

ELEVATION

50 m

19,149 × £103.65 = £1,984,800

PLAN

N.B. Wall thickness = 0.25 m

Error

Well within acceptable range

Office B

Identical dimensions but eight storeys included.
Therefore storey height = 3.75 m.

County Architect's Department was using a similar system.

In 1955—largely through the influence of Mr C. M. Nott, Chief Quantity Surveyor of Hertfordshire County Council—the Bedfordshire and Hertfordshire Branch of the RICS moved a resolution at the triennial conference of quantity surveyor members of the RICS suggesting that the profession should devise methods of analytically examining the cost of building, and should prepare methods of applying such analyses to the control of costs at design stage.

The resolution was supported by senior surveyors in public service, but, amazing as it may seem today, was only carried by a very narrow majority. Nevertheless, once the lead had been given, the RICS responded quite enthusiastically, setting up a Cost Research Panel and the Building Cost Information Service and encouraging cost awareness among its members.

Among the earliest users of cost planning were the County Architect's Department of Hertfordshire County Council and the Works Directorate of the then War Department. The pioneer work of these, and others, was so successful that design cost planning is now the normal practice in a profession which once was reluctant even to make a start with it.

Spatial costing
In the late 1960s and early 1970s a variation on the superficial and elemental methods was very much in vogue under the title of spatial costing. In this method the basic concept was the cost of a room of a certain type expressed in terms of its floor area. There is a high correlation between the cost of room finishes, fittings, ceilings and walls, and the activity for which the room is designed. If, at the brief stage of design, all that is available is the accommodation schedule (i.e. the list of required rooms) then it should be possible to forecast the cost of these items quite reliably as a function of the areas and, if possible, shapes of each room or space. The other major items, of structural frame, foundations, external envelope, and mains services would then be considered separately. The wall costs attaching to a room would be the cost of the finishings plus 50% of the structural partition; similarly with the floor and ceiling. The extra cost of external walls over and above the 50% partition costs, and the extra cost of roof over the ceiling costs, are added on a measured basis as are the other exlusions which have been mentioned.

A major difficulty is dividing up the normal Bill of Quantities measurement of the building into the room categories for cost analysis purposes. The cost of preparing a detailed analysis has been a contributory cause of the lack of data available to the profession for elemental cost planning. The room concept requires more complex analysis and is therefore even more expensive to use. It also lacks the simplicity of the elemental form and the clear communication of what is meant and included. Computer models which symbolise a particular building and can build up rates from the basic resource costs are more likely to provide a better solution in the future. They may by-pass the need for analysing old or "historic" costs and will be more flexible in use.

Objectives of modelling

Models for estimating and planning costs have evolved gradually. Their adoption by the profession at large has led to the establishment of what might be called "traditional" techniques. These have been discussed and referred to in this chapter, together with those that have been suggested but have not yet been widely used.

At this stage it is perhaps useful to consider what a good cost model should be attempting to achieve. Traditional and future models can then be tested to see to what degree they comply with this set of requirements.

The broad objectives can be listed as follows:

   (i) To give confidence to the client with regard to the expected cost of his project, i.e. economic assurance.
  (ii) To allow the quick development of a representation of building in such a way that its cost can be tested and analysed.
 (iii) To establish a suitable system for advising the designer on cost that is compatible with his own build-up of the design. It should be usable as soon as the designer makes the first decision that can be quantified, and should be capable of refinement, to deal with the more detailed decisions that follow thereafter.
  (iv) To establish a link between the cost control of design and the manner in which costs are generated and controlled on site. This involves dealing with the cost of resources at as early a stage as possible to aid communication between the design team and the contract manager.

Linked to these objectives will be some guiding principles which can be applied to the way we approach and verify the model. These may be summarised as follows:

   (i) The degree of refinement of the model should be tailored to suit the stage of design refinement. In other words it should call on as much design information as is available at the point in time when the model will be used. The cost data applied to this information should represent the degree of reliability that can reasonably be expected from an estimate at that stage.
  (ii) The cost data in the model should be capable of ascertainment, and continuous updating and evolution in the light of changes in external market and environmental conditions, without too much time being involved.
 (iii) The representation of the building or component in the model should bear an understandable relationship to design method (e.g. the arrangement and use of space) and if possible the manner in which the costs are incurred (e.g. the production method). Ideally the model should show the relationship between the client's objectives expressed in the brief and the

subsequent cost of resources used to achieve these objectives. This is, however, an extremely difficult task as many of these objectives will be of an intangible nature and at the present time it can only remain a guiding principle.

(iv) The model should cope with constraints imposed on design and be able to test the feasibility of a proposed solution within these constraints in order that definite decisions can be made.

(v) The results of the model should allow the designer to incorporate this knowledge into his drawings, specification and quantities, so that they form part of the strategic decision-making process.

Computer developments

Micro-computer techniques now enable the economic modelling of proposed building designs in the manner already discussed to be carried out rapidly and exhaustively. However, the recent development of computer-aided architectural designs systems has added a new twist to the situation. The more sophisticated of these systems model the project in 3-D as the architect designs it, producing not only elemental cost models but thermal performance models, day-lighting models, and so on. It is a very simple matter to write a computer program which will produce an outline elemental analysis from three-dimensional co-ordinates of the various corners of the building mass (most quantity surveying students could do this in a few hours); the difficulty lies in associating this with cost data sophisticated and reliable enough for the architect to be able to use by himself as he designs, or alternatively, to perfect a means by which the quantity surveyor or cost planner can directly interact with him while he works (writing letters or even telephoning will not be good enough). The danger is that a model prepared from over-simplified or incorrect cost data will look just as convincing on the screen, and be just as easy (or even easier) to call up by somebody who does not understand the complexities involved in cost forecasting. Architects, cost planners, and computer software houses must come to terms with this.

Chapter 8

Costs-in-Use Models

When talking about building costs we have been thinking principally of the capital cost of providing a new building, but of course the expenditure does not stop there. Once the building has been handed over and paid for it will continue to cost money—it will need to be maintained, decorated, heated, cleaned, repaired, and so on, and from time to time during its life quite expensive refitting may be required. Also each year the interest on the capital cost will have to be found, and perhaps a sinking fund paid into.

The term "costs-in-use" has been coined to describe a form of modelling technique to cope with this mixture of capital and running costs. We shall encounter three different applications of costs-in-use techniques:

    (A) Costs-in-use of alternative materials or constructions.
    (B) Costs-in-use of mechanical installations.
    (C) Costs-in-use of the total project.

We shall look at these in turn.

A. Costs-in-use of alternative materials or constructions

It has been felt by many people that cost targets have for too long been expressed purely in terms of capital cost, and that in order to meet these targets materials or constructions have been used which are low in first cost but which will require constant expenditure on maintenance and repair during the life of the building. If only, it is argued, the architect were allowed to spend more money initially on better materials these would pay for themselves in the long run.

As a simple example of this let us consider the walls of a lavatory in a good class building. To plaster the walls and paint three coats of gloss paint would cost about £3.00 per square metre, whereas glazed tiling would cost £10.00. As the tiling would last fifty years with little attention, and the plaster walls would need to be painted every five years or so at a cost of £1.00, the total cost at the end of fifty years would be £12.00 for the plaster walls against £10.00 for the tiling. Apparently therefore the better and more hygienic finish would cost less than the inferior work.

Similarly with roofs; a sound lead roof will last up to a hundred years and will then have quite a considerable scrap value whereas a built-up felt roof might have to be renewed three or four times during this period. The difference of 400% in the initial cost would appear to cancel out by the end of a century, and the trouble and inconvenience of having the roof stripped and relaid at intervals would be avoided by using the more durable material.

Of course, such examples are over-simplified, because we know that in comparing current and future expenditure we have to consider not the actual amounts to be spent in future years but these amounts discounted to present day value—that is, the sum of money which would have to be invested today in order to accumulate to these amounts by the time they are needed. As money invested at as little as 5% compound interest doubles in just under fifteen years there is obviously a considerable difference between the two figures.

At this juncture we can look at a simple example (the present day values are calculated according to the formulae in Appendix D).

EXAMPLE

It is desired to compare the costs-in-use of two types of cladding to a factory building. Cladding A will cost £500,000, will require redecorating every four years at a cost of £60,000, and will require renewing after twenty years at a cost of £700,000. The life of the building is assumed to be 40 years. The alternative Cladding B will cost £900,000, and will last the life of the building without any maintenance, although a sum of £150,000 is to be allowed for general repairs after 20 years. The rate of interest allowed is 3%, per annum compound.

Costs-in-use of Cladding A

		£
Initial cost		500,000
Present value at 3% of:		
Redecoration after	4 years £60,000 at 88.8p =	53,280
,, ,,	8 years £60,000 at 78.9p =	47,340
,, ,,	12 years £60,000 at 70.1p =	42,060
,, ,,	16 years £60,000 at 62.3p =	37,380
Renewal after	20 years £700,000 at 55.4p =	387,800
Redecorating after	24 years £60,000 at 49.2p =	29,520
,, ,,	28 years £60,000 at 43.7p =	26,220
,, ,,	32 years £60,000 at 38.8p =	23,280
,, ,,	36 years £60,000 at 34.5p =	20,700
		£1,167,580

C/forward £1,167,580

Costs-in-use of Cladding B

	£
Initial cost	900,000

Present value at 3% of:

Repairs after 20 years £150,000 at 55.4p =	83,100	
	£983,100	983,100
Saving by using Cladding B		£184,480

It would therefore appear to be justifiable to use the initially more expensive Cladding B, as this will prove much the cheaper in the long run. Note that the "present value" method of discounting has been used, as the "annual equivalent" method (see page 43) would have proved far more complicated in such an instance, where none of the payments or receipts are annual. There is no need to bother with sinking funds, as this is a comparison only and both claddings will be worthless at the end of the 40 years.

It is worth noting that the present value of Cladding A could have been evaluated even more quickly, with a slight loss of accuracy (because of averaging out the decoration costs to a yearly figure), as follows:

Costs-in-use of Cladding A

	£
Initial cost	500,000
Redecoration £60,000 every 4 years = £15,000 p.a.	
36 years purchase of £15,000 at 3%	
(see Appendix D, Table 4) at £21.83 =	327,450
Replacement at 20 years	
£700,000 less saving in decoration £60,000 = £640,000.	
Present value (3%) at 55.4p =	354,560
	£1,182,010

We shall see later that the loss of accuracy by this method is of no practical significance.

Disadvantages of "costs-in-use" assessment

The advantages of this method of comparing costs are self-evident; it enables us to consider the long term implications of a decision, and to provide a way of showing the cost consequences of short-sighted economies. Unfortunately there are a number of fundamental disadvantages, which explain why this technique for comparing the cost of the alternative materials and constructions is seen more often in the examination room than in real life. These disadvantages may be dealt with under two headings.

"Initial and running costs cannot really be equated"

(a) Where the building is to be disposed of by sale the maintenance charges will fall upon the purchaser, and so are of little importance to the vendor, who is responsible for the construction costs.

(b) Where the building is to be let, or used commercially, the initial cost comes out of capital, while the repairs and maintenance are deducted from the commercial receipts in calculating profit for the year. These maintenance charges are therefore paid out of untaxed income, whereas money spent at construction stage has to be raised as part of the capital cost and is eventually repayable. Repayment of, or interest on, capital expenditure is not normally deductable from receipts for the purposes of tax calculations. While this factor can to some extent be allowed for in the rate chosen for discounting, this does not fully deal with the fact that money for capital expenditure is normally more difficult to find and is subject to more constraints than money for current expeniture.

(c) Even with the publicly owned buildings it is an advantage to pay maintenance out of running costs instead of incurring a heavier debt due to high construction costs. In some instances, such as schools, the bulk of the construction costs may be paid by one authority while another authority will be responsible for running costs, so that there will be little incentive to provide an unduly high standard of building with a view to subsequent saving.

(d) Although built-in obsolescence is not yet a regular feature of the construction industry, undoubtedly circumstances change and although a building may be perfectly sound after the passage of years it may be too old-fashioned in design and accommodation to do the job that is required of it in modern conditions. Similarly with durable finishes, which although still in good condition may give a very old fashioned appearance to a building. Most readers will be familiar with instances where old joinery, tiling, and other finishes or fittings have been ripped out long before they are life-expired for this reason. This factor particularly applies in the competitive world of commerce; in a fashionable shopping street it is not unusual for a shop front or interior to be replaced after five or six years because it has begun to look out of date, or does not fit in with current merchandising ideas.

(e) In comparing figures of increased present-day expenditure against future costs of repair and renewal it must be remembered that once the money has actually been spent it is not possible to amend the decision in the light of future developments. As an example of this, supposing that very expensive finishes are chosen for a house to save repainting. If after a few years the owner finds himself short of money he still has to repay the annual interest on his expensive house, whereas if he had opted for a cheaper house he could have deferred the repainting for a year or two. (He could also redecorate his house in the lastest fashion each time, if he wanted to.) It is questionable practice to restrict the actions of future generations by committing them to high interest and repayment costs; this is just as bad as the other extreme of committing them to inflated running costs and maintenance costs by unduly low standards of design and construction.

(f) The previous arguments have suggested that DCF techniques over-emphasise the importance of running costs, but it can also be argued that they are unrealistic in an opposite sense, because it is most unusual to actually set money aside in this way to meet future expenditure. If, for instance, you had to meet repair bills this year for £90,000 it would be little compensation to learn that somebody discounted this to £20,000 in the year 1950—you would still have to find the £90,000.

"The future cannot really be forecast"

(g) While the capital costs can be estimated quite accurately the cost of maintenance is a pure guess. The amount of money spent on decoration and upkeep of a building is determined far more by the current policy of the body responsible for maintenance than by any quality inherent in the materials. Some owners will redecorate every few years, mend or replace worn or damaged work immediately, and continuously carry out a policy of minor improvements; others will spend the very minimum necessary to keep the building in operation.

(h) Major expenditure on repairs is normally caused by failure of detailing, faulty material, or bad workmanship, rather than by overall ageing, and so is almost impossible to forecast. A well designed and maintained piece of cheap construction might well last much longer than its theoretical life, while some quite expensive work could require early renewal because of, say, entry of water at a badly designed joint.

(i) Interest rates [which in general tend to reflect the current MLR (Minimum Lending Rate)] cannot be forecast with any certainty, particularly over long periods of twenty years or more;

remember that net interest rates are also affected by changes in taxation. Would you like to guess what the Chancellor will do in the year 2000—and whether he will be Tory, Labour, Marxist, or Anarchist?

(j) During the last thirty years there has been almost continuous economic inflation, and any building or maintenance work is likely to cost several times what would have been estimated, say, twenty years ago.

In order to demonstrate the effect of quite small misjudgements of the future, the example relating to Claddings A and B is now worked out again, assuming some slight differences to the assumptions previously made. Cladding A is redecorated every 5 years instead of every 4 years at a cost of £50,000 and lasts for 25 years instead of 20, costing £600,000 to renew. Cladding B has to be repaired after 15 years and again at 30 years, and interest rates average out at 4% instead of 3%. All these differences lie well within the range of error to be expected with careful estimates in normal times, and exclude either inflation or anything going badly wrong.

Revised costs-in-use of Cladding A

			£	£
Initial cost			500,000	
Present value at 4% of:				
Redecoration after	5 years £50,000 at 82.2p	=	41,100	
,, ,,	10 years £50,000 at 67.6p	=	33,800	
,, ,,	15 years £50,000 at 55.5p	=	27,750	
,, ,,	20 years £50,000 at 45.6p	=	22,800	
Renewal after	25 years £600,000 at 37.5p	=	225,000	
Redecoration after	30 years £50,000 at 30.8p	=	15,400	
,, ,,	35 years £50,000 at 25.3p	=	12,650	
			£878,500	878,500

Revised costs-in-use of Cladding B

		£	£
Initial cost		900,000	
Present value at 4% of:			
Repairs after	15 years £150,000 at 55.5p =	83,250	
,, ,,	30 years £100,000 at 30.8p =	30,800	
		£1,014.050	1,014,050
Saving by using Cladding A			£135,550

This calculation gives a completely different result to the original—the initially cheaper cladding proves to be much the cheaper in the long run also, and would still have life left in it at the end of 40 years if it were decided to keep the building in commission for a bit longer. The lesson it teaches is that calculations of this kind should not be used as the sole basis for decision unless the cost advantage of one of the alternatives is really massive—not the 15–20% of these examples.

A mathematical technique ("Monte Carlo simulation") for assessing the effect of probabilities in a situation such as this is given in Chapter 15, and this might assist decision-making in some circumstances. Alternatively, the problem can be solved by computer using a number of different values for the variables; this may enable the important ones to be identified.

Inflation

The last calculation did not take inflation into account at all, but some authorities suggest that it is this factor which really makes complete nonsense of any attempt at long term forecasting. This is to take too gloomy a view; inflation may be no worse than the other factors which we have discussed, because interest rates tend to rise during a period of rapid inflation. If, therefore, the original "Cladding A" example (page 116) were worked out on the basis of 10% annual inflation and 13% interest we would get much the same result as with no inflation and interest at 3%. (N.B. The compound interest table has been used for calculating the effect of inflation.)

Revised costs-in-use of Cladding A (10% annual inflation)

				£
Initial cost				500,000
Present value at 13% of:				
Redecoration after	4 years	£87,600 at 61.3p =		53,699
,,	,,	8 years	£128,400 at 37.6p =	48,278
,,	,,	12 years	£188,400 at 23.1p =	43,520
,,	,,	16 years	£275,400 at 14.1p =	38,831
Renewal after		20 years	£4,711,000 at 8.7p =	409,857
Redecoration after		24 years	£591,000 at 5.3p =	31,323
,,	,,	28 years	£865,200 at 3.3p =	28,551
,,	,,	32 years	£1,266,600 at 2.0p =	25,332
,,	,,	36 years	£1,854,600 at 1.2p =	22,255
				£1,201,646

This is very similar to the figure which we had originally, in spite of the vast increase in cost. However, we must remember that building costs do not necessarily increase in step with general inflation; in particular repair costs, which have a high site labour content and sometimes involve obsolescent materials, may well increase more than a general building cost index would indicate. At the same time it should be realised that income will tend to rise at roughly the same rate as inflation (otherwise building owners would go bankrupt) and this increase should offset the increased running costs. This is a further argument for ignoring the effect of inflation in costs-in-use studies.

However, it may be possible to take into account some aspects of differential inflation, where the price of one type of commodity or factor increases at a different rate to the alternative, although this is of course very difficult to predict. It may be influenced very much by the relative scarcity of different raw materials and other resources in the future.

Reasons for accepting increased capital costs

The rather obvious link between low first cost and high maintenance costs was mentioned earlier in this chapter, and could easily be taken for granted. It is only right to mention, therefore, that in spite of quite considerable efforts no evidence has been found from general user experience to suggest that increased capital expenditure on better materials and finishes necessarily produces lower maintenance costs.

Nevertheless there are still good reasons why a more expensive alternative may be preferred at design stage:

(1) For prestige reasons. The client may consider that his building is too important to have cheap and inferior materials and workmanship.

(2) As well as being more durable, expensive materials are often more pleasant to look at or to use.

(3) Replacement or repair may be inconvenient. The re-covering of a roof, or relaying of a floor, will upset the users of the building and could have severe commercial effects (customers prefer not to go into a shop or hotel where building works are in progress).

(4) Replacement or repair may be difficult, and therefore expensive. Repairs of the covering of an external cornice might involve scaffolding the whole building, for instance.

(5) The saving of money on a specific item may involve repairs out of all proportion to the saving. The use of iron instead of copper for slate nails would eventually necessitate the stripping and re-slating of the whole roof, for the sake of saving a few pence per square metre. Similarly the omission of galvanising on metal windows might involve the replacement of all the windows after some years.

(6) Obsolescence may not be a factor of any importance. Such buildings as churches, or especially cathedrals, employ the best materials in the hope that they will endure for hundreds of years.

In designing a new building therefore it is important to consider what its economic life is likely to be, and what changes it is likely to undergo during that life, before coming to a decision on construction and finishes. Obviously this can only be done to a limited extent as it is impossible to look too far into the future, but some types of building are inherently more subject to change than others, and this can be taken into account. Theoretically it might be possible to design a building so that all its components would begin to fail simultaneously at the end of its economic life; in practice this is not possible although the worst incongruities can be avoided. Expensive materials should not be chosen for the sake of their durability if they are likely to outlast the rest of the building, or if they will have to be replaced due to the failure of some other and inferior component.

B. Costs-in-use of mechanical installations

The conflict between capital outlay and running costs occurs in a pronounced form in the evaluation of heating and other mechanical systems, because considerable economies in daily fuel and staffing costs can be achieved by additional capital expenditure. We saw an example of this kind of thing in Chapter 4, when the cost consequences of a mechanical stoker for a boiler were calculated.

Many of the disadvantages of costs-in-use calculations which were set out earlier in this chapter will apply here also, although not so severely as in the previous case. This is because:

(a) The running costs of energy-consuming systems form a high proportion of their total costs-in-use (for this reason it is usually convenient to use the "annual equivalent" method for the costs-in-use study rather than the "present day value").

(b) The fuel consumption and staffing requirements (e.g. boilerman, lift attendant) of different kinds of systems can be calculated quite accurately, and cannot be so easily varied by client policy as can general building maintenance and decoration.

(c) Mechanical and electrical installations should be written off over a much shorter period of time than a general building fabric, both because of the more limited life of their components and because they become obsolete much sooner. Not many fifty-year-old buildings still have their original heating and electrical systems. Since one is forecasting over a shorter period any assumptions about cost, interest rates, and taxation are more likely to be valid.

The most simple forms of calculation are those related to capital/fuel costs of different heating systems—see example overleaf.

A more complex calculation is used to take into account the cost of additional thermal insulation of the building, for example double glazing. Such a calculation might have two different objects:

(i) To justify the capital expenditure on the insulation itself, because of savings in fuel cost.

Automatic gas-fired heating system:	£	£
Annual fuel costs	5,000	
5% interest on capital cost of system (including building work) £30,000	1,500	
"Sinking fund" to repay capital cost after 20 years at 3% £30,000 at 3.7p	1,110	
	£7,610	7,610

Electric storage heating system		
Annual fuel costs	6,800	
5%interest on capital cost of system £15,000	750	
"Sinking fund" to repay capital cost after 5 years at 3% £15,000 at 5.4p	810	
	£8,360	8,360

Annual saving on costs-in-use of gas-fired system		£750

(ii) To also justify the use of a low-capital/high-fuel-cost heating system, which would become more economic if the required heat loading could be reduced.

Very complex calculations are involved where the scope of the mechanical services are dependent upon the configuration of the building—for example, heat extraction systems might be necessary for a multi-storey bulding which has a very low wall/floor area ratio and would have to be taken into account in carrying out structural cost comparisons, and relative lift costs would be a factor in trying out alternative arrangements for a tall building.

Finally, in all these comparisons, it is likely that in the end the client's own (possibly subjective) views on acceptable levels of capital cost and running cost would be more important than the exact result of comparing them on an economically equal basis. It is important, however, that he should be given the facts (including these comparisons) before arriving at a decision.

C. Costs-in-use of the total project

In arriving at a decision on what kind of building to erect a forecast of the costs-in-use of the total project may be important for three reasons:

(i) To fix rentals of a development, such as an office block or service flats, where the owner will remain responsible for some of the running costs.

(ii) To see whether a client can afford to run the building when it has been erected—as in the case of deciding the optimum size of a new village hall.

(iii) To see whether increased expenditure on a building which is to be occupied by the client, such as a hospital, could reduce the general level of running costs by making it possible to operate with fewer, or less skilled, staff.

In all these cases the problem is usually a short term one—involving, say, five-year leases in the first instance and current staffing difficulties in the last, so that what is required is a fairly accurate assessment of expenditure in a typical year in the very near future rather than a "plus" or "minus" comparison with capital building cost. In the first of these cases there is little point in equating annual costs with increases or decreases in the capital cost of the development, as long as the rents will bear the likely charges. In the second case, since capital and running costs are almost certain to be met from different sources (perhaps an appeal plus grant for the first, and income from lettings for the running costs), much the same applies. It is only in the last of these three cases that such comparisons are likely to mean anything, although even here the main motivation is likely to be staffing problems rather than costs as such.

Information on maintenance costs

Without the existence of a large quantity of published data it would have been difficult for the practice of cost planning to take root, and one of the factors making costs-in-use studies so risky has been the lack of any similar body of information on maintenance costs. In order to remedy this situation a Building Maintenance Cost Information Service (BMCIS) has been set up by the RICS, to operate on a fairly similar basis to the earlier established Building Cost Information Service (BCIS). The new service was able to get off to a flying start as all the information which the government had accumulated on its own building maintenance costs has been made available to the Information Service. For continued success, however, it will be essential for a large number of major property owners to contribute to the store of information. A more detailed account of the contents of the BMCIS is included in Chapter 9.

Taxation and grants

One of the major assumptions which has to be made in costs-in-use calculations is the degree to which taxation will affect the final results. Taxation is a fluctuating variable, like other assumptions such as building life, component life, inflation, and interest rate. Different governments will have different policies towards the amount and type of taxation to be levied and this will directly or indirectly affect the amount the client pays for his maintenance. It is possible for a company to write off the cost of most operational and maintenance costs against profit before arriving at the net figure on which Corporation Tax is payable. In effect this means that the government is giving a very substantial discount on the cost of these items (52% in 1979–80). In practice, the benefit is probably not quite as great as the tax percentage, because the relief from tax does not usually occur until the next financial year after the costs have been incurred. The effect of this "tax lag" is to reduce the saving by the discounted value for the time elapsed between payment for the work, or service, and the time at which tax payment is actually due. Hence with a discount rate of 10% and a tax lag of one year, the real benefit becomes:

$$£0.52 \times 0.909 = £0.47 \text{ in every pound.}$$

This position becomes more complex when tax relief is allowed on initial costs. For example, to encourage investment in industrial buildings the government has allowed 54% of the construction cost to be written off against tax in the first year, and 4% per year thereafter until 100% of the capital cost has been accounted for (this means of course that only 2% can be written off in the final year). Each of these savings would need to be discounted using the present value table, bearing in mind once again that there is usually some form of tax lag. In addition to tax savings on initial cost it is also possible to receive direct grants from the government for building in specially designated development areas, as described in Chapter 5. These grants reduce the effective initial capital cost to the client. All these factors should be taken into account when undertaking a costs-in-use exercise. (However it should not be forgotten that the taxation relief is only available on profit and not every firm makes a profit every year.)

One last point to bear in mind is the influence of Value Added Tax. This is payable on all maintenance and repair work on buildings, but does not affect new construction as new work is zero rated.

Sensitivity analysis

We have already seen that there are a large number of assumptions made in any costs-in-use calculation, and that it is not always possible to assess the effect of changes in these assumptions realistically. One method of testing whether the results achieved by costs-in-use studies are satisfactory for decision-making purposes is to repeat the calculations in a methodical way, changing the value of a single variable (i.e.

assumption) each time. It is then possible to see how sensitive the results are to changes in the variable under consideration. If the results are plotted on a graph then a visual check can be made to see when, for example, one component becomes more attractive than another. Figure 8.1 shows the results of such a sensitivity analysis between two components where the calculations have been changed by varying the life of a building and the interest rate. These computations have been plotted in the form of a graph with present value on the Y axis and interest rate on the X axis. From a graph of this nature, the interest rate and building life at which one component becomes a better proposition can be clearly seen. The area at the crossover of the graphs for each alternative is not clear and, therefore, at these interest rates there is obviously very little to choose between the two. While this technique is of some advantage in testing the effect of changes in the assumptions it still assumes that the variables are static during the building life. If it is possible of assess the probable distributions of the likely occurrence of values for each variable then the Monte Carlo technique should be used to sample from these distributions. This technique is described in detail in Chapter 15.

FIG. 8.1. *Sensitivity analysis*

Summing up

The forecasting of running costs of a building will often be useful, but this does not always mean that a costs-in-use study (equating capital costs and running costs) will have much meaning for the client. Where such studies are justifiable the following points should be remembered:

(1) The shorter the period involved the more accurate the forecast is likely to be. As an alternative the use of an artificially high rate for discounting will have much the same effect by attaching little value to anything which may happen in the very distant future.

(2) While the results of the study will be of use as one of the factors to bear in mind in arriving at a decision, it would be most unwise to come to a decision about alternatives on a costs-in-use basis alone, unless the calculated advantage of one of them is very substantial.

Chapter 9
Cost Data

Introduction

In the chapter on traditional cost models it was postulated that the actual techniques used were merely the structure around which the professional cost adviser applied his judgement to make the techniques work. The model itself was ill-equipped to produce a reliable answer, and indeed reliability at any stage of refinement was entirely dependent upon the costs applied to the measured quantities in their various forms. If the right cost figure was applied to any of the single-price methods then they would be more reliable than if the wrong figure(s) were applied to the more detailed techniques. The factor that made detailed cost planning techniques more satisfactory was the control that was exercised as design developed. Even this control, however, was based on unit rates applied to abbreviated quantities (another model) and was, therefore, dependent on the reliability of cost information. At the end of the day any estimate was dependent on the prevailing market conditions at the time of tender, and this again required information in order that market trends could be detected.

So at the root of all this forecasting and control activity we find the need for cost data to supplement the numbers, areas, volumes, etc. which have been used to describe the building. It is this data that is critical in determining whether an estimate is reliable or not. One of the major problems in more recent models, in which computer techniques are used, is the need to ensure that the information on cost held within the memory of the computer (i.e. the data base) is reliable and relevant for all conditions of use of that model. Very often human intervention is not envisaged in the computer operation and professional judgement is left until the results have been tabulated. This is very often too late because the adviser has little chance of knowing why a particular figure has been generated without considerable investigation on his part. Also if he is going to adjust a result to what he feels is reasonable, he might as well have used his own judgement in the first place using a traditional model. There is a well-known computer maxim "Garbage in, Garbage out", which reinforces this view that wrong data used in any technique will produce incorrect results. The study of "what information should we use" and "where does it come from" is essential for the correct understanding of the use and development of costing techniques. First we need to understand what it is used for.

The use of cost data

If we were to look at the work being undertaken in a typical quantity surveying office we would find cost information being used for four main purposes:

(i) The control and monitoring of a contract, for which the contractor has already been selected, through interim and final account procedures.
(ii) The estimation of the future cost of a project and the control of design to ensure that this figure is close to the tender figure.
(iii) The "balancing" of costs in a cost plan to ensure that money has been spent in accordance with the client's priorities.
(iv) The negotiation of rates with a contractor for the purposes of letting a contract quickly.

Arising out of these activities are other uses which might well be the concern of a special section in a quantity surveying practice or research department of a polytechnic or university. These uses relate to the deeper understanding of the external political and economic trends, and the relationship between design decisions and the degree to which they affect cost. These studies usually require a more detailed level of investigation, involving the analysis of large quantities of data or the classification and structuring of the data in a particular way to assist in the development of evaluation models.

To incorporate all uses of data we can probably classify them under four main headings:

(i) *Forecasting of cost*
Under this heading would come such information as cost per square metre for various types of building, elemental unit rates, Bill rates, and all-in unit rates applied to abbreviated quantities. In the examples listed the data would almost certainly arise from an analysis of past projects, or "historic costs". These would be updated by the use of a building cost index, itself a form of cost data, and be projected forward to the proposed tender date by an intuitive or calculated prediction technique. In recent years the problems associated with historic costs (see later in the chapter) have spurred researchers and practitioners to develop techniques which rely on current resource costs (labour, plant, and material) to forecast the cost

of a project. This certainly helps in the negotiation of contracts and also in the reliable modelling of the building process. Resources are where the cost is generated, and the adviser is therefore dealing with the origins of cost. However, the problem lies in the acquisition of information on resource costs by anyone who is not a member of a large building organisation, and in the time-consuming nature of the task of synthesising costs from detailed resource inputs. In fact techniques employing resources to forecast cost have various ways of simplifying the problem to avoid the user being overwhelmed by too much data. These usually involve concentrating on the major items and quantities at the expense of those with less cost significance. It should be noted that even these techniques rely heavily on "historic" information regarding the *normal* time and quantity requirements for the resources needed for a particular item or building.

(ii) *Comparison of cost*
In this use of data the need is not so much to discover what the building or component will actually cost at the time of tender but to make a comparison between items with similar function, or buildings of different design, to decide which is the better choice. The problems of the tender market are not so critical here unless there is evidence that there will be a change in the cost relationship between the alternatives by the time the decision takes effect. The criterion in choosing data for this task should be that it is structured in such a form that if the design or specification of an item is changed the use of the cost data will reflect the true change in the cost of the commodity.

(iii) *Balancing of cost*
In determining a budget for the cost control of a building it is necessary to break down the overall cost into smaller units. These smaller units are used not only for cost checking purposes but also to allow a cost strategy to be developed for design. This strategy will attempt to spend money in accordance with the client's requirements, by allocating sums of money to the various major components of the building. Data for this use is usually obtained from past projects, and it may be in the form of actual costs or as a proportion of the total cost of a similar project. At the stage that this information is used the design will not be developed (and may not even have commenced) and therefore the categories used for this breakdown will tend to be broad and probably not exceed forty items for any one project. The data can therefore be described as "coarse" as opposed to refined.

(iv) *Analysis of cost trends*

Of paramount importance in any prediction technique which seeks to project costs into the future is the information that tells us what is happening to costs in the industry over a period of time. By looking at the way in which costs for different items are changing in relation to one another, or changing between one point in time and another, it is possible to have a better chance of selecting the specification which will suit the client's financial requirement over the short and long term. It will also allow us to obtain a more reliable prediction of what the market price to the client will be when he eventually goes out to tender. These trends may be shown as the change in the cost of materials and labour, or they may be a detected change in the total cost of a particular type of building or component. When data is used for the detection of cost trends the cost is very often related to a base year cost, in which case the presentation of the information is in the form of an index. It should be clearly noted that the detection of a cost trend does not necessarily imply that it will continue into the future. Indeed it is very unwise to extrapolate a cost movement without taking into account all the political, social, and economic factors that contribute to a change in cost levels. The number of variables involved in such an evaluation is enormous, and consequently the establishment of what future costs will be is nearly always left to the professional experience of the cost adviser. He will probably take account of economic reports, but even these differ widely in their predictions. It has been said that where you get two economists discussing a particular economic problem you are likely to get three different opinions!

If these are the major uses of cost data, we can now look at the problems in retrieving and storing the information for these particular applications.

How reliable is cost data?

Nearly all data used in cost planning techniques has been processed in some way, very often with a corresponding loss in accuracy and certainly with some loss of context. The published information received by the quantity surveyor appears to relate to a "typical" building in a "typical" location with only a brief summary of the contributing factors to such a cost (i.e. the explanatory variables) included. The feedback of such cost information centres in the main around the Bill of Quantities.

Figure 9.1 shows a diagrammatic representation of traditional cost retrieval and planning practice.

FIG. 9.1. *Traditional cost retrieval*

In theory, information on wages, materials, and plant is collected on site and fed to the contracts manager; he then passes this raw data on to the estimator who uses it together with data from other projects to forecast his next tender price. The consultant quantity surveyor then analyses the contract Bill of Quantities to provide him with data which he then uses to forecast the cost of the next similar building and to control the cost during the development of design. When this new design has been built, the feedback cycle starts all over again. Notice that in the diagram no feedback into the general system is shown from the area of building performance cost (i.e. maintenance and operational costs). Although some public authorities in recent years have attempted to obtain data on these costs and pass this information to the design team for consideration in their choice of detailing and specification this is by no means common practice. In the private sector, the time involved, the lack of clients involved in large programmes of building, and the tax skeletons in the cupboard, have all contributed to a reluctance to collect and divulge occupation costs.

The above procedures, although they represent the usual practice, are fraught with problems. Let us consider the contractor's estimating feedback cycle first of all. The difficulties are as follows, and are further considered in Chapter 14.

(i) Although records of labour and material costs are kept on site, the information is kept primarily for the payment of wages and checking of invoices and secondly for monitoring progress on site as an aid to contract management. These purposes dictate a format of recording which is not compatible with the way in which the estimator prepares his estimate. The grouping of items into "operations" for reference to the contractor's programme creates difficulties in rearrangement for the pricing of a Bill of Quantities based upon the Standard Method of Measurement requirement to measure items as fixed "in place". Consequently feedback to the estimator tends to be at a very general level of, for example, ". . . we were a bit low on plaster rates in this contract Jack . . ." rather than more specific data.

(ii) Even if site data could be related back to the estimator it is unlikely to be of very great benefit. Performance of the labour force varies considerably from day to day according to such factors as weather, supervision, obstruction by other trades, and psychological pressures. It is unlikely that individual performance on one contract is likely to be repeated on another. The estimator can only hope to get close to the total labour content of the project and hope that good site management will avoid wastage of this resource.

(iii) For work where "labour only" sub-contractors are used no record of the performance of labour will be available, and therefore an increasingly large area of work is no longer subject to scrutiny and analysis.

(iv) Material use and costs will also be a variable between sites, and here again no firm data can be expected for the estimator to use. The amount of materials used will depend on such factors as ordering, site control, degree of vandalism, and of course the competence of the work force.

(v) Plant cost will depend on good site management, the amount and type of plant available from stores, or on hire, and the amount of disruption affecting the contract period. Once again it may be difficult for the estimator to relate data obtained from one site to another.

The problems with feedback mean that very little data is kept in the contractor's office. The data base for the majority of estimators consists of a "small black book" of labour and material constants, a list of addresses and telephone numbers of suppliers and sub-contractors, and a good deal of experienced judgement!

No wonder that it has been suggested that a tender represents "the socially acceptable price" rather than a scientific appraisal of the resource needs of a project. Indeed there is some evidence to show that estimators bid randomly within plus or minus 10% of the actual contract cost excluding profit. This is considered to be the limit of their ability to reliably forecast what the job will cost and is discussed later in this chapter.

The problems with the retrieval of site data set the scene for the problems the quantity surveyor will find when he analyses the priced tender document. The vast majority of his cost information arises from the Bill of Quantities and yet as we are beginning to see, this document may be based on incorrect assumptions which just happen to work in most cases and are convenient for the estimator to use. It has been said that the only reliable figure in the Bill from the client's point of view is the tender figure. If we start to break this composite sum down into smaller units for estimating purposes then we are liable to find error in each individual sub-section when considered in isolation from the other sections. The greater the number of categories the greater the degree of error for the following reasons:

(i) We know that the rates in the Bill of Quantities are not true costs, but they are not even true prices in the sense of a price on a supermarket shelf. The contractor is not offering to "sell" brickwork at so many pounds per square metre, his accepted offer is for constructing a whole building and the rates are simply a notional breakdown of his total price for commercial and administrative purposes. There is thus no reason why any individual rate should be justifiable in relation to either cost or competition.

(ii) The way in which the contractor prices his preliminary items of plant, scaffolding, etc. will vary from one firm to another. Some will include these items in the work rates whilst others will place them in the preliminaries section.

(iii) The same applies to the contractor's profit and overheads. Consequently the "cost" of any individual trade, element, or

Bill item will vary according to these two factors.

(iv) It may be in the contractor's best interest to "load" those parts of the building which are executed first, such as excavation and earthworks, to improve his cash flow (i.e. obtain his money quicker on interim valuations to help finance the rest of the work). Although if this is overdone it is likely to be challenged by the quantity surveyor before accepting the tender, these sort of discrepancies can occur on a sufficient scale to distort any analysis of the Bill.

 (v) In a similar fashion, the contractor may anticipate variations to the contract and reduce the price of likely omissions whilst increasing the unit rate of any items which are likely to increase in quantity.

(vi) In addition to the deliberate pricing method of each contractor there are all the variations in unit rates caused by different assumptions being made by each estimator with regard to the resource requirements. These variations tend to be highest in high-risk trades such as excavator and carpentry, and lowest in those most easily controlled such as glazing and concrete work. The assumptions made will relate to the estimator's view of his firm's expertise and economic structure.

(vii)   In an estimate for a complex product such as a building it is inevitable that some mistakes will be made. These will tend to cancel each other out but sometimes there is an error of cost significance in a single item which may not be spotted by the quantity surveyor.

If other factors such as the contractor's previous experience of the particular design team (e.g. pricing the architect or quantity surveyor!), knowledge of the locality, and experience of the type of building proposed are taken into account it can be seen that data obtained from Bills is likely to be highly variable even for contractors who are tendering for the same job. If we now consider the Bill rates of contractors tendering for different projects then we can expect variability due to all the above factors plus a good few more. These additional items will relate to the site and contract conditions for each particular job and will include:

(i) *The site conditions*
Under this heading we can include the problems of access; boundary conditions especially the problems of adjacent buildings; soil bearing capacity and consistency; topography and the orientation of the building (which may well affect manoeuvrability on the site and the type of resources, particularly plant, that can be used).

(ii) *Design variations*

The way the building is designed has an enormous effect on the efficient use of resources, and on production method and time. For example if there is a good deal of repetition of formwork then it is reasonable to expect lower unit rates if this fact has been communicated to the estimator. Similarly wet trades requiring drying and curing time will possibly create more delay than if a dry form of construction is used. The extra costs, if any, will be represented in the rates or will result in a redistribution of prices, for example, more money in preliminaries for the longer supervision required and the plant not fully employed, and less money in the work sections of the Bill.

(iii) *Contract conditions*

The impact of these is very difficult to anticipate particularly with regard to their effect on unit rates. In general it can be assumed that the more onerous the terms as far as the contractor is concerned the more likely it is that a higher estimate will be given. However, when a contractor is short of work or particularly wants a job, say for prestige purposes, then the effect of "tough" clauses may be less dramatic than would normally be expected. Any contract which requires more working capital for the project, or additional risk, is almost certain to incur a cost penalty which will be passed on to the client. In addition, conditions relating to the length of the construction period, particularly a shortening of the time, and also the phasing of the works, both of which may result in uneconomic working, will influence the estimator's rates and particularly the preliminary items.

(iv) *Size of contract*

For each contractor there is an optimum size of contract that will suit his particular structure and resources. Large firms very often create "small works" sections of the main company to deal with those contracts which are small or of a specialist nature, such as restoration work, and which cannot carry the overheads of a giant corporation. Small firms on the other hand find it difficult to gear themselves up to a multi-million pound project with its specialist plant, complex labour relations, and sophisticated supervision and control requirements. The size of the firm in relation to the contract for which it is bidding will therefore affect its approach to the estimate. The unit rates for a large project should include an allowance for the economies of scale that could be expected. However, the problems of site working, the lack of advanced mechanical production plant, and the nature of the industry do not always allow these economies to be made.

(v) *Location*

This factor will obviously affect the problems of accessibility to the production resources. The transport of plant, men, and materials to site, with perhaps accommodation of the workforce on remote sites, makes this an important consideration. On top of these problems are those of local climate which may affect the starting on the site, the degree of protection required and the interruption of the works programme. Despite these problems it should be noted that only the Housing Cost Yardstick, of the old principal government cost limits, identified location as a cost variable and this particular yardstick divided the country into regions. The other yardsticks made no allowance for regional variations but did take the problems of a particular site into consideration by use of an "abnormal" allowance. A contractor's estimator is likely to pass on the problems of a particular area as an extra cost to the client if he has had experience of that location. This again will create variation in the rates due to different allowances being made.

All the problems listed contribute to the wide variability in Bill rates. Derek Beeston of the Property Services Agency found that the variability tended to be different for each trade. He looked at the major items in each work section (or trade) and compared the unit rate for each identical item in a large sample of Bills of Quantities from different Department of the Environment projects. He expressed the degree of variability in the form of the "coefficient of variation", which enables a comparison to be made between the variability of items of different value and is given by the formula:

$$\text{Coefficient of variation} = \frac{\text{standard deviation}^*}{\text{arithmetic mean}} \times 100\%.$$

So in concrete work for example the cost per cubic metre may be £30.00 and the standard deviation £5.00:

$$\text{Coefficient of variation} = (5/30) \times 100\%$$

$$= 16.67\%.$$

This can now be compared with plaster work with a cost of £3.00 per square metre and a standard deviation of 30 pence:

$$\text{Coefficient of variation} = (30/300) \times 100\%.$$

$$= 10\%$$

---

* This and other statistical terms are defined in Appendix C.

The standard deviation on its own would not allow the degree of variability in each trade to be compared.

The results of his investigations showed the following:

Excavator	45%	Joiner	28%
Drainlayer	29%	Roofer	24%
Concretor	15%	Plumber	23%
Steelworker	19%	Painter	22%
Bricklayer	26%	Glazier	13%
Carpenter	31%	All trades	22%

It is no surpise that excavator, with its high risk problems due to weather, soil conditions, accessibility, etc., should have the highest variability. The ranking of some of the others is perhaps unexpected and a detailed investigation would need to be undertaken to discover the reason for their particular performance. However, the table does illustrate very clearly the problems of using Bill data. Once again success depends on the skill of the user in determining what rate to use against a particular measured quantity.

The contractor's bid

If we accept the problems associated with obtaining reliable feedback from site and the rather arbitrary value given to unit rates in the Bill of Quantities then we might wonder how the contractor arrives at his "bid" for a particular contract when he is in competition with others. The theory is that the estimator *knows* how long it will take a team of craftsmen and labourers to execute a job; that he *knows* the precise amount of material required including wastage; and that he *can define* the exact output of each item of plant to be used and the time it will be on site. He then brings together all these factors for each trade and adds on the *measured* cost of supervision and overheads to arrive at the net cost of the job (excluding profit). The process is essentially *deterministic;* the method assumes that the estimator can determine the exact amount of resources and their cost. However, every contractor knows that this is not possible.

Research in the field of estimating has suggested that while the above process is theoretically adopted it is in fact very often used to justify a target that the contractor has in mind from the very beginning. Brian Fine, who used to work for one of the largest UK building companies and is now a management consultant has suggested that contractors may bid at what they consider to be the "socially acceptable price". This is not well defined but is considered to be the price which society is known to be prepared to pay for a particular type of building. For commercial projects this price would probably be related to the income of the office block or output of the industrial plant, whilst for projects of a social nature it may be related to the known funds available or in the case of government funding it may be a defined cost yardstick. It is considered that this value of the building is relatively easily calculated and that generally the building is buildable at around the socially acceptable price. By bidding at this value the estimator overcomes the problem of being unable to predict resource requirements for the project. As the client is probably basing his anticipated cost on what has been successfully built before it is therefore likely that the estimator will have put forward a reasonable estimate. He then uses his "constants" to justify his bid.

It is unlikely that many contractors consciously go through the above process, and indeed they very often react strongly to the suggestion that they do. However they will occasionally admit that they can write down the cost of the job before they start pricing it, or that they work out the yardstick before pricing a government job! Many clients assist the contractor in this respect by naming the value of the contract when enquiring if the contractor is willing to tender. In addition the building grapevine of sub-contractors, who probably quote several times for the same job but for different contractors, will ensure that the anticipated contract sum is well circulated. It is strange that despite the wide variation in Bill rates the final tender figures are considerably closer together than one would be led to expect. A coefficient of variation for the spread of tenders on a project tends to be in the range of 5–8% and this can be applied to a wide range of projects.

Support for this non-deterministic argument as to how contractors estimate is strengthened by the following observations:

   (i) The name of the project appears to influence the cost of the job. A good example of this phenomenon is the decision by a number of hospital boards to let nurses' homes as a separate contract to the main hospital development. The reason for this decision was that the nurses' homes were costing appreciably more than comparable students' accommodation in the education sector. Contractors had apparently applied the same criteria of complexity, difficulty, and high cost that is associated with hospital projects to the far simpler problem of the nurses' home. Hence the high cost and of course the suggestion that the *real cost* was not being estimated.

   (ii) As stated previously in the chapter, it is not possible to establish accurate constants of labour, plant and material that can be applied to the job that is to be estimated. A typical output of a gang of bricklayers on site may be as shown in Fig. 9.2.

      Data of this nature may be of very little use in estimating the next job. On the graph opposite, week 6 results in a negative output, i.e. the gang have had to pull down something they constructed the week before because it was unsatisfactory or

Fɪɢ.9.2. *Weekly output of bricklaying gang*

the subject of a variation order. This is not an uncommon experience, but will it happen on the next job? If confident predictions cannot be made then an intuitive assessment in the form of the socially acceptable price is perhaps the answer.

(iii) In a competitive tendering market it appears that contractors take their place in the bidding order by chance. As would be expected with chance, in the long term they appear to win contracts in direct proportion to the number of contractors they are bidding against. J. C. Pimm of Management Procedures (Building) Ltd looked at four companies, the number of contracts they had bid for, and the number of competitors identified by the total number of bids. From this information and knowing the number of contracts actually won, he produced the following table:

Company	No. of contracts won	No. of bids	Bids per contracts	Per cent if won by chance	Per cent actually won
A	41	249	6.1	16.4	17.0
B	36	183	7.0	14.2	15.4
C	19	88	4.6	21.6	21.1
D	35	202	5.8	17.3	17.1

It can be seen that there is a very high correlation between those actually won and the number expected to be won by chance, assuming that each contractor took his place randomly in the bidding list. This is supported by Brian Fine who suggests that contractors can only estimate within plus or minus 10% of the actual cost. If this is so then each contractor needs to add on a "mark-up", to the estimate, to allow for the fact that if he is awarded the contract he is likely to have made the largest error. If this is not allowed for, then the mark-up will come out of the expected profit, or end up as a loss. The actual amount to be added should depend upon the number of contractors bidding. The probability of the lowest tenderer having made a large error increases with the number of competitors. In practice, very few firms consciously allow for this factor, but they probably note its eventual impact on the profitability of a project.

(iv) If the estimation of cost was really a deterministic exercise then the constants used in the estimate would be absolute and unchanging unless, of course, they were amended as the result of ascertained cost feedback. However, what happens when an estimator or his firm loses a number of bids in succession? They reduce their rates! This may be done on a lump sum basis, or the amount may be spread through the rates in the Bill. For a firm (or its estimator) to survive they must get work. This practice suggests that the estimate does not mean very much in terms of an accurate prediction. If the firm does get the job and they think it will be "tight" they put their best management on the project and very often they get a better return than on a job where they foresaw a large profit and did not maintain such tight control! The lower price that they are bidding could be the socially acceptable price.

It would not be fair to suggest that the concept of socially acceptable price has been thoroughly substantiated on the basis of the few arguments considered. However, doubt has been cast on the deterministic estimating process and this in turn will influence the way in which we look at and use cost data. Obviously the factors of supply and demand related to the capacity of the industry, and its workload, will influence the level of the contractor's bid, and the relationship between these factors and the socially acceptable price has not yet been well defined. However, it is important to realise that market conditions do reflect the economic standing of the country and this aspect may well have more impact on "historic" cost data, and the price society is prepared to pay for its buildings, than any other.

The structuring of cost data

In addition to the difficulty of acquiring reliable cost data there is the problem of what to do with it once acquired. The need for a system of cost planning to have access to cost data at a number of different levels of complexity postulates a hierarchy of cost groupings or even a series of interlocking hierarchies, because some of the criteria to which cost data will be applied are of a different type and not merely a different scale.

One such hierarchy, which we will encounter in Chapters 11 and 12, is based upon the concept of design cost elements. This is a highly pragmatic breakdown of a project for design cost planning purposes which, apart from its inherent faults, suffers from the disadvantage that it does not meet the requirements of any of the other functions in the design/build process.

Another hierarchy is the Standard Method of Measurement format used for Bills of Quantities, which is only of very limited use for other purposes. However, because the information provided in the Bill of Quantities is generally of a high quality, is tied back into the contract, and is available to the builder without further trouble, its format does tend to pervade process documentation rather more than might be expected.

Operational cost centres which are useful for actual control on site are difficult to relate, except at the highest levels of generality, to the estimating and commercial systems of the industry. Because of the obstruction to communication between builder and designer which is caused by the price mechanism there has been little attempt to link site operation costs to design criteria.

A number of efforts have been made during the last twenty years to devise an integrated system of groupings of building work which would meet the needs of all participants in the project, from the point of view of design process, costing, communication, organisation, and feedback. It is argued that such a system would reduce duplication of effort (it is alleged that the same piece of building work may be physically measured up to fifteen times for various purposes), improve communication between the parties, and permit a far higher quality of costing and cost feedback. The CI/SfB system whose use is encouraged by the RIBA is one such effort, but is somewhat too design-orientated to have found much favour elsewhere. A much more complex version of the same basic system, CBC, was developed in Scandinavia and relied heavily on computer use. In Britain the Department of the Environment set up a Data Co-ordination study with substantial resources and a large measure of contribution from industry and the professions, it being their very reasonable view that this was the only way of obtaining results that would be useful, and acceptable, to all. Unfortunately this work has now ceased, without producing much more than a number of very interesting reports and the *Construction Industry Thesaurus*, which is used mainly for library and information purposes.

Little real progress has therefore been made in this field, but there is plenty of background reading available.

Sources of data

So far in this chapter we have dealt with some of the more general problems of cost information associated with its use, retrieval, and structure. Although these problems should be identified it has to be recognised that the quantity surveying profession has been using data obtained from Bills of Quantities for scores of years with reasonable success. Contractors, too, have been able to prepare realistic estimates from the very general feedback that they get from site. The problems associated with data should not therefore be allowed to obscure the fact that the present data sources available to the industry have allowed a simple and reasonably effective system of cost forecasting and control to develop.

From the point of view of the client's cost adviser, information can be obtained from two main sources. Either he can use the data passing through his own hands in his office or he can obtain the information from published material found in the technical press, price books, and information systems. Of the two there is no doubt that a quantity surveyor would usually prefer to use his own data, for the following reasons:

(i)   The data is from a project of which he knows the background. He is therefore aware of all the problems associated with the project, its location, the market conditions, complexity, etc., which influenced its price. We have already said that traditional cost modelling and the successful use of data requires sound professional judgement. This judgement is better served by using information which is known to the quantity surveyor by his involvement in the project rather than that received second hand, in an abbreviated form, through a published source.

(ii) The further detailed breakdown of any structured information is available should he require it. To take the example of an elemental cost analysis, the firm will have available the priced Bill of Quantities, the dimensions, the working drawings, and the contract should they wish to find further information on why an element cost a certain amount or what were the prevailing market conditions at the time. It is very unlikely that this level of detail will be available in published data, however well prepared. To take another example, several quantity surveyors prepare their own cost indices because again they know the weightings and costs included and these can be manipulated to suit the needs of a particular project.

(iii) There is a shorter time lag between receiving raw data, processing it, and being able to use the structured information in the office. This is particularly relevant to cost indices where the published information may be anything up to six months behind the times.

(iv) The choice of classification and structure of the processed data is under the control of the firm. It is therefore possible to ensure that the details which are most relevant to that particular practice are emphasised and identified rather than having to accept a standardised published format. If errors and ambiguities occur it is also easier to spot them in your own system than in somebody else's.

Having established the preference of most quantity surveyors for their own information it would be unrealistic to suppose that any but the largest firms, or organisations which deal mainly with one type of building programme, could exist upon the data passing through their offices. The range of projects undertaken by most practices is considerable, varying from government and local authority buildings to commercial and leisure buildings for individual and corporate clients. The variety of specification, location, size, and shape of this range is also large and it is therefore most unlikely that the office will have up-to-date information which it can apply to all its new projects. The common unit rates which each quantity surveyor will gather from his handling of project information will help him in preparing his approximate quantities estimate, but a wide variety of data at the "coarser" level of elements and single-price rates is unlikely to be readily available. While he can probably make intuitive assessments, particularly of cost per square metre, it is helpful to have a check available in the form of published information to reassure him of his own judgement. Indeed it is probably the primary role of published information to provide data which allows the practitioner to check on his own knowledge and to provide a context for his own decision making. The following are the major published sources of this type of data. It will be seen that they apply almost entirely to conditions in the UK and the absence of a similar range of information on costs in other parts of the world makes the cost planner's task overseas much more difficult. Such information as exists is often of a more condensed statistical nature.

(i) *The technical press*
   There has been a steady improvement in the quantity and quality of cost information appearing in the journals and magazines concerned with design and building management. This is largely due to the increased demand from clients for better cost control, the tighter yardsticks and cost limits, and the recognition that there was previously very little disseminated information in the cost area. With this stimulation of interest, editors have found it profitable to give more space to cost forecasts and analysis than that provided in the past.

The type of information that can now be found in these publications includes elemental analyses; resource costs and measured rates; cost indices with future cost projections; regional economic reports; analysis of the economic performance of the industry; and cost studies of different types of building. Indeed with the rapid increase in the level of resource costs and measured rates over very short time-spans the technical press has, in many instances, replaced the standard price books as a source for quick reference material. Most journals are published weekly or monthly and this allows a comparatively short time lag between the reception and publication of current information. Typical examples of these journals are *The Architects' Journal, Building, Building Trades Journal,* and *Building Specification.*

(ii) *Builders' price books*

A traditional source of useful information has been the price books which are normally published annually by several well established organisations. These too have expanded the scope of their contents to keep pace with current demand. However, in periods of high inflation they have suffered the big drawback of having to prepare their information well in advance of the year of publication. This time lag of several months means that the rates included are forecasts of what is likely to happen at a sometimes unknown point of time in the year ahead. Despite these problems it is not unusual to find an assortment of these books on the shelves of all the building professions. Some of the most familiar are *Spon's Architects and Builders Price Book, Laxtons Price Book,* and *Hutchins Priced Schedules.*

Their popularity stems from the comprehensive nature of the data included and indeed the list of sub-sections is extensive:

    (a) Professional fees for building work.
    (b) Wage rates in the industry.
    (c) Market prices of materials.
    (d) Constants of labour and material for unit rates.
    (e) Prices for measured work (in accordance with the SMM).
    (f) Building cost index.
    (g) Approximate estimate rates and comparisons.
    (h) Cost limits and allowances.
    (i) European prices and information.

As with data from any source, considerable care should be exercised in the use of the information. For example, in the "Prices for measured work" section of the 1984 "Spons" the contract envisaged is situated in the outer London area, about a million pounds in value, and it is assumed that a reasonable quantity of work for all items is required. The prices include 10% for overhead charges and profit and if preliminaries are required to be included then at least 15% should be added on top of the published rates. The user is expected to make all allowances for changes in the location, size of contract, and market conditions.

(iii) *Information services*

With the advent of cost planning techniques and the need for a wide range of information on different types of project, it was realised that most offices would require information additional to that normally found in any one particular practice. The suggestion was made that if firms could be persuaded to supply their own elemental cost analyses to a central body then a large pool of information could be gathered which could then be disseminated to the contributing members. If these analyses could be supplemented with other more general information on trends and economic indicators then a useful service would be provided for the profession. Therefore, in April 1962, the RICS set up the Building Cost Information Service (BCIS), under the direction of Mr Douglas Robertson, to undertake this work. The service has since become well established and a valuable source of knowledge in the industry. Since 1972 the service has been available to organisations outside the quantity surveying profession. Although the original intention was to establish a data bank of elemental cost analyses this was never keenly supported by members, the reason for their lack of contributions being probably the expense and time involved in the preparation of an analysis which they themselves might never use again. The process of preparing an elemental analysis from a traditional Bill of Quantities is explained in Chapter 11, and its cost can easily run into hundreds of pounds. You would have to be pretty sure that this expenditure would be money well spent before committing your firm to this time and effort. The problems of confidentiality of cost information obtained from contract Bills of Quantities have been largely overcome by obtaining permission from the contractor before publishing the cost information. The number of published detailed analyses is now down to less than fifty per annum, and with the decline of theoretical elemental estimating (involving the adjustment of elemental unit rates) it is unlikely to grow much beyond this figure. In recent years, therefore, the information service has concentrated on other areas of cost study which could not easily be undertaken in the professional office, and it is in these other areas that it now provides the major contribution to the practitioner. A summary of the major sections of the service is given below:

Section A *General and background information*

This is a very broad and comprehensive section ranging from the statistics relating to the performance of the construction industry to current resource costs. It includes cost indices, building activity indicators, labour hours and wages, regional trends, and a briefing on the current economic and political climate.

Section B   *Publications digest*
This section contains a summary of important papers, articles and books related to the economics of buildings.

Section F   *Cost studies and research and development papers*
These papers are analytical studies of particular aspects of building cost or of cost planning systems.

Section G   *Detailed cost analyses*
This section contains the analyses submitted to the service and presented in accordance with the standard rules for elemental analysis developed by the BCIS. Each analysis contains a general description of the project including market conditions, contractual arrangements, number of tenderers, etc., a list of elemental costs, a brief specification, and a schematic drawing.

Section H   *Concise cost analyses*
These are much briefer forms of analysis with costs broken down into only seven major elements. The job description and specification is also reduced to give only a review of the major design variables. The analyses include summaries of the detailed forms found in Section G, plus summaries of published analyses found in the technical press.

Section Z   *Reference indexes*
This is a comprehensive cumulative reference index to sections A-H.

Some time after the BCIS became established it was realised that there was a similar need relating to the cost of maintenance. Therefore, in April 1971, after a pilot service had been operating for a year, the Building Maintenance Cost Information Service was launched. It was sponsored in collaboration with the School of Architecture and Building Technology at the University of Bath by the former Ministry of Public Building and Works (now part of the Department of the Environment) and had similar aims with regard to cost information for maintenance as did the BCIS with regard to capital cost. It is now an independent organisation to which anyone can become a subscriber. The service collects information from many relevant sources and disseminates it by regular mailings, but its unique data are derived from its own subscribers who, like those of the BCIS, are expected to contribute to the service. The arrangement of the service is also similar to that of the BCIS but in lieu of the detailed analyses there are three new sections. The full list is as follows:

Section A   *General background information*
Section B   **Publications digest**
Section C   *Case Studies*
These studies relate to maintenance management and control as exercised by various private and government organisations.

Section D   *Occupancy cost analyses*
The maintenance equivalent of the BCIS elemental cost analyses, these sheets break down the annual cost of maintaining and operating a building into major categories of expenditure such as cleaning, decoration, etc. Details of specification and a general description of the building are given to assist in using the data.

Section E   *Design/performance data*
There is a strong relationship between design and building maintenance, particularly in the early years of occupation, and this section identifies some of the major problems and suggests remedies which can be applied. The section is supplemented with sketches for ease of comprehension.

Section F   *Research and development papers*
Section Z   *Reference indexes*

Other cost information services are available but these two are definite leaders in their respective fields.

Since April of 1984 the BCIS has been operating a computer-based service accessible from a member office through a micro-computer, modem and telephone line. Initially this just provides data available in the manual system, but eventually a more comprehensive system with the possibility of members sending information up the line may be established.

(iv) *Government literature*
As the government has gradually become the major client of the building industry it has steadily increased its involvement in the research and development aspects of cost forecasting and control. Local authorities have very often led the way in developing new contractual arrangements, cost planning, and computer methods. In addition, central government has promoted a number of working parties in the industry and has sponsored research in several areas relating to cost. Most of the major government departments which undertake large building programmes have standardised their procedures for budgeting and have made recommendations as to normal cost planning and control practice. These guidelines are sometimes related to cost yardsticks which provide a good deal of cost information (especially at the brief stage) in their own right. A very useful publication that appears twice a year is the *Construction Forecasts* for the following two years published by the National Economic Development Office (NEDO) through

HMSO. Although publicly financed, NEDO is not a government department or agency and it is not involved in implementing government decisions. The information it supplies is extremely useful in assessing the likely demand for builidng in each sector of the industry in the short term period, which information can then be related to likely cost predictions. At one time attempts were made to prepare a forecast over longer periods and on a regional basis but, although this was a useful government strategic planning tool, circumstances changed too fast and frequently for it to be of real benefit to the practitioner. NEDO is also of course responsible for providing the indices for the adjustment of fluctuations using the Formula Price Adjustment method. Although government departments have had to curtail their activity in recent years due to cutbacks in expenditure they still provide a ready source of information on a wide variety of topics.

(v) *University or polytechnic research*
As quantity surveying has developed into a degree discipline it has been recognised that there is a need to establish a foundation of research which will be of benefit to the profession. The educational institutions are therefore beginning to establish programmes of work which will assist in developing a general theory for cost prediction and control, and to investigate the reasons for, and the degree to which, costs change related to design and economic variables. Papers on this research are beginning to be published and it is envisaged that, providing funds are forthcoming, this will provide a larger source of cost information in the future.

(vi) *Technical information systems*
For a large number of years there have been office library systems available to the building professions which contain a collection of the current trade literature relating to building products. Their major purpose is to provide a ready reference for the practitioner on specification and performance of a wide variety of building products. At one time it was not uncommon to find current price lists included, but with the problems of updating this information so frequently such cost information is very seldom published and circulated except on request. The use of such services for costing purposes, admittedly never their major role, has now largely died out.

Whilst the firm's own data and published data represent the two main sources for the cost planner, there is a further source available for some types of work, which in some ways is a combination of the two. This is the obtaining of information from specialist sub-contractors, specialist consultants, or even sometimes a building firm. Like published information this suffers from remoteness, but because there is usually an element of personal contact involved it is then possible to explain and discuss exactly what is involved. Such information can be very useful in connection with various forms of roofing, flooring, windows, doors, cladding, finishes, framing, landscaping, and in particular engineering services. It is helpful to know the people with whom one is dealing, since there is clearly little other guarantee of the soundness of such advice.

If prices are obtained from specialist sub-contractors there are several additional points to watch. Not only must the cost planner remember to add the builder's profit and perhaps discount allowance to the figures quoted, but if the field is one with which he is not familiar he should obtain an indication of the extra facilities which the builder may have to provide. In some sectors of industry a price for site installation simply covers the cost of sending a specialist supervisor, the builder having to do most of the hard work. Other people may be almost entirely self-sufficient.

Analytical and synthetic cost data

It will have been seen that cost data may either derive from the analysis of a total project cost (the traditional elemental cost analysis being a good example of this), or may be synthesised from its component parts (as in traditional builders' estimating, or the preparation of approximate quantities).

Both these approaches have their part to play and the choice of the best one in any particular circumstances is important. The analytical approach tends to give a good forecast of total cost (since it derives from the analysis of such a total cost in the first place), but can be suspect in relation to the cost of individual parts. The strengths and weaknesses of synthesis are exactly the opposite — very good for evaluating or comparing the costs of particular detail solutions, but the sum of such parts may not be a good guide to the market price of the whole.

In the preparation of a major cost estimate both methods could well be used in the appropriate places.

Generally

An attempt has been made in this chapter to paint, with broad strokes of the brush, a picture of the use, problems, and sources of cost data. It is a vital primary need of the cost adviser and one which will receive far more attention in years to come. As modelling techniques develop so will the need for different data and information structures that will suit the new methods. The direction for these ideas will almost certainly be along the lines of representing the way costs are incurred on site. It therefore seems likely that more attention will be given to the feedback of information from site and subsequently the presentation of resource costs in such a way that they can be related to design development.

One last point, do not forget that the data included in Bills of Quantities is confidential and the contractor's permission must be sought if any analysis etc. is to be published.

Chapter 10

Construction and Use of a Building Cost Index

One of the most important items of cost data, particularly with regard to forecasting techniques which rely on historic (i.e. past) information, is a cost index. The object of the cost index is to measure changes in the cost of an item or group of items from one point in time to another. A base date is chosen and is usually given the value of 100, all future increases or decreases being related to this figure. For example suppose the base date cost of employing a craftsman on site is £80.00 per week and the current figure is £120.00 per week. £80.00 would be given the value 100 and £120.00 would be represented by the figure 150, derived in the following manner:

$$\frac{(120 - 80) \times 100}{80} + 100 = \text{Cost index in relation to base } 100 = 150.$$

As the base is 100 the number of points of any subsequent index above 100 (in this case 50) also represents the percentage increase since the base date. However, if we are comparing costs over time in which the data we wish to update is not at base year cost, but has an index of say 120, then to arrive at the percentage increase in cost where the current index is 150 the following calculation is adopted:

$$\frac{150 - 120}{120} \times 100 = 25\%.$$

Notice that the answer is **not** the difference in the number of points on the index scale, i.e. 30.

Use of index numbers

There are a number of uses to which index numbers can be put in the construction industry and these can be summarised as follows:

(i) *Updating elemental cost analyses.* This is perhaps the most common use for the quantity surveyor and is an essential part of the theoretical elemental cost planning process. Tender information of past projects can be brought up to current costs for budgeting purposes, although it should be realised that great care is required when updating information beyond a period of, say, two years.

(ii) *Updating for research.* It is extremely difficult to obtain large quantities of cost data relating to the same point in time in order to analyse trends and patterns for cost research. By bringing cost information, obtained at a number of different points in time, to a common date by the use of an index, a much larger sample of data can be examined.

(iii) *Extrapolation of existing trends.* By plotting the pattern of costs measured by an index it may be possible to extrapolate a trend into the future. However, there are very great dangers in attempting this. During the 1960s it was possible to identify an increase in cost of about 5% per year. Extrapolations were undertaken using this figure for projects one or two years ahead. This worked quite well for a number of years until 1970 when the cost of building to the client suddenly rose by about 10%. Many quantity surveyors (and other professions) had not foreseen this rise and were heavily under-valued in their budgets. Since the 1970s the erratic behaviour of inflation rates has meant that extrapolation purely on trends is not possible.

(iv) *Calculation of price fluctuations.* The National Economic Development Organisation has produced a series of indices for building trades based upon the resource costs of each trade. By applying the indices to work undertaken during a specified period, it is possible to evaluate, to an acceptable degree of reliability, the increase in costs of resources to the contractor since the tender date. This enables the financial control of contracts which contain a fluctuations clause to be exercised more speedily and with less ambiguity. Formula Price Adjustment, as it is known, is now well established and will probably be used more widely in years to come.

(v) *Identification of changes in cost relationships.* If a cost index is prepared for the different components of a building, or for alternative possible solutions to a design problem (e.g. steel *v.* reinforced concrete frame), then it is possible to see the changes in the relationship between one component and another over time. It may then be possible to identify when one solution appears to be a better proposition than another.

(vi) *Assessment of market conditions.* Quantity surveyors are particularly interested in the price their clients have to pay for a building. If the index will measure the market price, as opposed to the change in the cost of resources, then a measure of current market conditions can be obtained which is of enormous benefit in updating and forecasting cost.

Methods of constructing an index

Over the last two or three decades there have been a number of attempts at providing a reliable cost index. They include the following:

(i) *The use of a notional Bill.* In this method a typical (or synthesised) Bill of Quantities is chosen and repriced at regular intervals by a competent quantity surveyor based on his experience of current rates. Unfortunately rates vary so much that it is extremely difficult to assess the current tender situation in such a way that a reliable index can be obtained from the resultant totals. This method is now to all intents and purposes obsolete.

(ii) *Semi-intuitive assessment.* This method is based upon trends in resource costs combined with tender reports by quantity surveyors. By receiving reports on current tenders from each of the project quantity surveyors in his organisation an experienced practitioner can adjust his knowledge of the changes in material and labour costs to prepare an index for the current market situation. This works quite well where the market is stable or steadily changing, but these judgements are extremely difficult to make at a time when the economy is subject to "stop-go" conditions. This method has been superseded by the tender-based index described later.

(iii) *Analysis of unit price for buildings of similar function.* If data could be found giving, say, the cost per square metre of all schools of a certain type being built in the country at one point in time, then the average of these costs could be used to provide the basis of an index. If the exercise were repeated at regular intervals for that type of building then a regular index could be established. Problems arise, however, due to such large design variables as specification and shape. Such an index would also be only applicable to buildings which are homogeneous in function and standard and for which there is a regular building programme to provide the data. This method is used by the Nationwide Building Society to establish trends in house prices, and as such provides a fairly reliable indication of price movements in that particular market.

(iv) *Factor cost index.* If a typical building is analysed into its constituent resources and the cost of each resource is monitored over time, then a combined average index can be prepared which measures the change in the total cost of the building over the same period. Each resource (labour, plant, and material) would need to be given due importance in the index according to its value in the total building. The construction of, and problems associated with, this type of index are described in more detail later on in this chapter.

(v) *Tender based index.* There is a great need for quantity surveyors to have a measure of the market price their client has to pay for his building. The accepted tender figure based on the pricing of a Bill of Quantities is a record of the market price for a particular building at a specific point in time. If the measured items in the Bill are repriced using a standard schedule of base year prices (to give a base year "tender"), then an index can be constructed by comparing the current tender figure with the new derived base year total. Short cut methods are available to avoid repricing the whole Bill. Details of this method are provided later in the chapter.

The factor cost index

It has already been explained that this uses changes in the cost of resources to build up a composite index. To illustrate the method let us look at the construction of a simple index for the cost of a brick wall. We will assume that the following table represents the cost of the constituents at base year level in the first column, and then at today's date in the second column. The final column represents the index resulting from these figures (calculated as described previously).

Cost per square metre of wall

	Base year	Current	Index
	£	£	
Bricks	20	28	140
Mortar	2	3	150
Labour	8	10	125
		÷ 3	415

Average index = 138.34

However in the above example no account has been taken of the fact that bricks as a proportion of total costs are ten times more important than mortar, all the resources having been given equal status. Consequently a very rapid rise in the cost of mortar would have a disproportionate effect on the composite index, and this would not be representative of the increase in the cost of a brick wall as experienced by the contractor. To overcome this problem the resources need to be "weighted" in accordance with their importance as follows:

	Index	Base year weighting		Extension
Bricks	140	20		2,800
Mortar	150	2		300
Labour	125	8		1,000
		30	÷ 30	4,100

Average weighted index = 136.67

The effect of the weighting is to reduce the index in this example because mortar (which has increased most in price) does not now share equal status with bricks and labour.

A further problem arises at this point. Suppose for some reason the labour force becomes more productive over the time period, by say 25%. Then at base year costs the value of the labour would have been £6.00 instead of £8.00. This will affect the amount of labour involved in building a brick wall and consequently its cost. This change, although affecting the cost to the contractor and possibly client, will not be represented in the index unless the weightings are changed.

	Index	Current year weighting		Extension
Bricks	140	20		2,800
Mortar	150	2		300
Labour	125	6		750
		28	÷ 28	3,850

Average revised weighted index = 137.5

This is a very real difficulty with the factor cost index because it is not easy to judge productivity over time, particularly with regard to the construction of whole buildings. In fact in the majority of cases, weightings in building factor cost indices are assumed to remain constant until a revision of the index is undertaken and a further analysis of the importance of each resource is made.

Where an index uses the base year weightings for each calculation then it is known as a Laspeyres index. Where the index uses weightings obtained from the current year or point in time that is under consideration then it is known as a Paasche index. Both names derive from their original authors.

Another factor not considered in the above examples is the contractor's profit and overheads. Profit, particularly, can be a function of market conditions and it would be difficult to devise a reliable quantitative measure for this variable. This is why a number of factor cost indices have incorporated an additional component, called a "market conditions" allowance, very often based on the professional judgement of its author.

The brick wall was chosen to illustrate the essential ingredients and problems of an index of this type. When constructing an index for a complete building the task becomes more complex although the same principles apply. A typical procedure can be summarised as follows:

(1) A typical building (or group of buildings) is selected for analysis into its constituent proportions of labour, plant, and material.

(2) Analysis takes place and the building resources are allocated under various headings to suit the representative cost factors for which information is available. For example if use was being made of published information for material indices (such as those prepared by the Department of the Environment) then the different materials in the building would be analysed according to the structure of that published data.

(3) The different types of labour (corresponding to different wage-fixing bodies) would be identified and the basis for evaluation of a unit of labour cost identified. Usually this would include the following:

(i) Changes in the hourly or weekly wage rate as determined by agreement of the parties to the wage-fixing body.

(ii) Changes in employer's "on costs" and contributions such as holidays with pay, national insurance contributions, etc.

(iii) Changes in the agreed standard working week.

(iv) Changes in the average hours worked per week, as recorded in government statistics. This item and the preceding one will affect the degree to which overtime rates are paid for each unit of labour output.

In addition two other factors may be considered.

(v) Changes in productivity. One method of obtaining a gauge of productivity is to take the total quantity of materials used by the industry, priced at "standard rates" (i.e. constant figures) and divide by the total building labour force. If the output per man increases over a particular time period then it is assumed that this is the result of productivity and the labour weighting should be reduced accordingly.

(vi) Change of location. It may be necessary to assume a particular geographical position for the typical building in order that regional differentials can be ignored.

The labour unit cost for each type of craftsman and labourer would be computed and then weighted according to the importance of each in the total labour force. The resultant weighted average for labour would be carried forward for further weighting with other resources.

(4) Material rates for comparison with base year prices are selected. Although it is possible to identify a long list of cost significant materials and calculate a separate index for each it is more usual to rely on published statistics for this type of information. The Department of Trade and Industry regularly publishes indices of materials for a range of material classifications. It is then merely a question of analysing the typical building according to the published material types to obtain the weighting to be applied to each material index.

(5) Plant types, together with their weighting, are identified and a standard method of evaluation adopted. This may be based on an average of hire rates for the particular item or it may be calculated by considering purchase price, depreciation, maintenance, starting time, etc. to establish a standard resource unit cost which can form the basis of.the index. In many published forms the change in the cost of plant is ignored.

(6) When the weighted index for each of the three basic resource types is computed they are then brought together and weighted again, this time in accordance with the importance of each within the total building cost.

Typical values for weighting are:

Labour	35–45%
Material	50–60%
Plant	5–10%

The final weighted index represents the change in cost between one point in time and another for the typical building chosen. Any subjective judgement to take into account market conditions, productivity, etc. can then be made if it is considered necessary.

It is important to realise what the cost factor index is actually measuring. It measures the change in the cost of resources to a contractor for a "typical" building. It does not directly measure the change in the price the client must pay, and although the "market conditions" allowance attempts to rectify this situation the source may not necessarily be reliable. Neither does it measure the change in cost of a specific building under consideration by a quantity surveyor. It is unlikely that the "typical building" will have the same mix of resources as the client's project; however on many occasions the difference will not be cost significant.

To try and minimise this difference the "typical" building may be more of an economic model than a likely real-life building, having, say, a mixture of light concrete block and clay block partitions so that a change in the cost of only one of the alternatives will not unduly distort the index on the one hand nor be ignored on the other. In spite of these drawbacks the method is very suitable for identifying trends in resource costs and relationships. It is particularly useful for evaluating cost fluctuations in contracts which allow for reimbursement of any changes in costs to the contractor that occur during the contract period.

The tender-based index

The main shortcoming of the factor cost index from the private quantity surveyor's point of view is that it takes little or no account of the tendering market. A much more attractive proposition appears to be an index which takes as its source of information the tender document itself. This should record what is happening in the market place and therefore be much more useful in updating prices for a design budget.

In essence the tender figure is compared with a figure produced by pricing the same tender document using standard rates at the base year prices. From the two resultant figures an index can be calculated showing the increase or decrease in cost to the client within the current tendering market. There are drawbacks with the method, such as the questionable validity of Bill of Quantity rates, and the remote chance of obtaining priced Bills for jobs which are comparable except for date of tender.

If, however, a large enough sample of projects is taken then the difficulties can be dealt with by "trampling the problem to death". If an appreciable quantity of projects is analysed it is hoped that all other differences except current levels of cost will cancel themselves out. An obvious difficulty here is the work involved in analysing all the rates in scores of Bills. Fortunately it has been found that much time can be saved by taking only the few largest items in each work-section and this results in a negligible degree of error.

The procedure for preparing and using a typical tender-based index can be summarised as follows:

(1) Prepare a priced list of typical BQ items at the prevailing base year pricing levels (usually with an allowance for preliminaries included). This is of course a time-consuming task and the current published forms of this index tend to use the Department of the Environment's Schedule of Rates, which is readily available. This is a very comprehensive schedule and is more than adequate for the majority of buildings.

(2) Take the priced document for the lowest tender received and note the format (e.g. work-section, elemental).

(3) For each section of the format (e.g. excavator, concrete work) pick the largest value item in the section, then the second, and so on until a total of 25% of the section value is achieved. (It is of course the value of the item as extended in the cash column, and not its unit price, with which we are concerned.) This procedure is repeated for all sections with the exception of preliminary items, PC sums, profit and attendance on PC items, and day-work percentage additions.

(4) For each of the items selected find the corresponding unit price in the base schedule of prices. The difference as an addition or subtraction from the base year rate is then obtained by compar-ing the Bill unit price of each sample item with its equivalent base year price.

(5) The extended base year value is calculated for each item (i.e. weighted by its quantity). The total of all the extended items at base year prices is then compared with the total of all the extended items for each section to obtain an index.

(6) The index obtained for each section is then weighted according to the value of that section as a proportion of the whole tender Bill for the project being considered (less preliminaries, PC sums, contingencies, etc.), and a combined index for all sections obtained.

(7) The preliminaries are usually dealt with by considering them as a percentage addition to the other items in the Bill, excluding dayworks and contingencies, provided that the rates in the base schedule include an allowance for the preliminary items. In that case the index figure arrived at so far is not a true one, since net Bill rates have been compared with gross base rates. So, if the "false" index of Bill items is 130 and the value of the pre-liminaries in the current tender is 10% (as a percentage of the remainder of the Bill) then the final index would be:

$$130 + \left(130 \times \frac{10}{100}\right) = 143.$$

(8) To obtain an average index for publication rather than for one particular job, the index numbers for all the tenders which have been sampled in a specified time period are averaged by taking either the geometric or arithmetic mean. The difference be-tween the mean of the current and proceeding quarters is used to gauge the movement in tender prices. The geometric mean is usually taken when relative changes in some variable quantity are averaged, because the arithmetic mean has a tendency to exaggerate the "average" annual rate of increase.

A number of simplifications have been made in the above procedure for the purpose of clarity. For example, in practice, problems arise with items that cannot be matched (these are generally overlooked in the item selection process), and also where a sample amounting to 25% of a section's total cannot be obtained. The rules governing the index being used should always be carefully consulted in these situations to discover the method to adopt.

The resultant index has several advantages over a simple factor cost index from the point of view of the client's quantity surveyor:

(i) It measures the change in the cost *to the client* of a particular project over time, taking full account of market conditions in addition to the change in cost to the contractor.

(ii) It is relatively simple to operate once a base schedule of prices has been obtained.

(iii) It allows comparison of the price obtained by tender for a specific project with the national or regional building price trend. This could assist in deciding whether to call for fresh tenders from another group of contractors, or not.

(iv) It allows the relationship between the market for buildings of different function and locality to be plotted.

(v) It is not based on other indices and therefore any inherent inaccuracies are not compounded.

There are however one or two problems which have to be acknowledged:

(i) To overcome the problems due to the variability of price rates in Bills of Quantities a large number of projects are required for each index. It is suggested that at least eighty are required for a suitable sample, but this condition is seldom met. Unless access to this quantity of Bills is easily available the trend being plotted may be erratic and not typical. Very few organisations have access to this number of projects and therefore most firms cannot prepare their own index by this method.

(ii) The index relies heavily on the base year schedule which will have to be regularly revised to take into account new products, new methods of measurement, etc. This is a time-consuming and costly task.

(iii) Because of the lack of projects at any one point in time the average index may have to rely on an unbalanced sample containing more jobs of one particular function and location than is considered desirable. This may lead to errors in the trend plotted.

However, despite these problems there is no doubt that the tender-based index represents a major breakthrough in the measurement of trends in market prices to the client.

Published forms

There are a large number of published indices which are available to the construction industry and the major sources are listed below, classified under the two major index types.

Factor cost indices

There are a large number of these indices available to the industry in published form, and in addition there are several operated by private firms. Of those that are published perhaps the following are the most familiar:

(i) *The BCIS building cost index.* This is a long established index available from the Building Cost Information Service, which was originally based on a breakdown of four types of project into their constituent resources. With the introduction of the NEDO Price Adjustment Formula, which produces a factor cost index for each trade or work-section, the BCIS decided in 1977 to construct six indices using the NEDO information together with weightings obtained from a study of forty Bills of Quantities. The Bills were divided into three main building types in order that an index could be prepared for each. These were:

BCIS Index No. 6   Steel framed.
BCIS Index No. 7   Concrete framed.
BCIS Index No. 8   Brickwork construction.

In addition indices were prepared for the following:

BCIS Index No. 5   General building cost index comprising 25% steel frame, 25% concrete frame, and 50% brickwork construction buildings.
BCIS Index No. 4   General building cost index (excluding M & E) which is similar to the previous index but excludes electrical, heating, ventilating, and air conditioning and lift installations.
BCIS Index No. 9   The mechanical, electrical and lift cost index.

All indices exclude any element of external works. The weightings obtained from the analysis for indices 6, 7, and 8 are shown in Table 10. To construct the index for any point in time it is necessary to multiply the NEDO index by the weighting and then calculate the arithmetic mean of the extended totals. The base date would be that of the NEDO index. Note that following the publication of the NEDO series II work categories the index has been extended.

TABLE 10. WEIGHTINGS FOR BCIS COST INDICES — SERIES II REVISION

Work category	Per cent weighting			
	Steel framed	Concrete framed	Brickwork construction	General construction
1. Demolitions	—	—	—	—
2. Excavation	1.89	1.98	1.43	1.68
3. Hardcore	1.18	0.70	0.94	0.94
4. General piling	—	0.35	—	0.09
5. Sheet steel piling	—	—	—	—
6. Concrete	8.08	10.03	4.63	6.84
7. Reinforcement	2.15	7.71	1.85	3.39
8. Structural precast units	2.60	3.69	1.22	2.18
9. Non-struct, precast components	2.67	5.80	1.17	2.70
10. Formwork	3.53	6.20	1.13	3.00
11. Brickwork & blockwork	8.22	10.20	15.62	12.42
12. Stone	—	—	—	—
13. Asphalt work	1.01	1.82	0.49	0.95
14. Slate & tile roofing	0.90	0.20	3.15	1.85
15. Asbestos Cmt sheeting	0.18	—	0.05	0.07
16. Plastic Ctd steel roofing	3.65	0.16	—	0.95
17. Aluminium sheet roofing	0.59	0.15	0.01	0.19
18. Felt roofing	0.52	0.88	0.50	0.60
19. Felt roofing on metal	3.03	—	0.59	1.05
20. Carpentry, board, flooring	3.17	2.37	7.45	5.11
21. Hardwood flooring	—	0.05	0.06	0.04
22. Tile & sheet flooring	0.95	1.01	1.57	1.28
23. Jointless flooring	—	—	—	—
24. Softwood joinery	3.22	1.60	8.35	5.38
25. Hardwood joinery	0.37	0.44	1.24	0.82
26. Ironmongery	0.77	0.89	1.89	1.36
27. Steelwork	0.04	0.23	0.24	0.19
28. Steel windows/doors	3.11	0.88	0.25	1.12
29. Aluminium windows/doors	0.63	3.82	1.35	1.79
30. Metalwork	1.09	1.50	1.56	1.43
31. Cast iron pipes	0.24	0.30	0.12	0.20
32. Plastic pipes	0.39	0.26	0.96	0.64
33. Copper pipes	0.24	0.51	0.88	0.63
34. Steel pipes	0.30	0.06	0.06	0.12
35. Boilers, pumps, etc.	0.08	0.07	0.67	0.37
36. Sanitary fittings	0.63	0.43	1.87	1.20
37. Insulation	0.23	0.11	0.80	0.48
38. Plastering	0.83	1.16	2.99	1.99
39. Beds & screeds	1.93	2.57	1.58	1.92
40. Dry partitiions & linings	0.73	1.54	2.47	1.80
41. Tiling & terrazzo	1.39	1.91	1.28	1.47
42. Suspended ceilings	1.13	2.43	0.55	1.16
43. Glass	2.34	1.00	1.52	1.60
44. Decorations	2.45	1.29	3.40	2.64
Electrical	8.42	8.10	9.52	8.89
Heating ventilation and air conditioning	11.31	11.31	13.70	12.50
Lift	0.82	3.85	0.45	1.39
Structural steel	12.99	0.44	0.44	3.58

By kind permission of the Building Cost Information Service.

(ii) *"Building" housing cost index.* This index is based on fixed weightings of specified labour, materials, and overheads found in typical house building and is published in "Building" magazine.

(iii) *NEDO formula.* This index, or more correctly this series of indices, is prepared by the Property Services Agency of the Department of the Environment who have based it upon a large number of Bills of Quantities in order to arrive at typical proportions of labour, materials, and plant in each of 34 (series 1) or 48 (series 2) work categories. The indices are based on market prices, nationally agreed wages, etc., and therefore do not take into account the problems of a contractor on a particular site. Although primarily provided for the assessment of price fluctuations on contracts where there is a fluctuations clause they can be adapted for use in a composite building cost index as already demonstrated with the BCIS format. The indices are published by HMSO.

(iv) *DOE cost of new construction index.* This index is prepared by the Department of the Environment and published in *Housing and Construction Statistics* (HMSO). It relates to the cost of construction completed in a given quarter and attempts to take into account the movement in material prices and labour including an allowance for productivity based upon the output per operative.

There are a number of other cost factor indices which appear in the technical press and builders' price books. The derivation of the indices is not always known and therefore they have not been included here, and should be used with caution.

Tender-based indices

As tender-based indices are a comparitively recent innovation there is not the long history of results that could be found with factor cost indices. However the number of institutions and practices producing an index of this type is steadily growing.

(i) *DOE (DQSD) index of building tender prices*
This index gives the level of pricing contained in tenders for new work accepted by the Department of the Environment in the UK compared with a fixed price base. However it should be realised that since 1974 many of the contracts used in the index have contained the NEDO formula method of adjusting fluctuations instead of being tendered for on a fixed-price basis, and this tended to downturn the index for some years. The construction is similar to that already described in this chapter, where a sample of items is taken for each work-section up to

25% of the value of the particular trade. This index was the original tender price index and has formed the basis for the others which have followed. It is published in Housing and Construction Statistics (HMSO).

(ii) *BCIS tender-based index*
The method of construction is similar to the DOE form just described. Two indices are however prepared, one relating to fluctuating contracts and the other to fixed price. This goes some way towards overcoming the problem of the different allowances made in the tender figure for future variations in price. The sample of jobs from which the index is derived is not restricted to government projects, and therefore it can be expected to cover a wider range of building type than the preceding index. For a small fee the BCIS will undertake the preparation of an index for a priced Bill from any of its members in order that a tender can be compared with the national average.

(iii) *Davis Belfield and Everest tender price index*
Again the method of construction is similar to (i) above, the only difference being that the index is based only upon schemes in the London area, includes non-government jobs, and is probably based upon a smaller sample. The index is published in *The Architects' Journal*.

Other indices are available which are in general use but do not strictly fall under the previous two headings. One example is the Nationwide Building Society's Index of House Prices which measures the change in cost to purchasers of different house types in different regions of the UK based on mortgage information. It should be used for guidance purposes only, as house prices vary widely depending on such factors as size, location, specification, and fashion; it is of course substantially affected by variations (usually upward) in land values which may be considerably greater than building cost fluctuations.

Another example is the DOE price index of local authority house building, where a number of priced items are extracted from Bills of Quantities for traditional one- and two-storey houses in each quarter, and the index prepared from the average change in price of these items only. The items are considered to be of major cost significance and factors are applied to each item according to base year weightings, thus following the approach of a Laspeyres index. To obtain a national price index it is necessary to employ fixed regional weights, not only because the amount of building varies greatly from one region to another, but because price levels, and the rates of change in prices, vary too.

Comparison of index performance

The degree to which an index performs or moves depends on two factors:

(i) The market factors influencing the components represented within the index.

(ii) The weightings applied to the components within the index.

This is true whether we are considering a tender-based or a factor cost index. In the latter case it is comparatively easy to see that if you measure an increase of 20% in the price of one material then if all other factors remain unchanged the index will go up by an amount equivalent to the weighting of that material in the total index, multiplied by 20%. With the tender-based index this process is obscured by the contractor's pricing method, and the fact that material cost is not shown as a separate item. However, the increase in the cost of this material *will* be included in the unit rates by the contractor and *will* be subsequently weighted by the quantity of the items containing that material. It will also be weighted a second time when the work sections themselves are weighted. The tender-based index will in addition include for any extra charge in the rates for increased overheads, profit, or above-normal resource costs due to the current market situation. It is these features that produce the distinctive performance of a tender-based index compared with the factor cost type.

By way of comparison let us look at the performance of the BCIS General Construction Cost Index (factor cost type) with the BCIS Tender Price Index (tender-based) for the years 1974 to 1982. The movement of each index is shown in Fig. 10.1 superimposed upon the industry activity indicators of contractors' new orders and contractors' output of new work expressed at constant 1975 prices. As can be seen the tender-based index reflects a more erratic trend in the cost to the client and generally falls behind contractors' cost from 1974.

In the previous period of 1970 to 1974 the reverse had been true caused by the capacity of the UK industry (i.e. its ability to fulfil the work demanded) being over-extended by a large increase in new orders. During this period contractors were not only able to pick and choose projects, but were therefore also able to increase profit margins. However, some of the increase in tender prices was due to each contractor trying to out-bid his competitors for the limited pool of labour and other resources that were available.

When the British government took steps at the end of 1973 to avoid overheating the economy, they cut public sector expenditure in a drastic way, mainly by reducing the public sector building programme. The industry then went into recession, jobs were hard to obtain and over the next two years the cost to the client remained fairly stable.

FIG. 10.1. *Relationship of cost indices to trends in new orders and output of contractors' work. (Reproduced by kind permission of the Building Cost Information Service)*

This is reflected in the tender price index but the factor cost index continued to rise through nationally agreed labour rates and material price increases, but these were not necessarily reflected in the cost to the contractor on site. To obtain a work force in 1972 and 1973 each contractor had to pay well over the national wage agreements to obtain his labour force and even outbid his competitors for materials. When the recession began to bite there was obviously some slack in the system and the client benefited in the return to normality.

From 1976 to 1979 the two indices rose in parallel to one another indicating that no more slack was able to be taken up and the increase in resource costs was now being reflected in tender prices. The Labour government was maintaining the government capital programme and there was a period of relative stability. With the return of the Conservatives in 1979 and their emphasis on monetary controls to defeat inflation, government expenditure on buildings was cut yet again. The impact can be seen in the stabilisation and even fall of price to the client whereas resource costs continue to rise. It is difficult to know for how long this can continue. Already bankruptcies are hitting an all time high and contractors cannot sustain their operations for ever by absorbing the increase in resource costs from their reserves. The reader will notice a strong correlation between the industry's output and the tender-based index suggesting that workload has a very strong influence on the price to the client.

In any comparison of index performance the important fact that must be realised is that each index is measuring a *different* movement of cost or price. Even where the form of the index is the same, the difference in the weightings attributed to each component by individual indices will result in a different value for each at the end of all the calculations. In using an index it is essential that the user is quite clear what trend in cost he wishes to measure, and then picks the form and weighted structure that best suits his objective.

Generally

It has already been stated that there are a number of problems associated with the construction of cost indices. These problems can also create difficulties in the use of the index and these together with some more general points are summarised below:

(i) The index will usually be measuring a trend for a typical or model building type, and may not necessarily be measuring the change over time for the particular project that you are developing.

(ii) Where the base date is several years old then the question should be asked as to whether the index is being based on outdated criteria. This particularly applies to a factor cost index using base year weightings. It may be that the balance of resources has changed considerably in the intervening period and this is not represented in the index. Over quite a short period the "mix" of resources on a typical bulding may alter as a result of the very changes in cost that the index is trying to record; for instance a rise in metal prices may cause a substitution of plastic for lead and copper in plumbing and roofing work. In the longer term changes in technology may not only make the base "mix" untypical but may also distort its prices; as new techniques and materials come into greater use their price tends to decrease proportionately, whilst the cost of obsolescent technology tends to rise faster than the general rate of increase. However, every index must have *some* history in order that trends can be identified.

(iii) Regular publication of the index is required, otherwise the user is put in the position of having to forecast the immediate past (i.e. the time between the last publication and the present) as well as the future. Three months is probably the maximum delay that should be expected.

(iv) The index should be published at regular fairly short intervals in order that trends can be determined. General trends over long periods of time can be ascertained from a yearly index. However a quarterly or monthly index is essential if an indication is required of a sudden change in the building market, or of course if seasonal variations are to be measured.

 (v) The basis of construction of the index must be known in order for it to be used intelligently. The choice of a tender-based or factor cost index will be dependent on what the user wishes to measure, but in addition the weightings of any index are important in judging whether the results can be applied to the project under consideration.

(vi) Short term changes in an index are unreliable since the inherent errors in the system of compiling the index may well be the equivalent of several points on the scale.

(vii) In the tender-based indices, a good sample of Bills must be used if bias due to regional variation and building function is not to distort the results.

(viii) When plotting a trend in an index it is sometimes advisable to use a logarithmic scale for the index against a natural scale for time. The advantage of this method is that if costs are rising at a regular percentage every year then the index values will be shown as a straight line. Any deviation above or below this line will show immediately as a change in this regular pattern and will assist in detecting a new trend. Figure 10.2 shows the principles involved using a 20% proportionate increase as an example. If a natural scale is used for the index then an exponential curve results for the 20% increase and comparison is more difficult.

The quantity surveyor obviously has a duty to keep himself aware of past, current, and future economic trends, and he will use this awareness in coming to a conclusion on the extrapolated index value which he will use in estimating for a future project. Of course no one has yet proved that he or she can accurately forecast the future, and this particularly applies to future index numbers. Providing reasonable care has been exercised the quantity surveyor should not be blamed if his forecast turns out to be wrong due to changed economic or political factors that were unforeseen at the time of making the estimate. In recent years it has become common practice and far more sensible to give a range of anticipated future costs based on the possibility of certain events occurring. In any case it is most important that everything should be made explicit when the original estimate is given. The details should include the index which has been used, the point or range that has been chosen together with the reasons for this choice, and of course the time scale for the project which has been assumed when making the forecast.

Which type of index to use

By their very existence it is obvious that all cost indices have a role to play in assisting the cost adviser to determine the market forces affecting his project. The choice of index will however be determined by the use to which the index is put.

(i) For short term forecasting, allowances for fluctuations, etc. then the factor cost index can be used.

(ii) For general estimating and cost planning purposes the tender-based method will more reliably measure the change in the cost to the client. It also has the advantage of being able to measure the performance of a tender, region, or building type against the national average.

(iii) For very long term forecasting and budgeting the use of a unit price index based on cost per square metre or unit of accommodation may be more applicable.

Fig. 10.2. *Showing typical cost increases plotted against natural (LH) and logarithmic (RH) vertical scales. A proportionate rate of growth is one which increases annually by a constant percentage of its immediately previous value (e.g. an increase of 20% on an index value of 100 gives 120. A subsequent increase of 20% would give 144, not 140). Note the characteristic shape—straight, concave, convex—of the index graphs in the second diagram, making them much easier to identify visually.*

Chapter 11
Elemental Cost Analysis

This chapter deals with the theory and practice of elemental cost analysis, which is currently used by the quantity surveying profession at large, and which, in spite of a number of failings which have become apparent over the years, has made possible a degree of control over costs which was previously unknown. It is the experience gained with this system, and the attitude of mind which it has engendered, which has led the way to the more fundamental approaches to cost control.

Elemental cost analysis was developed in order to provide data for design cost planning. It is therefore necessary to look first at the requirements of the latter.

What are the essential features of a cost plan? The obvious requirement (common to any form of estimate prior to tendering) is that it should anticipate the tender amount as closely as possible, but there are two particular requirements that must be fulfilled before the estimate becomes a cost plan.

Firstly it must be prepared and set out in such a way that as each drawing is produced it can be checked against the estimate without waiting until the whole design is complete. This enables any necessary adjustments to be made before the drawing is used for the preparation of quantities. The second particular requirement of a cost plan is that it should be capable of comparison with other known schemes in order to see whether the amount of money allocated to each part of the building is reasonable in itself and also is a reasonable proportion of the whole. From the point of view of economical building this second requirement is possibly even more important than the first.

How can one scheme be compared with another? The first suggestion which would occur to a surveyor would be to look at the priced Bills of Quantities for the two contracts. Suppose we look at the summary pages of the Bills for two different schools.

These trade totals tell us very little. We can see that the second school is dearer than the first, it is in fact larger; but it is difficult enough to try and compare the rather varied trade breakdowns without having to make repeated mental adjustments for the difference in size between the two buildings. So a first step is to divide each trade total by the superficial area of the schools in order to obtain comparative prices per square metre. (We could use the cube instead, but we have seen that for this type of building it is a less accurate indicator of comparative building cost than the area.)

	Clay Green School £	Woodley Road School £
Preliminaries	38,200	86,000
Excavation	16,160	19,320
Concrete work	86,610	181,950
Brickwork and blockwork	102,870	67,430
Masonry	7,300	—
Asphalt work	14,100	—
Roofing	49,770	26,030
Carpentry	51,550	69,880
Joinery	100,900	124,050
Steelwork and metalwork	126,440	131,900
Plumbing, engineering, and electrical work	213,000	266,550
Floor, wall, and ceiling finishes	91,150	88,850
Glazing	9,760	17,020
Painting and decoration	26,090	24,780
Drainage	28,840	22,330
Site works	73,260	52,980
	1,036,000	1,179,070
Insurances and summary items	3,500	25,300
Contingencies	20,000	20,000
	£1,059,500	£1,224,370

The resulting summary is shown in the table on page 174.

We now have the costs on a more truly comparable basis. Clay Green has a steel frame with timber pitched and tiled roofs and mainly brick faced external walls with "window holes", while Woodley Road has a reinforced concrete frame with felt flat roofs on strawboard decking and large wall areas of metal windows with concrete panel in-filling.

As we would expect, Woodley Road shows a far higher total for concrete work, and a lower figure for brickwork, roofing, and steelwork. At Clay Green there are some asphalt covered concrete flat roofs and the crawlway floor duct is tanked in asphalt, whereas at Woodley Road the floor ducts are waterproof rendered.

The glazing figures allow for the larger window area at Woodley Road, while the drainage and site works figures are consistent with Clay Green being on a larger and more rural site with a consequently greater extent of works. The differences in floor, wall, and ceiling finishes and decoration are simply due to a higher standard of specification at Clay Green.

	Clay Green (2,000 m²) Cost per m²	Woodley Road (2,500 m²) Cost per m²
	£	£
Preliminaries	19.10	34.40
Excavation	8.10	7.70
Concrete work	43.30	72.80
Brickwork and blockwork	51.40	27.00
Masonry	3.70	—
Asphalt work	7.00	—
Roofing	24.90	10.40
Carpentry	25.80	28.00
Joinery	50.50	49.60
Steelwork and metalwork	63.20	52.80
Plumbing, engineering, and electrical work	106.50	106.60
Floor, wall, and ceiling finishes	45.60	35.50
Glazing	4.90	6.80
Painting and decoration	13.00	9.90
Drainage	14.40	8.90
Site works	36.60	21.20
	518.00	471.60
Insurances and summary items	1.80	10.10
Contingencies	10.00	8.00
	£529.80	£489.70

However, while the effect of these differences in specification can be traced to some extent in the trade costs per square metre, the inclusion of parts of several elements of the building in one trade section makes it impossible to carry comparisons very far. For instance, the figures for Woodley Road for concrete work are affected by:

(1) The reinforced concrete frame in lieu of structural steelwork.

(2) Some concrete walls in lieu of brickwork.

(3) The concrete facing panels in lieu of faced brickwork.

We do not know how much of the difference is due to any one of these causes. Similarly the steelwork figures are affected by the omission of the steel frame and the increased area of higher quality metal windows at Woodley Road. These are compensating differences and in fact the two figures do not reflect the scale of the variations between one school and the other in this section. Other sections are similarly affected—the rates for carpentry and joinery are almost meaningless without detailed breakdowns.

Although the figures which we have obtained are interesting, they do not enable us to make any really valid cost comparisons. We do not know whether the steel and the concrete frames are competitive in cost, and we cannot tell how much is saved by a felt roof instead of a tiled one.

In order to be able to make such comparisons we shall have to split up the Bill of Quantities in a different way. We shall have to divide the work into "elements".

An element has been defined as "That part of a building which always performs the same functions irrespective of building type", and, we might add, irrespective of specification. What list of elements shall we use?

The possibilities are nearly endless. We could use as few as six, for example:

(1) Sub-structure and ground floor, complete with finishes.
(2) External and internal walls, complete with finishes.
(3) Upper floors including staircases, complete with finishes, and proportion of frame.
(4) Roof, complete with finishes and proportion of frame.
(5) Services.
(6) Site works.

Alternatively we could use any greater number within reason— some authorities use over 40. Points to bear in mind in arriving at a decision are:

(a) The definition of an element as stated previously. Any element chosen must be capable of being defined exactly, so as to ensure uniformity between the elemental breakdowns of any number of contracts even if the breakdowns are done by different people.
(b) The element must be of cost importance.
(c) The element must be easily separated, both in measuring from sketch drawings and in analysing Bills of Quantities.
(d) The list of elements chosen should be capable of being reconciled with those used by others, for comparison purposes. Unless the surveyor belongs to a very large firm or other organisation he will frequently need to make comparisons with analyses published in *The Architects' Journal* and elsewhere, or with analyses obtained from the Building Cost Information Service of the RICS.

To take an example of the last point, in most published forms of cost analysis the cost of parapet walls and copings is included under "roof".

The reader might prefer to include it under "external walls" (it would make the analysis of traditional Bills easier) but he would then be unable to compare his own cost information on these two elements with the published information, as the basis of measurement would be quite different.

The Standard Form of Cost Analysis

As the use of elemental cost planning has increased, some differing forms of cost analysis have been developed, both by those independent authorities and firms who are building up their own cost records and by journals which publish cost information for the benefit of their readers. The weekly magazine *The Architects' Journal*, as we have seen, was one of the pioneers in this field, and produced a detailed set of rules for their published analyses, while the RICS Building Cost Information Service and others used somewhat different rules.

It was obviously desirable that a uniform set of rules should be established, so that users could benefit fully from cost data prepared outside their own organisation. The RICS therefore set up a working party to standardise cost analyses; this proved to be difficult because, in practice, it is not possible to define a set of independent functional elements which can be related to a Bill of Quantities and so any standard cost analysis becomes a compromise between independent functions on the one hand and ease of producing the data from traditional documentation on the other.

In December 1969 the first Standard Form of Cost Analysis was published by the Building Cost Information Service of RICS; in addition to its sponsorship by the RICS the Form is also supported by the chief quantity surveyors of all the main government departments which are concerned with building programmes. It is this wide measure of support which gives the Form such importance, as anybody using a different format will become largely isolated from the cost experience of the rest of the profession.

As an example of a practical elemental breakdown, the headings in the current Standard Form of Cost Analysis are as follows:
(Please note that the third level of detail is no longer used by the Building Cost Information Service in its published analyses.)

1. **Sub-structure**

2. **Superstructure**

    2.A. Frame
    2.B. Upper floors
    2.C. Roof

    2.C.1. Roof structure
    2.C.2. Roof finishes
    2.C.3. Roof drainage
    2.C.4. Roof lights
  2.D. Stairs
    2.D.1. Stair structure
    2.D.2. etc.
  2.E. External walls
  2.F. Windows and external doors
    2.F.1. Windows
    2.F.2. External doors
  2.G. Internal walls and partitions
  2.H. Internal doors.

3. Internal finishes

  3.A. Wall finishes
  3.B. Floor finishes
  3.C. Ceiling finishes
    3.C.1. Finishes to ceilings
    3.C.2. Suspended ceilings

4. Fittings and furnishings

  4.A. Fittings and furnishings
    4.A.1. etc.

5. Services

  5.A. etc

6. External works

  6.A. etc.

This summary is sufficient to enable the principle to be understood, and full details of all the sub-divisions are given in Appendix A. Most other forms of elemental analysis are basically similar, but in order to be successful they must incorporate the same sort of hierarchical principle. It will be seen that the Form can be used at different levels of generality—the six element groupings *Sub-structure, Superstructure, Internal Finishes,* etc.; the elements themselves 2.A., 2.B., 2.C., etc.;

or the sub-elements 2.C.1., 2.C.2., 2.C.3., etc.; but because the detail is grouped in this way an analysis into six items only will be quite compatible with a fully detailed analysis of another project. The construction of the list therefore required a careful selection of elements each of which was significant on its own but which could form part of a larger significant group.

One or two forms of analysis which have been used differ by including finishes, windows, and external doors in the external walling element, and including finishes, internal doors, and partitions in the internal walling element. This is more logical but means splitting finishes between external and internal walls, which is difficult to do when analysing a traditional Bill of Quantities.

We can see that if the costs per square metre of Clay Green and Woodley Road schools could be expressed in terms of these elements it would enable us to find the answers to the questions which we were asking (which is the cheaper frame, how do the two roofs compare in cost) and these figures would enable us to cost plan a third school basically similar to Woodley Road but with a steel frame.

The Standard Form and CI/SfB

It has been a source of disappointment to many people that the elements themselves, their grouping, and their coding are not the same as in Table 1 of the CI/SfB system of classifying construction data. This system is widely used by the architectural profession for coding and classifying design information, and also to a much more limited extent for coding production drawings and project data. Many of the CI/SfB element definitions are specially modified when used for cost analysis purposes, so that as far as most of the elements are concerned the main differences between the two forms lie in the coding and grouping rather than in the content of the elements themselves, so that it is possible to sort the Standard Form data into CI/SfB format, though with a good deal of trouble. It is claimed that a great opportunity has been lost to provide the cost analyses in a form which could be instantly assimilated in the architect's elemental design records; it would certainly have been very convenient for the architect to have a record of typical costs filed with his design information.

However, in preparing the Standard Form (SFCA) it was considered important for the detailed costs at each level of the anlaysis to equal the cost of the relevant group at the preceding level. Thus (to look at the elemental breakdown of the Standard Form, reproduced as Appendix A) the costs of all the elements 2.A to 2.H added together should give the total cost of the "group element" 2 (superstructure), while the costs of the sub-elements 2.C.1 to 2.C.4 added together should give the total cost of the element 2.C (roof). CI/SfB Table 1 is arranged rather differently (with document indexing rather than cost planning as its primary purpose), so that its "group element" (2–) is "Primary Elements" including external wall construction (21), roof construction (27), etc. while (3–) is "Secondary Elements", (4–) is "Finishes" and (5–) is "Services". The total roof costs would therefore be distributed among four "element groups".

It might be considered that it would be worthwhile accepting this disadvantage for the sake of compatibility. However, there is a more important issue involved.

We have already seen that the so-called "elemental costs" which we obtain at present are not true costs at all, but are only a breakdown of a Bill of Quantities in which money may have been allocated to the various parts of the work in a quite capricious manner, quite apart from the overall level of pricing of the Bill itself. It would therefore be dangerous to detach these "costs" from the analysis and index them for the use of an architect as though they were scientific data like thermal insulation values.

One day it may indeed be possible to do this; but at present it is vital that this cost data should only be used by a qualified quantity surveyor who has the experience and knowledge necessary to assess and manipulate it. The cost analyses themselves however are referenced to CI/SfB Table 0 ("Built Environment") and so can be filed within the CI/SfB system.

There is, however, a real disadvantage in the lack of compatibility which becomes apparent if a project is to be designed by elements. The architect will probably use the CI/SfB elements for this purpose, and if the cost plan is based on the Standard Form elements then difficulty is bound to occur. Thus, we must accept this incompatibility, but only as a necessary evil at the present time.

Preambles to the Standard Form

In the Standard Form there is rather more information to be given about the size and nature of the building than was previously customary.

The gross floor area is measured in the normal way, that is the overall area at each floor level within the containing walls; but the basement floors (grouped together), the ground floor and the upper floors (grouped together) are each required to be shown separately.

The definition of "enclosed spaces" means that open entrance areas, etc. are excluded from the gross floor areas, although even a light enclosing member such as a balustrade will suffice to include the area. It is possible that doubt might arise when a wall becomes so pierced by blank openings that it no longer acts as an "enclosing wall"; obviously a mere series of columns does not meet the definition.

Although "lift, plant, tank rooms, and the like above main roof slab" are to be included in the gross floor area, we have the option of excluding these if we are prepared to allocate their costs to "Builder's Work in Connection". If the plant room is only required because of the existence of a particular service it seems quite logical to adopt the second course.

Roof and wall areas in the Preambles to the Standard Form

These are both measured gross over all openings, etc., the roof being measured on plan area. As it is "walls of enclosed spaces" which are required, parapets, gable ends of unused roof spaces, etc. would not be included in the wall area. The roof on the other hand is measured across overhang and would presumably include roofs over open entrance porches and other areas which do not count as "enclosed spaces". If there are substantial areas of open covered way it would probably be better to exclude them from the elemental analysis altogether, and deal with them under "Site Works".

The wall area is not shown on the Form, except in calculating the wall-to-floor elemental ratio. This is $\dfrac{\text{wall area}}{\text{floor area}}$; the lower the ratio the more economical the design.

Interdependence of elements

Although it is quite easy to define a cost-planning element it is more difficult to divide a Bill of Quantities up into elements which comply with this strict definition. A major difficulty is that an indivisible building element may combine several functions (some of which it shares with other elements).

For example "external walls" may have all or some of the following functions:

   (i) Keeping out the weather.
  (ii) Thermal insulation.
 (iii) Sound insulation.
 (iv) Supporting themselves (dead loads, wind loads).
  (v) Supporting floors and roofs.
 (vi) Transmitting light and ventilation (curtain walls).

If an external wall only performs a few of these functions then it is obviously unreasonable to compare its cost with that of a wall which performs a greater number. It is therefore usually necessary to refer to the "frame" and "window" elements in order to arrive at a true indication of the wall's cost performance, and similar cross-references may be required when costing other elements.

Preliminaries, insurances, and contingencies

These may be shown as separate costs per square metre (treating them, in fact, almost as extra elements) or they may be allocated proportionately among the other elements. This is an important point and deserves some consideration.

First, preliminaries and insurances. The cost of any or all of the following items (mostly at the contractor's discretion) may be included in the preliminaries or insurances sections of a priced Bill of Quantities for a new project.

Huts, temporary buildings, latrines.

Canteen, mess-rooms, tea-boy, welfare.

Hut and attendance on clerk of works, site architect and surveyor.

Mechanical plant, including tower cranes, excavating and concreting plant, lifts, dumpers, etc.

Scaffolding.

Non-mechanical plant and small tools.

Water for works.

Temporary electricity supply.

Consumable stores.

Temporary fencing and hoardings, temporary roads and standings, car parking space.

Agent, foreman, and other site supervisory staff.

Timekeeper and site clerks.

Watchmen and security lighting.

Heating of building for drying out.

Temporary weather protection.

Attendance on sub-contractors and artists.

National Insurance payments.

Superannuation.

Guaranteed week (wet time), travelling time and expenses, subsistence and lodging.

Redundancy payments.

Training levies.

Anticipated increases in costs of labour or material.

Bonus or other supplementary payments.

Making good damage and defects.

Fire insurances, third party insurance, and any other insurances required by client.

Public liability or contractor's all-risk insurance.

Head office expenses (overheads).
Profit.

However, almost any of these items (and certainly any of the major ones) may be included in the rates for the building work instead of being shown separately; some contractors do not price preliminaries at all while others do price preliminaries but in such a way that it is impossible for the surveyor to find out what is or is not supposed to be included. Sometimes at the last minute the contractor may have second thoughts about a tender and adjust it by adding a lump sum to preliminaries, or taking one off.

It must be realised that any large differences between the amounts of money inserted against the preliminaries items on one job and on another are less likely to be caused by genuine contractual differences (site conditions, access, etc.) than by the different pricing habits of the two contractors. Some of the principal items such as profit, supervision, scaffolding, plant, and overheads could affect the level of pricing by 15 to 20% according to whether or not they are included in preliminaries.

As these pricing habits are to some extent regional it may be possible for the surveyor's department of a local authority, or for a firm of surveyors whose work is confined geographically, to consider preliminaries and insurances as a separate element with some degree of consistency. But it would be safer on the whole to add preliminaries and insurances to each element as a percentage in order to give a common basis of comparison. If we refer back to the summaries of the two schools, Clay Green and Woodley Road, we can see that the trade prices for the latter appear low by comparison because preliminaries and insurances have been priced more fully.

If it is decided to include preliminaries and insurances in the elemental rates it will be necessary to make additional separate allowances when estimating for a project with some abnormal feature, such as a site on a mountainside or an uneconomically short contract period.

We have also to consider contingencies. Unlike preliminaries the contingency sum is an arbitrary amount fixed at the architect's discretion. It is not really part of the contractor's tender but is an amount he is instructed to add to his tender in order that there may be a cushion to absorb unforeseen extras. It normally has no effect on the level of pricing of the Bill and is better treated as a separate element rather than a percentage on the remainder of the work.

Analysis of final accounts

Upon first consideration it might seem a good idea to analyse the final account instead of the tender, since this will give a more accurate picture of the actual cost of the building. The objections are twofold; firstly it would be much more difficult to analyse both Bill and Variation Account than to analyse the Bill alone; and secondly the analysis would not be available until perhaps three or four years after a tender analysis and so would only be of historic interest. The differences between the tender and final account are not usually great enough to invalidate an analysis obtained from the Bill of Quantities.

System

Whatever methods of cost breakdown and whatever methods of cost planning are chosen they must be adhered to rigidly. Otherwise not only are the figures useless for reference purposes but the whole idea of working to a system is lost. It cannot be too strongly emphasised that the whole technique of cost analysis depends upon working in accordance with a fixed method; this is why standard forms should be used. There is plenty of scope for rough working but the forms must be used at all vital points, so that there is no possibility of preliminaries (for instance) being left out because the surveyor who did the previous estimate believes in showing them separately whereas the man using this estimate for reference supposes that they are included in the rates.

In most cases the forms and instructions issued by the Building Cost Information Service can be used, thus ensuring compatibility with information obtained from other sources.

Preparation of an elemental cost analysis

The aim of cost analysis is to provide data for use in elemental cost planning; as little time as possible should be spent on it consistent with a fair degree of accuracy. Meticulous allocation of trivial sums of money, or the identification of insignificant changes in specification, should be avoided. If there is no time to prepare a full analysis an outline analysis will be better than nothing and may take less than an hour to prepare. For the preparation of an elemental cost analysis we shall require a priced Bill of Quantities, a drawing showing plans and elevations, and a list of elements. It would also be very helpful to have the sorted slips or dimensions although these are not essential.

Each item in the Bill has to be allocated to one or more elements until every item has been dealt with and the elemental totals will equal the total of the tender. Once an office has adopted a certain form of analysis it will be possible to prepare the Bill with subsequent analysis in mind; this will ease the task of the analyser considerably and will make it unnecessary to refer to slips or dimensions. It is not necessary to depart radically from the usual order of billing as long as the main elements can be kept separate within each trade or section of trade.

For instance, the "sawn softwood" section of woodwork could be billed under headings of roof timbers, upper floors, stud parititions; and the "reinforced concrete" section of the concrete work could be separated into sub-structure, frame, upper floors, roof, and staircases. This should not involve lengthening the Bill greatly as there will be very little duplication of items between different elements; the concrete work is the only section where this should occur to a significant extent.

A Bill prepared in this manner will be useful not only for analysis but will be convenient for interim valuations and for the contractor's use in bonusing and site organisation generally. The so-called Northern system of taking-off, where the Bill is written straight from the dimensions, lends itself to the preparation of a sub-divided Bill of this sort.

Any further breakdown of the tendering Bill into a completely elemental format is very unpopular with builders' estimators, since design cost planning elements are of little significance to them and a good deal of re-arrangement into trade order has to be carried out by them.

This is a convenient point to mention the ingenious Bill which was pioneered by Hertfordshire County Council, in which each trade of each element was printed on a separate sheet and coded so that the Bill could be shuffled into either elemental or trade order at will. The usual arrangement was for the Bill to be sent out in trade form for tendering, and put into elemental form for subsequent use.

Another development is the Master Bill for tendering, which can be used where a contract consists of several buildings each of which requires a separate Bill which in turn is divided into trades and/or elements. In order to avoid inundating the contractors who are tendering with masses of paper the section Bills are re-abstracted into a Master Bill which is used only for tendering. This Master Bill is in strict trade order and contains no sub-headings or sections apart from those required by the Standard Method of Measurement. The additional expense of preparing this Bill may be worth while because busy contractors naturally prefer a two hundred page Bill to a pile of Bills containing up to a thousand pages, and keener tendering will probably result. By using this method it is possible to have the section Bills divided into elements without bothering about trade divisions, which are only really required for tendering purposes.

Further refinements are possible when Bills are prepared by computer. Providing that all the dimensions are given elemental code references the Bill can be sent out to tender in traditional form and after tenders have been received the computer will be able to print an elemental version of the Bill. In some systems the Bill rates are also fed into the computer so that the elemental breakdown will be completely priced as well.

Before going any further there are three terms which must be defined in order that the processes of cost analysis and cost planning may be understood.

Elemental cost is the cost of the element expressed in terms of the superficial area of the building.

Element unit quantity (sometimes also called *quantity factor*) is the actual quantity of the element, expressed in square metres for such elements as floors, roof, walls, finishes or in terms of number for elements where this is not practicable.

Unit cost is the cost of the element expressed in terms of the element unit quantity, e.g. 1,000 m² of internal walling costing £1,200 gives a unit cost of £1.20 per m².

Elemental ratio is the proportion which the unit quantity of one element bears to that of another. A commonly used example of this is the ratio of external wall area to gross floor area.

When analysing a Bill of Quantities there are three different ways in which items may be allocated:

(a) The description of the item may indicate the element to which it belongs, in which case there is no necessity to refer to slips or dimensions.

(b) The item may be too trivial to spend time on, in which case it may be allocated as seems most obvious or as is most convenient.

(c) It may be necessary to refer to the dimensions in order to allocate the item correctly. Since it would take far too long to refer to the taking-off for every item in the Bill, the analyser must use a good deal of discretion about this. In cases of doubt he would be influenced very much by the cost importance of the item.

Element unit quantities

Unfortunately a simple analysis of cost into elements will not satisfy all our requirements. It will give us a money total for each element and we can divide each total by the floor area to get the elemental cost per square metre, but it does not give us the unit quantities or the unit costs. We need these if the analysis is to be of much use. Some commonly used element unit quantity factors are set out below as a guide; where "none" is marked the elemental cost per square metre is the only basis of cost comparison.

Work below lowest floor finish. Area of lowest floor.
Frame. Area of floors relating to frame.

Upper floors. Area of upper floors.

Roof. Area on plan of roof measured to external edge of eaves, but excluding area of rooflights.

Rooflights. Area of structural opening measured parallel to roof surface.

Staircases. Number and total vertical rise of staircases, or area on plan.

External walls. Area of external walls excluding window and door openings. Basement walls given separately.

Windows. Area of clear opening in walls.

External doors. Area of clear opening in walls.

Internal walls and partitions. Area of internal walls excluding openings.

Internal doors. As for external doors.

Ironmongery. None.

Wall finishes. Area of finishes.

Floor finishes. Area of finishes.

Ceiling finishes. Area of finishes.

Decorations. None.

Fittings. Often none, but where appropriate the total length of benches or other details might be given.

Plumbing and hot water. Number and type of sanitary fittings, number of hot and cold draw-offs.

Heating services. Heat load in kW, cubic capacity of accommodation served.

Gas services. Number of outlets.

Electrical services. Number of points, total electrical load.

Special services. Such information as will indicate the extent of each service (e.g. for lifts the number, capacity and speed of each and number of stops should be given).

Drainage. None.

External works. None.

As well as giving the consolidated unit quantities and costs for each element it is common practice to sub-divide them into categories of different construction or finish and give quantities and cost for each. For example, for a building of 2,400 m^2 of total floor area:

ELEMENT: Upper floors

    Total cost of element: £57,000

    Cost per m^2 of total floor area (elemental cost) £23.75

Unit quantity and cost	
Element unit quantity	1,000 m^2
Unit cost per m^2	£57.00

Sub-division	£
550 m^2 of 150 mm r.c. slab	at £55 = 30,250
350 m^2 of 225 mm r.c. slab	at £70 = 24,500

100 m² of 25 mm softwood boarding on
175 × 50 mm joists   at £22.50 =   2,250

£57,000

While these sub-divisions are very useful as explanations of how the total cost is affected by specification it must never be forgotten when using them that the greater the detail in which a priced Bill of Quantities is analysed the less reliable are the results. It might well be found that a Bill for the same job priced by another builder would give completely different figures at this level of breakdown, though quite similar in total.

The overall unit costs will be found particularly useful when preparing early estimates of cost before specification details are available.

Obtaining unit costs from elemental analysis

In order to obtain unit costs as well as elemental costs from our analysis we will have to elaborate our form of abstract somewhat, particularly if we are going to keep separate costs for the different forms of structure or finish within each element.

There are two problems to solve: the separation of the costs within the element and the recording of areas and other quantities. Such things as areas of walls, floors, and finishes can be obtained most easily from the Bill, but sizes of window and door openings may be difficult to get from this source (particularly where there are fanlights, sidelights, or windows glazed directly into frames) and it may be necessary to refer to the dimensions or the drawings. There is also the difficulty of areas which occur more than once, for instance the areas of concrete in floors will be duplicated by the formwork areas and these must not be added in again, but areas of concrete floors and hollow pot floors will require to be added together. As it would be asking far too much to ask a junior to differentiate between such cases the analyser will have to take the responsibility of recording areas himself. No attempt need be made to separate constructions which differ only in detail (such as 100 mm, 125 mm and 150 mm floor slabs), because the aim is to obtain overall unit rates for basic constructions, not "Bill Rates" for individual items.

The analysis in its final form

This is one of the places where a standard form, preferably the SFCA form, should always be used.

It is not necessary to fill in too much specification detail if the analysis is for office use as it should be possible to refer to the contract papers if anything more than a very broad outline is required.

There should be a reference number for the analysis so that a list of analyses can be kept, and there should also be a cost index value so that allowance can be made for changes in market prices when comparing with past or future jobs.

Note that elemental costs continue as a running total but unit costs cannot be carried forward, as a total of them would be meaningless.

Summing-up

The information should be in a standard form and should also be in a suitable form for use; costs which require measurement of details in order to apply them to an estimate will not be very helpful at cost plan stage.

The taker-off should be trained to anticipate the analysis in the setting out of his work, as he has information at his fingertips which it may take hours to find subsequently. The analyser who turns up the dimension sheets referring to doors, and who finds all the gross opening sizes set out together, squared and totalled, will be grateful to the taker-off who spent a few minutes of his time arranging this.

Doing a few elemental analyses is an excellent introduction to cost planning. The surveyor who has spent some time extracting element costs from a Bill of Quantities will soon realise which items within the elements have an appreciable cost effect and which do not.

Chapter 12
Elemental Cost Planning and Control at Design Stage

A complete system of cost planning and control at design stage would comprise:

(1) Establishment of the brief.
(2) Investigation of a satisfactory solution.
(3) Cost control of the development of the design.

It is unfortunately true that the amount of time and effort spent by the cost planner on each of these three aspects is usually in inverse proportion to their relative importance, often being almost entirely concentrated on the third aspect, with perhaps a little advice being given on the second. Sometimes the amount of effort required to keep the design development within cost limits actually stems from unwise decisions made at the earlier stages without the benefit of cost investigation. In fact if the strategy is right, the design development should present few problems.

Although the establishment of the brief and the investigation of a satisfactory solution are shown as two separate and consecutive functions there may well be a certain amount of iteration involved—design investigation may itself suggest modifications to the brief, which in turn may require to be investigated. This is all to the good, and will probably result in improved performance. Even if it involves, as it will, a good deal of abortive work by the cost planner, his actual work at this stage is relatively cheap compared to the benefits which may be derived. The cost control of design development on the other hand demands more resources and if possible should not be carried out until the most satisfactory solution has been defined. Substantial iteration between the second and third stages of the process brings nothing but disadvantages.

The formulation of the brief, whether for social or profit development, will require the application of techniques referred to in the earlier chapters of this book, and in this process the quantity surveyor will be co-operating, probably on a team basis, with not only those professionals concerned with the actual building design but also representatives of the client's organisation, as well as valuation surveyors, accountants, and possibly planners. As the investigation of a satisfactory design proceeds further into the realms of building configuration he will tend to become increasingly involved with the architect and his consultants to the gradual exclusion of the other parties. At some point in this process he is likely to turn to an elemental basis for his cost modelling procedures.

Elemental cost planning and control procedures

For a project which is to be designed prior to contractor selection, a suitable sequence of procedures would be as follows, although these would be subject to some amendment where the contractor was to be selected at an earlier stage, or where construction was to proceed concurrently with design. However, the first-mentioned situation is still the normal one.

1. *Preliminary estimate(s) based on overall m^2 floor area prices*
   This really has nothing to do with elemental techniques at all, but is mentioned here as being the minimum contribution that the cost planner should be making to the initial formulation of the brief, prior to the first elemental estimates. No drawings, and only the vaguest of information, are required at this stage.

2. *Preliminary cost plan(s)*
   These are produced in order to evaluate the architect's first sketch designs, or even sometimes to help the architect select a configuration. It is really a misnomer to call these "cost plans" at all, since they are unlikely to be used, as they stand, for subsequent cost control procedures, and it would be more accurate to refer to them as "elemental estimates". However, the former title is more impressive and seems to be more often used. Some kind of sketch drawings are needed for their production, but they can be very simple.

3. *Cost plan*
   When the architect has produced his final sketch drawings, and these have been approved by the client, the formal cost plan should be produced. This will probably be based upon the last of the elemental estimates but developed in as much detail as a full cost analysis, and will form the basis for the system of cost control. It will make everyone's life much easier, and the process of cost control more efficient, if the design then proceeds as closely as possible in accordance with the details of the cost plan. For this reason this expensive document should not be produced until both the architect and the client are satisfied with the design.

4. *Cost checks*

As the architect produces his working drawings, they will have to be checked against the cost plan to see whether the assumptions which were made still hold good. This is a time-consuming business, and the adjustments which have to be made if major discrepancies emerge are even more so. The process can be minimised if the cost plan was prepared in considerable detail and if the architect has followed it closely. The task of cost checking can also be minimised by not doing it thoroughly because of the vast amount of work involved in the changes which have been made, and in the further changes which would be necessary to get the project back on target. If this point is ever reached then the money which the client has spent on cost planning and control can be regarded as wasted, and if the débâcle is not of his making he will have every right to feel cheated by his professional advisers.

5. *Tender reconciliation*

When the tenders are received they should be reconciled with the cost plan. If all has gone well this will be a matter for the cost planner alone—simply putting his records straight. However, if some reductions have to be made because of cost over-run this will help him to make the most economical suggestions. If the foregoing procedures have been carried out these should only be of a minor nature.

6. *Post-contract ("real-time") cost control*

This does not fall strictly within the title of the chapter, but the cost planner must continue to monitor the cost of the project whilst construction proceeds, in the light of the provisions which the contract makes for adjusting the contract sum. This stage is at least as important as those which have gone before.

We can now proceed to examine these various stages in more detail by working through an example in which the techniques described in this and preceding chapters can be applied to the design cost planning of a small office block in a provincial city.

Preliminary estimate

This will be an approximate estimate; it could hardly be otherwise in view of the lack of information at the quantity surveyor's disposal. There are exceptions to this, for instance where the project is one of a series (such as a chain of service stations) and information has been accumulated on a number of almost identical buildings, or where the first estimate has to be calculated according to a government formula and the building will be tailored to fit the estimate.

As the scheme is worked out in more detail it may become apparent that the building which the client wants, with a proper balance between economy and quality, will cost either more or less. It would be possible to reduce or increase the quality of the specification to get back to the original figure, but the architect or quantity surveyor should not automatically assume that the client will want this to be done. He may be more concerned with getting the building that he wants than with 5% on the cost; on the other hand he may not, but the decision is his. The difference between this approach and the old situation of a large and unexpected gap between estimate and tender is that the client makes his choice consciously, with a knowledge of the amount of money which his decision is costing (or saving) him.

In the case of commercial projects such as speculative offices and flats it is often possible to charge higher rents if a better standard of amenity and finish is provided, so that the budget to an extent is flexible and the cost disadvantages of larger and more luxurious public spaces, more and faster lifts, better fittings, and so on will have to be considered in relation to income. The acceptable final cost may be quite different to the original rough estimate due to the decisions taken as the scheme develops.

A client for a private house may find his ideas becoming more ambitious as the drawings progress, and again provided that he is kept informed of the consequences of his decisions he may prefer to have the house he wants instead of the cost he first thought of.

In the preparation of the estimate previous experience of the architect is most valuable, as there are some men whose designs always come out above average costs just as there are those who usually manage to achieve a low-cost design. At this stage the surveyor is likely to be told "This will be an economy job" and only a knowledge of the people concerned will tell him how far he can let this affect his estimate.

The surveyor should never allow the amount of his estimate to be influenced by opinions expressed by interested parties, or worse still by the amount that the client would like the job to cost, unless these also coincide with his own judgement. When an estimate has worked out at £850,000 it is all too easy to remember that the architect said it was to be a £500,000 job. The danger then is that the surveyor may assume that the estimate must be too high and reduce it a little in order to make the difference less breath-taking. Remember that it is the man who has prepared and possibly signed the estimate who will be held responsible for it.

The preliminary estimate, like all others, must make quite clear what is and is not included. This is a proper place to use a form, with a definite section to show inclusions and exclusions. Such items as complete internal decoration, joinery fittings, office partitions, venetian blinds, light fittings, floor finishes in offices and flats for letting, site works, special plant, shopfitting, should be specifically dealt with, not just forgotten about or covered by some vague overall clause.

Make sure that professional fees are clearly included or excluded; some clients think that the estimate shows their total commitment unless they are told otherwise. If fees are shown it is important to get them right. Allow for surveyor's fees on the post-contract work as well as for the preparation of the Bills of Quantities, allow for structural and other engineering consultants, and for the reproduction of documents including drawings, Bills of Quantities, and final account. Where the contract is remotely situated allow something for expenses. The final total of fees may be quite a shock, perhaps over 12% even for quite a large job.

The estimate must also be specific in relation to building costs. If it is based on present day costs it should say so, and also make it clear that it is subject to revision in the event of increases (or decreases) in cost. There have only been one or two short periods when building costs have been fairly static in the last thirty years. If the estimate is based on anticipated costs at some future date the basis of calculation should be set out in the estimate so that revision can be made if the prediction proves to be inaccurate. The man who could accurately forecast economic conditions two years ahead would be in demand in other fields than quantity surveying!

As the preliminary estimate cannot be related to the cost plan except in total it is not worth preparing in greater detail than is necessary for its primary purpose, that is to give an approximate estimate of cost. And, although cost planning is much more than the preparation of an estimate, it gets off to a very bad start if the first estimate is wrong. This stage is therefore very important indeed.

Finding the right rate at which to price floor area is not easy and the most reliable starting point is a similar job from office experience. To adapt the superficial area rate from one job to another when shape is not known requires consideration of seven different factors, as follows:

(1) Market conditions.
(2) Size, number of storeys, etc.
(3) Specification level.
(4) Inclusions and exclusions.
(5) Services.
(6) Site and foundation conditions.
(7) Other factors.

The example used will be a new 2,400 m² six-storey office block in a provincial city with shops on the ground floor and offices on the upper five. The previous job on which the estimate will be based is a similar four-storey block in outer London, again with shops on the ground floor and offices above. The total floor area was 1,235 m^2 and the tender price 12 months previously was £364.35 per m^2.

1. *Market conditions*

This adjustment deals with the changes in building prices and in tendering conditions between the time when the previous job was priced and the anticipated date of tender for the new project. For this purpose one of the published cost indices previously described would probably be used, but when the estimates which are being compared are not too far apart in time (up to a year or so) it is quite possible to make the adjustment for market conditions without using a published index, but simply by adding a percentage for increases based on known labour and material fluctuations. For this purpose the proportions of labour, material, and plant content given in Chapter 10 should be used, with a heavier bias towards materials if the contract is for an expensive building with good finishes and high-class materials. In making this calculation the figures should be taken as fractions of the gross contract amount without deducting overheads and profit, since these will rise in proportion to increases in prime cost.

Let us assume an increase of 10% on this contract, ascertained by comparison of indices; £364.35 per m^2 + 10% = £400.79.

2. *Size, number of storeys, etc.*

The new provincial block will have a larger plan area; this will tend to reduce the proportion of external wall area to floor area (assuming a similar plan shape) and hence should reduce the cost per square metre a little.

However, the new block will have six storeys instead of four, and this will have the effect of increasing the cost, as it is a general rule that high building costs money. But the difference between four and six storeys is not critical and the probability is that this and the previous factor will cancel each other out.

A further point to consider is that on the outer London block one quarter of the floor area was set aside for shops whereas on a six-storey block one-sixth of the area will be shops. As shop areas are usually left in an unfinished state for the shopkeeper to fit out according to his tastes this part of the building will be cheaper than the rest, and by reducing the proportion of the building allocated to shops we shall be increasing the overall price per square metre. Let us suppose that the saving in floor, ceiling, and wall finishes will be £40 per m^2 of floor area (this can be got from an elemental analysis).

Therefore for the outer London block we have:

$$1,235 \text{ m}^2 \text{ at } £400.79 = £494,969$$

Shops 25% = 309 m² at £400.79 minus ¾ of £40 = £370.79 = £114,574
Remainder 75% = 926 m² at £400.79 plus ¼ of £40 = £410.79 = £380,391
£494,965

Using the same rates for the provincial block we now get:

Shops 16²/₃% =   400 m² at £370.79 = £148,316
Remainder 83⅓% = 2,000 m² at £410.79 = £821,580
£969,896

$$£969,896 \text{ divided by } 2,400 \text{ m}^2 = £404.12 \text{ per m}^2.$$

3. *Specification level*
The specifications will be roughly similar, but the architect has decided that the cheap flooring used in the offices on the London block was a mistake and wants to allow an extra £7.50 per m² for this. The client also wants Portland stone facings instead of cast stone used on the previous job.

The adjustment for the flooring is easy. Allow an extra £7.50 per m² over the area of the offices, say two-thirds of the total floor area. 1,600 m² at £7.50 = £12,000 which is equal to £5.00 per m² of floor area when divided by 2,400. Calculations like this can be done by simple proportion if preferred [(1600/2400) of £7.50 is £5.00] but it is quite easy to make a mistake when doing this and the longer calculation is more easily checked.

The stone will be a little more difficult to allow for. The area of external walling in an office building of this sort should be about 10% more than the floor area (again check this with several analyses if possible), but not all the wall area will be stone. We will assume that 25% of the area is stone and that natural stone facing will cost £85 more per m² than cast stone.

Then extra cost of stone is

$$(110/100) \times 2,400 \times ¼ \times £85 = £56,100$$

which is £23.37 per m² of gross floor area.
The total cost after allowing for changes in specification is
therefore £404.12 + £5.00 + £23.37 = £432.49 per m².

It is important to note that the rate has already been adjusted for inflation and therefore any specification adjustments must be done at prices ruling at date of tender of new scheme and not those ruling when the previous or example job was carried out.

Note that a number of assumptions have been made regarding the London building which could have been made much more accurately if a cost analysis had been available.

4. Inclusions and exclusions

The client wants the office tenants to do their own partitioning and decorations, whereas on the London job these were provided by the building owner.

This particular adjustment will most easily be carried out by extracting the relevant figures from the Bill of Quantities for the London job.

	£
PC sum for office partitioning	13,750
Add for profit and attendance	685
Decoration in offices, say	1,500
	£15,935

The figure must be adjusted for increased costs, also for five-sixths of the building being offices instead of three-quarters.

$$£15,935 \text{ divided by } 1,235 \text{ m}^2 = £12.90$$
$$£12.90 \text{ plus } 10\% \text{ increased costs} = £14.19$$
$$£14.19 \times {}^4/_3 \times {}^5/_6 = £15.77 \text{ (cost of partitions and decoration on new building to be omitted).}$$

The total after allowing for exclusions is therefore
£432.49 minus £15.77 = £416.72 per m².

5. Services

Services are a major part of a modern building, and represent a large proportion of the cost. On a project of any size there will most likely be consulting engineers for heating, plumbing, and electrical work, and they will normally provide an estimate of the cost of the services for which they are responsible. The estimate would be adjusted as follows:

PROVINCIAL OFFICE BLOCK

Estimated figures received from consultants:

	£
Space heating	90,000
Plumbing	27,500
Electrical installation	60,000
Lifts	71,250
	248,750

Builder's work, attendance,
profit   15,000
                                                 £263,750

£263,750 ÷ 2,400 = £109.90 per m².
Amount allowed for services in outer London block = £127,500
(including builder's work, etc.)

£127,500 divided by 1,235 m² =	£103.24 per m²
Add 10% increase as main estimate	10.32
Total for outer London block	113.56
Total for new block	109.90

Reduction £3.66 per m²

The total after allowing for services is therefore
£416.72 minus £3.66 = £413.06 per m².

In view of the early stage at which this estimate is being prepared the engineering consultants may not feel able to give an estimate for services, but it is important that they should be asked to do so. This will avoid the situation which might arise if the surveyor were to include his own assessment of the cost and this proved to be different to the amount required by the consultants when they prepared their detailed scheme. The resulting arguments would do little to improve either the harmony within the professional team or the client's confidence in the team as a whole. Nevertheless it is quite possible that the consultants, being asked to establish a preliminary cost target before they have much idea of what is required, will play safe and allow themselves a sum of money sufficient to cover any eventuality.

This is common enough to be met with by most surveyors from time to time. If the surveyor feels that the services are taking rather a large slice of the whole cake he could draw the architect's attention to this as tactfully as possible; the architect as leader of the team is the man who will have to decide about this. The surveyor must bear in mind however that prices per square metre for services are extremely difficult to estimate (because little elemental cost data exists at present) and should try to co-operate with the various consultants rather than to raise difficulties.

If there are no consultants appointed, or if at this stage they will not commit themselves, then the surveyor would be better not making any adjustment to the estimate for ordinary services unless there are glaring differences between the outline requirements for the two buildings. In future, however, it may be more common for the surveyor to be closely involved in the cost planning of the engineering services.

Special services such as lifts should always be adjusted, as their cost bears practically no relation to the area of the building. The adjustment should be done as a comparison of lump sums as shown above.

6. Site and foundation conditions

Both sites are in congested city areas. The new provincial job will probably require piled foundations, which must be allowed for. Either the cost of piled foundations per square metre can be obtained from a suitable analysis or a certain number of piles allowed for, as follows:

$$\text{Say 90 piles average 6 m long at £45 m} = £24,300$$
$$£24,300 \text{ divided by } 2,400 = £10.13 \text{ per m}^2.$$

Note that the complex of pile caps and ground beams in connection with the piles will cost at least as much as conventional foundations, so there is no saving to set against the cost of the piles.

The total after allowing for site conditions is therefore £413.06 plus £10.13 = £423.19 per m^2.

7. Other factors

The wage rates in the provincial town will be slightly lower than in outer London. The difference is very small, and there is little evidence to show that this type of building costs less in provincial towns. No adjustment is made for this.

The client is anxious to have the building erected as quickly as possible and the contract period is likely to be very short. This will tend to increase the price, both because the site labour force will need to be larger than is economical and because the number of local contractors who can be relied upon to work to a tight programme is small and competition will therefore be very limited. The contract price may also have to include a good deal of overtime. An addition of 2½% will therefore be made to the estimate.

The total after allowing for other factors will be £423.19 plus 2½% = £433.77 per m^2.

Now let us see how this estimate would be set out on an appropriate form (Fig. 12.1) (it must be assumed that the question of professional fees is dealt with in a covering letter).

It may be that the estimated cost is higher than the client can afford, or more than he wants to pay. It would be very dangerous to reduce the amount of the estimate for this reason, or on some vague grounds such as a general reduction in standard, although of course adjustments could be made for specific items such as (on the basis of the above example) cheaper lifts, or a return to the cheaper floor finish. But if the total of the estimate is much too high it is best to face facts, and either

PRELIMINARY ESTIMATE OF COST

PROJECT: *Office Block, Midtown*

DATE OF ESTIMATE: *10. 2. 80*   ASSUMED DATE OF TENDER: *Sept. 1980*

GROSS FLOOR AREA: *2,400 m²*

BASIS OF ESTIMATE:	£ per m²
Office Block, London (Sept. 1980)	
1235 m²	*364·35*
ADJUSTMENTS:	

1. Market Conditions:
   RICS Cost Information Index. Add 10%   *36·44*
   400·79

2. Size, number of storeys, etc:
   6 storeys in lieu of 4 — see notes   + *3·33*
   404·12

3. Specification level:
   See notes. Wood block flooring /
   Portland Stone   + *28·37*
   432·49

4. Inclusions and exclusions:
   Office partitions and decorations
   excluded   − *15·77*
   416·72

5. Services:
   See consultants and notes   − *3·66*
   413·06

6. Site and foundation conditions:
   Piling (90 No 6m long)   + *10·13*
   423·19

7. Other factors:
   Tendering (as notes) add 2½%   + *10·58*
   433·77

   Professional fees   *excluded*

   £ *433·77*

Total estimated cost *2,400 m²* @ £*433.77* = £ *1,041,048*

INCLUDED (and as above)	EXCLUDED (and as above)
	Floor, ceiling, and wall finishes in shops.
	All furnishings, fittings, blinds.
	Electric light fittings (except in public spaces).

FIG. 12.1. *Preliminary estimate of cost*

reduce the size of the building or get the brief substantially modified.

It is the easiest thing in the world to cut an estimate by 10% (or by any other percentage) under the influence of the client's pleadings and the architect's optimism; but it must be made clear that an overall 10% cut in costs means more than a 10% cut in standards as much of the structural work cannot be reduced.

This example of the two office blocks assumes that there is a comparable scheme already in the office. When we come to elemental estimating, an exact comparison of use is not vitally important (costs per square metre of external walls, windows, doors, floors, etc. will not vary much between a library or an office block) but the costs per square metre of the buildings themselves will vary considerably because of the differing proportions of these items in them. If there are no truly comparable schemes in the office it may be possible to get information from another surveyor, or as a last resort to use published information.

When working from one's own information it is best to use one building as an example because the variables in design and tendering are known, but it is often helpful to supplement this with published information for similar buildings, in which case as many examples as possible should be obtained to try and average out all the variable factors. As stated previously, published information is particularly useful for checking and comparison of an estimate prepared from one's own information.

The preliminary cost plan ("elemental estimate")

There are advantages in doing a preliminary cost plan as soon as the first sketch drawings are available, so as to see whether the architect's initial solution is possible within the cost limits which have been set. This will be particularly true if the shape or design is rather unusual, or looks inherently expensive.

There are some advantages in using a "short list" of consolidated elements for preparing the preliminary plan, as the only measurable items will be the main floor and wall areas and there is unlikely to be a specification as yet.

For the purpose of this example a short list is assumed, and four main areas need to be measured, as follows:

(a) Ground floor area.
(b) Total floor area.
(c) Area of external walls, including windows and doors.
(d) Area of internal walls, including windows and doors.

Let us look at an example, based on the architect's first sketch design for the six-storey office block as shown in Fig. 12.2:

FIG. 12.2. *Architect's first sketch design for provincial office block*

Ground floor area 30 + 22.5 = 52.5 multiplied by 7.5 = 393.75 m².

				m²
Total floor area	6	× 393.75 m² =		2,362.5
plus tank room	8 m ×	6 m =		48.0
				2,410.5

External wall area	4/30 m ×	27 m =	3,240
Tank room	28 m ×	2.5 m =	70
			3,310

Internal wall area, say	1,200

Already we can see that the ratio of external wall area to total floor area looks rather high (33:24), and we may feel that this is going to prove an expensive building. However, the preliminary cost plan will confirm or reject this theory better than any amount of conjecture. The best rates for pricing would be those obtained from an analysis of the outer London block, since we based the first estimate on the same job. We must remember to add the 10% price increase and the 2½% tendering differential so as to keep the two estimates on the same basis, unless circumstances have changed in the interim when the total of the estimate will have to be revised. Again a standard form should be used.

The form shown in Fig. 12.3 is an example of the sort of thing required. Some of its features would vary according to the preferences of the individual office; for instance some people might prefer to show the preliminaries as a separate item, or to make a separate element of the frame. On the other hand it would be possible to combine the finishes with the relevant structural items, as is done by Hertford-shire County Council. However, the selected arrangement should be standard within the office so that the recorded information can be kept in a suitable manner. The overall rates for preliminary cost planning can be obtained when doing the ordinary analysis and filed separately, and being large omnibus items there is perhaps less risk than usual in poaching prices from more than one job.

Let us return to the particular example. The establishment of rates for the various elements will have been complicated in this instance by the different proportion of unfinished shops compared to the outer London job. The rate for floor finishes for example will have been obtained as follows:

		£
Rate per m² for floor finishes on outer London offices		15.20
Add 12½% increased costs and tendering		1.90
		£17.10

		£
1,235 m² at £17.10	=	21,119
Shops 25% = 309 m² at say £5.50	=	1,700
Balance 926 m²	=	19,419

Which is £20.97 per m².

		£
New provinical block 2,410 m²		
16²/₃ shops = 402 m² at £5.50	=	2,211
83¹/₃ remainder = 2,008 m² at £20.97	=	42,108
Total 2,410 m²	=	44,319

which is £18.38 per m².   £18.38

Add say ¾ of £7.50 for more expensive floor finish in offices (as approximate estimate)	5.63
	£24.01

From an examination of the first preliminary cost plan shown in Fig. 12.3 we can see that the scheme is likely to prove more expensive than the amount of the first approximate estimate (£1,041,048). A little of this increase is no doubt due to the slightly increased size of the building (2,410 m² instead of 2,400 m²) but the cost per square metre of floor area is also increased from £433.77 to £445.86. While the increase is not very large (it could be got rid of by a small reduction in the level of specification) it does make us wonder whether this is the most

PRELIMINARY COST PLAN NO. 1

PROJECT *Office Block, Midtown*

DATE OF COST PLAN 3. 4. 80

ASSUMED DATE OF TENDER *Sept 1980*

		Total Cost £	Cost per m² of floor area (divide by 2411)
GRD. FLR. AREA (A) 394 m²			
TOTAL FLR. AREA (B) 2411 m²			
EXTERNAL WALLS (C) 3310 m²			
INTERNAL WALLS (D) 1200 m²			
Work below lowest floor finish	£		
(A) 394 × 167·50		65, 995	27·37
Upper floors inc. frame			
& stairs (B-A) 2017 × 67·50		136, 148	56·47
Roof inc. frame			
(A) 394 × 90·00		35, 460	14·71
External walls			
(C) 3310 × 110·00		364, 100	151·02
Internal walls			
(D) 1200 × 27·50		33, 000	13·69
Floor finish			
(B) 2411 × 24·00		57, 864	24·00
Ceiling finish			
(B) 2411 × 15·00		36, 165	15·00
Wall finish			
(C+2/D) 5710 × 7·00		39, 970	16·58
Decoration			
(B) 2411 × 2·50		6, 027	2·50
Fittings		1, 500	0·62
Services		263, 750	109·39
Drainage		5, 000	2·07
Site Works		15, 000	6·22
Contingencies		15, 000	6·22
		1, 074, 979	445·86
Professional fees		—	—
		1, 074, 979	445·86

(Inclusions and exclusions as approximate estimate unless otherwise stated)

FIG. 12.3. *Preliminary cost plan*

economical solution to the design problem. At this point the figures in
the right-hand column (cost per square metre of floor area) come in
very useful in enabling us to make comparisons with other contracts. It
certainly seems as though the external walls are costing a lot, which
confirms our first thoughts on looking at the plan, but we now have
figures to prove the matter. Although it would be practicable to build
this scheme within the budget it would be worth the architect's while to
see whether an alternative shape would be possible.

The rather unsatisfactory appearance of the first preliminary cost
plan should lead to the consideration of alternative schemes. It may
not always be possible to improve wall/floor ratios very much, due to
site restrictions or other unalterable factors. But let us suppose that in
the case of the provincial office block the architect has been able to
produce an acceptable alternative design (Fig. 12.4):

$$\text{Ground floor area} \frac{33 + 29}{2} + \frac{14 + 10}{2} = 43 \text{ multiplied by } 9 = 387 \text{ m}^2.$$

$$
\begin{array}{lr}
 & \text{m}^2 \\
\text{Total floor area } 6 \times 387 = & 2,322 \\
\text{plus tank room} & \underline{48} \\
 & 2,370
\end{array}
$$

$$
\begin{array}{lr}
 & \text{m}^2 \\
\text{External wall area } 23.4 + 13 + 9 + 19.6 + 29 + 9 = 103 \times 27 = & 2,781 \\
\text{Tank room as before} & \underline{70} \\
 & 2,851
\end{array}
$$

Internal wall area say 1,200 m^2 as before.

The approximate cost for this scheme is shown in preliminary cost
plan no. 2 (Fig. 12.5).

This is a much more hopeful design with an estimated cost of
£1,025,477, slightly below the approximate estimate. The allowance
for site works has been increased, as additional treatment to the front
areas would be required owing to the front elevation being set back on
the splay.

It should be realised that outline elemental estimates will not be
completely accurate, although the comparisons obtained from them
will be valid enough. Each of these breakdowns would only take a few
hours of a senior assistant's time, and each hour spent at this stage is
worth days spent on cost checks of minor elements later on. This is
where cost planning really pays for itself.

This is the place for a word of warning. Because we are dealing in
such large figures at preliminary cost plan stage it is vital that all

FIG. 12.4. *Revised sketch plan for provincial office block*

arithmetic, and if possible all measuring, should be checked. A silly mistake in calculating the principal areas would have dreadful consequences later on, and just because it seems (and is) simple the preliminary cost plan must not be taken lightly. The same remarks apply to the preliminary estimate, which we dealt with in the previous section.

It is also important to remember that there are many other considerations in designing a building besides cost, and that the surveyor must not be tempted to try and usurp the architect's function when the shape and type of building is under consideration. The surveyor must be prepared to give the architect all possible assistance at this time, but should avoid making detailed suggestions about matters of planning and architecture which are entirely the architect's responsibility.

The cost plan

We now come to consider the cost plan itself. This may take many forms, but all the different systems have much common ground. The plan will almost certainly be prepared by elements and the cost will be expressed per square metre of floor area even if it is calculated in a different manner, in order to be able to make comparisons between other schemes of different size on a common basis.

If there is a cost target it will by now have been set up with some degree of finality and the architect will want to go ahead with the working drawings. Since cost planning involves cost control the architect must design in accordance with the cost plan, which must be available before the working drawings have proceeded very far. What do we need in order to prepare such a plan?

(1) A drawing and a standard of specification to which the cost plan can be related.

(2) A cost analysis of a comparable project.

Opinions differ on how detailed the specification information should be when the cost plan is prepared and this is a suitable place to discuss the issues involved.

By training, and often through bitter experience, the quantity surveyor likes to deal in solid facts. His natural inclination therefore is to try and get as much detailed information as possible from the architect before preparing the cost plan, and if this is not completely forthcoming to fill in the blanks himself. When the cost plan is complete he can supply the architect with a detailed list showing the type of construction and finish on which the cost is based, and the architect knows that although he may alter anything in the specification at will, any such deviation may have an effect on the planned cost. The quantity surveyor may also feel that this specification gives him some protection in the possible event of an architect failing to design within the agreed limits, since these limits are written into the cost plan and are not just assumed.

However, this procedure is open to the objection that the quantity surveyor appears to be taking the whole of the responsibility for design out of the architect's hands and into his own. The alternative way of dealing with this problem is to leave the responsibility for design entirely where it belongs, with the architect. When the cost plan is prepared the architect's ideas on specification are incorporated into it, but if these are not forthcoming the surveyor does not provide them for himself. Instead be devises a target cost for the element based on standards of cost performance achieved elsewhere and it is left to the architect to design as he wishes within that cost. If the element, when designed, costs more than the sum of money allocated to it then it must either be redesigned or the elemental cost increased at the expense of other elements.

That the philosophy behind this approach is sound few will deny, but the first alternative is the one preferred by most surveyors. Apart from the factor already mentioned (of protection against an unco-operative architect) it is said that most architects prefer the discipline of a specification to the imposition of a cost figure for the element which is unrelated to specification and may necessitate several attempts at design before it is achieved. The "detailed specification" method also has the advantage that if the architect works to the agreed specification then subsequent cost checks will be unnecessary.

PRELIMINARY COST PLAN NO. 2

PROJECT *Office Block, Midtown*

DATE OF COST PLAN *10.4.80*

ASSUMED DATE OF TENDER *Sept 1980*

	Total Cost £	Cost per m² of floor area (divide by 2370)
GRD. FLR. AREA (A) 387 m²		
TOTAL FLR. AREA (B) 2370 m²		
EXTERNAL WALLS (C) 2851 m²		
INTERNAL WALLS (D) 1200 m²		
Work below lowest floor finish £		
(A) 387 x 167·50	64,822	27·35
Upper floors including frame		
& stairs (B-A) 1983 x 67·50	133,853	56·48
Roof inc. frame		
(A) 387 x 90·00	34,830	14·70
External walls		
(C) 2851 x 110·00	313,610	132·32
Internal walls		
(D) 1200 x 27·50	33,000	13·92
Floor finish		
(B) 2370 x 24·00	56,880	24·00
Ceiling finish		
(B) 2370 x 15·00	35,550	15·00
Wall finish		
(C+2/D) 5251 x 7·00	36,757	15·51
Decoration		
(B) 2370 x 2·50	5,925	2·50
Fittings	1,500	0·63
Services	263,750	111·29
Drainage	5,000	2·11
Site Works	25,000	10·55
Contingencies	15,000	6·33
	1,025,477	432·69
Professional fees	—	—
	1,025,477	432·69

(Inclusions and exclusions as approximate estimate unless otherwise stated)

FIG. 12.5. *Revised preliminary cost plan*

In order to prepare an elemental cost plan the analysis of a comparable project will be required. It is not necessary that the buildings should be for a similar use as long as there is some reasonable compatibility as buildings. For instance a police-station and a health clinic are both public buildings with fairly similar storey heights and divided into both small and large rooms; the elemental analysis of a police-station could therefore be used to prepare the cost plan for a health clinic if nothing better was available whereas between say a church and a block of multi-storey flats there is no resemblance whatever.

The cost plan must be prepared on a standard form, for reasons that have already been emphasised in connection with analyses and preliminary estimates. The form should show the chosen list of elements, contingency sum, preliminaries and insurances (if separate), and fees. It is common practice to allow a "design margin" of between 1 and 5% as a design contingency in addition to the contract contingency, and this margin may come in useful during the cost check when it can be absorbed into any element that needs it. The cost plan should also show the cost index value which is being used. The first page of a typical form is shown in Fig. 12.7 (page 215).

Method of relating elemental costs in proposed project to analysed example

There are two ways of doing this, either by using unit costs of the elements or by proportion. In spite of what may be thought to the contrary these are really two ways of doing much the same thing; in both methods the unit quantity of the element (e.g. area of external walls) is first measured from the sketch drawings of the proposed project.

Using the first, or "unit cost" method this quantity is priced out at the unit rate per square metre for the same element obtained from the analysis. This gives the total cost of the element, and the total is then divided by the floor area of the proposed project to give the elemental price per square metre.

When the second, or "proportion" method is used the ratio of unit area to floor area in the proposed project is compared to the corresponding ratio in the analysed example, and the elemental cost per square metre is adjusted in proportion to the difference in the two ratios. With this method one is not concerned with the actual unit cost (either in total or per square metre) at all, although the total cost for the element will be required for comparison purposes at cost check stage.

In order to illustrate the systems in use, two examples are worked out on page 209 using both methods. It will be seen that either method

METHOD OF RELATING PROPOSED PROJECT TO ANALYSED EXAMPLE (1)

Analysed example: Total floor area 5,000 m²
External wall area 4,000 m²
Wall/floor ratio 0.80
Cost of external wall per m² of floor area
(elemental cost) = £37.50
Cost of external wall per m² of wall
(unit cost) = £46.875

Proposed project: Total floor area 4,800 m²
External wall area 3,600 m².

Elemental cost of external walls on proposed project:

UNIT COST METHOD   PROPORTION METHOD

3,600 m² of wall at £46.875 = £168,750   Wall/floor ratio = $\dfrac{3,600}{4,800}$ = 0.75

£168,750 ÷ 4,800 = £35.156   £37.50 × $\dfrac{0.75}{0.80}$ = £35.156

(Total cost 4,800 × £35.156 = £168.750)

METHOD OF RELATING PROPOSED PROJECT TO ANALYSED EXAMPLE (2)

Analysed example: Total floor area 5,000 m²
Internal doors 35 No.
Cost of doors per m² of floor area
(elemental cost) = £1.05
Cost of doors each (unit cost) £150

Proposed project: Total floor area 4,800 m²
Internal doors 50 No.
Cost of doors each £165 (better quality).

Elemental cost of internal doors on proposed project:

UNIT COST METHOD   PROPORTION METHOD

                                   Quantity   Quality
                                   adjustment   adjustment

50 doors at £165 = £8,250

£8,250 ÷ 4,800 = £1.72   £1.05 × $\dfrac{5,000}{35}$ × $\dfrac{50}{4,800}$ × $\dfrac{33}{30}$ = £1.72

(Total cost 4,800 m² × £1.72 = £8,250)

will allow differences in quality as well as quantity to be adjusted quite easily.

What are the advantages and disadvantages of the two methods? The proportion method is the logical choice for use where the elemental cost per square metre is regarded as an index of performance rather than the result of a specification. But the unit cost method is more in line with the traditional quantity surveying approach and many surveyors would feel less likely to make mistakes when using it, as the unit cost is much more easily envisaged than a proportion sum, particularly if the workings become complicated. The unit cost method is more easily related to approximate quantities either at cost plan or cost check stage, and we must remember that at one or other of these stages fairly detailed quantities have got to be introduced.

If the analysed example will not yield all the necessary information for preparing the cost plan it must be obtained elsewhere:

(1) By taking a price from another analysis. This is potentially dangerous; we have seen how a priced Bill of Quantities will probably contain compensating errors and that these will be incorporated in the analysis. However, if we take items from more than one analysis we may get cumulative instead of compensating errors; it would be possible to take a number of elements from different analyses all of which are priced too low and this would make the total of the cost plan quite unrealistic. This cannot happen where a single analysis is used throughout.

    If prices are obtained from other analyses it is wise to collect as many examples of the same item as possible so that any errors are likely to cancel out in the average so obtained.

(2) By the use of approximate quantities. These are likely to be very approximate indeed (remember that we have no working drawings) and herein lies the danger; one is much more likely to leave things out than to put extraneous items in. Therefore when using approximate quantities the surveyor must be very careful to include *all* the items which are included in the description of the element (e.g. skirtings and their screeds with "floor finishes", or rainwater pipes with "roofs"), and also to include the percentage for preliminaries, insurances or contingencies if these are included in the elemental rates. Needless to say, the quantities must be priced at the same level of market rates as the cost plan itself, although the rates will be higher than ordinary Bill of Quantities prices because of the need to include the cost of secondary work which has not been measured separately.

    The approximate quantities themselves will be similar to those normally employed by surveyors for estimating purposes except that the elements must be kept separate; so that the plastering on the underside of a concrete roof slab, for instance, could not be included in the overall rate for the roof but would be worked out separately as part of "ceiling finishes".

Examples of use of information from analysed building:

ANALYSIS. Total floor area 2,000 m²

    Element: Internal partitions. *Elemental cost* £13.50 m²

		£
1,400 m² of 75 mm breeze partition at £6.50		9,100
900 m² of 225 mm and 300 mm brick walls at £16.50		14,850
120 m² of glazed partitions at £25.40		3,048
2,420		26,998

    Average unit cost = £26,998 ÷ 2,420 = £11.16 m².

PROPOSED PROJECT. Total floor area 3,100 m²

    Total area of partitions (measured roughly from drawing) 3,500 m²

In some offices it is the custom to keep a complete schedule of prices for use when pricing approximate quantities; this certainly gives a consistent level of pricing but it is doubtful whether any but the largest organisations would find the preparation and maintenance of such a list to be an economic proposition.

Ordinary surveyor's dimension paper can be used for the preparation of approximate quantities, the left-hand set of columns for the measurements, squaring, and description and the right-hand set for the quantity, price, and extension. (An example of this is shown in Fig. 12.6.) If we do not know the type of partition required, or if the proportions of various types are likely to be similar to those of the analysed example we can use the average unit rate, or work by the proportion method:

    3,500 m² at £11.16 = £39,060 total cost ÷ 3,100 = £12.60 m² elemental cost.

But if even at this stage we can see that the proportions of the various sorts of partition are quite different to the analysed example we must use the individual unit cost as shown overleaf.

When severely altering the proportion of items like this it is necessary to watch out for any freak rates. For instance, it is possible that the rates for glazed partitions in the analysed example may have been much too low, and being a very small part of the whole job this will not have had much effect on the total price. On the proposed project

Total area of partitions 3,500 m²			£
20% 75 mm breeze parition	=	700 m² at £6.50	4,550
10% 225 mm brick wall	=	350 m² at £16.50	5,775
60% glazed partition (cheaper type)	=	21,00 m² at £22.50	47,250
10% timber stud partition (no rate for this, price built up by approximate quantities)	=	350 m² at £11.50	4,025
			£61,600

£61,600 ÷ 3,100 m² = £19.87 m² elemental cost.

however the proportion of glazed partition has been increased from 10 to 60% and such an error would be much more serious. Again this emphasises the point which has been made before, that the smaller items in the analysis may well have the least reliable prices.

Elemental costs

By whatever means the total cost of the element has been obtained it should always be expressed per square metre of floor area, for two reasons.

Firstly, for comparison of reasonableness with other buildings. If the partitions (for instance) are costing far more per square metre of floor area than on other buildings of the same type it is worthwhile investigating the reasons. These may be perfectly sound; the cost may include built-in cupboards, there may be a greater degree of insulation required between rooms, but it is also possible that there is inefficient planning of the accommodation and this would also be reflected in other elements.

Secondly, the elemental price per square metre enables the importance of any extravagance or economy to be judged in a way that is not possible when considering unit prices only. Let us consider the unit costs for three different specifications of internal doors:

(a) Hardboard faced skeleton framed flush doors hung on steel butts to softwood frames, no architraves. *Unit cost* £22.50 *per m²*.

(b) Plywood faced semi-solid core flush doors hung on steel butts to softwood frames with softwood architraves. *Unit cost* £41.25 *per m²*.

(c) Mahogany veneered plywood faced solid core flush doors hung on solid drawn brass butts to mahogany frames with mahogany architraves. *Unit cost* £87.50 *per m²*.

							£	

Office Block, Midtown

External Walls

Main Areas

						£	

21·5 22·5	m² 484	Curtain Walling all as the Curtain	1576	m²	131·25	206,850·00
12·1 22·5	272	Walling Co's				
23·4 22·5	527	approx quotation dated 17·4·80				
13·0 22·5	293	Quote - £110 m² Profit				
	1576	attend 5% £5·50				

Scuff.   £3·00

Sundries £6·50
            £125·00
Prelims
and ins. 5% 6·25
            £131·25

	m²				£	
21·5 4·5	97	Shopfronts (left blank) Stone trim only	151	m²	25·00	3,775·00
12·1 4·5	54	to cols.				
	151					

2		m²				£	
	7·5 27·0	405	Stone faced concrete walls	648	m²	197·40	127,915·00
	9·0 27·0	243	£ Stone fcg. 150				
		648	Conc wall 35 Scaff. 3				
			188				

Prelims   9·40
and ins.
            197·40

Continued   £ 338,540·00

FIG. 12.6. *Use of dimension paper for approximate quantities*

From a comparison of the unit costs it would seem that specification (c) is prohibitively expensive for normal work compared with the more usual specification (b). Yet to adopt the better specification in a typical school of 3,000 m² with 70 internal doors would only increase the elemental cost per square metre by about £1.08, and to use the completely inadequate specification (a) would only save £0.44. Considering that the total cost per square metre of the school would be around £300 these increases and decreases are quite insignificant. On the other hand a marginal difference in some other elements, such as the particular choice of hardwood for wood block flooring, which may only alter the unit price by 10% will have as great an effect upon the cost of the school per square metre as a 100% difference in door prices.

It will soon become obvious to the surveyor which items need the most time spent on them at cost plan stage—in other words, which elements have the greatest cost significance. It would be worthwhile to use approximate quantities for a major element such as external walling where a difference of one or two pounds in the unit cost per square metre would have an important effect on total cost, and to check the cost plan very closely when drawings subsequently become available; such elements as internal doors or ironmongery on the other hand can be dealt with much more rapidly.

Presentation of the cost plan

The cost plan should be presented as neatly as possible; it will almost certainly be going to the client and should reflect credit on the surveyor who has prepared it. To what extent expense should be incurred in order to give the plan an impressive appearance is a matter for individual preference.

Another matter for personal decision is the extent to which the detailed build-up of the plan should be made available to the architect. Whether this should be done in all cases will depend upon the degree of mutual confidence which exists and also upon the available facilities for copying a large quantity of rough working.

With the cost plan should go the specification upon which it is based; this will necessarily be more in an outline form than the type of specification which will eventually be embodied in the Bill of Quantities. It may either be included as part of the cost plan itself or prepared as a separate document; a typical example is shown in Fig. 12.8. If a separate document is used it is important that there should be a space for each specific item so that it can be quickly seen whether everything has been dealt with or not. The specification should preferably be filled in by the surveyor in consultation with the architect rather than being sent to the architect for him to fill in himself.

COST PLAN

PROJECT. Office Block, Midtown

DATE OF COST PLAN. 12th November, 1980

ASSUMED DATE OF TENDER. July, 1980

TOTAL FLOOR AREA. 2390 m^2

Note: This Cost Plan is based upon the attached outline specification, and both documents should be read together.

	Unit quantity	Unit cost £	£	Total cost £	Elemental cost per m^2 £
1. WORK BELOW LOWEST FLOOR FINISH. Grd. Flr. Area 390 m^2	390 m^2	167.50		65,325	27.33
2. STRUCTURAL FRAME 2390 m^2	-	-		68,710	28.75
3. UPPER FLOORS					
225 mm Hollow pot Floor	386 m^2	33.00	12,738		
150 mm In-situ r.c.	1585 m^2	22.50	35,662		
			48,400	48,400	20.25
4. STAIRCASES					
R.C. staircases	25 m rise	670.00	16,750		
One 25 m rise					
One secondary staircase 21.5 m rise	21.5 m rise	500.00	10,750		
			27,500	27,500	11.51
	Continued		£209,935		87.84

FIG. 12.7. *Front sheet of typical cost plan*

OUTLINE SPECIFICATION

in connection with Cost Plan

for

Office Block, Midtown

WORK BELOW LOWEST FLOOR FINISH   12th November 1980

Foundations to walls   In-situ concrete piles
and/or columns   average 6 m long (approx.
                                        90 No.) reinforced concrete
                                        pile caps and ground beams

Basements, walkway ducts, etc.   Semi basement 1.5 m
                                        approximately 8 m x 4 m
                                        for boilers.
                                        Also lift pits approx.
                                        0.75 m deep in waterproofed
                                        concrete.

Rising walls   Clay common bricks in
                                        cement mortar built off
                                        ground beams (approx.
                                        0.75 m high generally to
                                        d.p.c.)
                                        Reinforced concrete walls
                                        (0.3 m thick) around stair
                                        well and lift pits.

Ground floor slab   Generally 150 mm slab rein-
                                        forced with fabric on
                                        building paper and hardcore.
                                        Note thickness of hardcore
                                        to make up levels (0.6 m
                                        average).

D.p.c's. and membranes   Lead-cored bituminous
                                        d.p.c. in walls. 3 coat
                                        Synthaprufe or similar on
                                        g.f. slab. 2 coat asphalt
                                        tanking to semi basement.

STRUCTURAL FRAME

Generally   Reinforced concrete beams
                                        (at 3.5 m c/c) and columns
                                        similar to Outer London
                                        House.

FIG. 12.8. *Specification notes to accompany cost plan*

Cost checks on working drawings

After the cost plan has been prepared and agreed it will be the surveyor's task to see that the work shown on the working drawings and measured in the Bill of Quantities corresponds with the plan, as otherwise the tender figure is likely to be quite different from the amount of the estimate. Any necessary adjustments must be made before the Bill is prepared, not afterwards.

For this purpose all drawings should be cost checked as they come into the office; this must be a matter of routine and a rubber stamp should be made so that the drawing can be marked when the check has been done.

Unfortunately this stage in the surveyor's work (the receipt of working drawings and subsequent revisions and details) is usually a hectic one and there is not time to spare for things like cost checks. Again it is unfortunate that these checks can best be done by the more senior man, who is usually very busy in other directions.

Where the cost plan has been based upon approximate quantities tied to a fairly detailed specification, and where the design has proceeded in accordance with it, the work involved in cost checking will be minimal. If, however, the design has been radically changed for some reason it may be better to start the process again and prepare a fresh cost plan at as early a stage as possible rather than attempting to check the detailed drawings against a cost plan prepared for a somewhat different building. Cost checking procedures, as will be seen from the next few pages, are quite the most time-consuming and error-prone part of the whole process and the more they can be legitimately minimised the better. Should it prove to be necessary to undertake a thorough cost check of the whole design (perhaps because the cost plan did not give the architect sufficient guidance), then the drawings will have to be prepared by elements if the feedback from the cost checks is to be of any real use.

The extent to which cost checking should be carried out will depend upon:

(1) The amount of extra time which the surveyor can be allowed. This will vary from job to job, but it must be realised that if lack of time prevents essential cost checks from being carried out then the whole attempt at cost planning will largely be a waste of time.

(2) The amount of apparent alteration from the cost plan. If the cost plan was based upon a very similar project for the same architect and client and the details of specification and design were therefore known fairly well, the cost check may entail little more than a quick glance at the drawings to see that nothing is substantially different. Even where the circumstances are not quite as ideal as

this it may still be possible for the surveyor to satisfy himself by
inspection that the drawings show what the cost plan envisaged.
The drawings should be stamped and initialled, even so.
(3) The amount of detail in the cost plan. If it was possible to take
out fairly full approximate quantities the cost check may simply
consist of comparing these quantities with the working
drawings.
(4) The degree of confidence which exists between surveyor and
architect. If the architect is known to be cost conscious, capable
of and enthusiastic about cost design, the cost checks will be
much less important than where this confidence is lacking.
(5) The familiarity of the project. Most surveyors would feel fairly
confident of cost planning a school, whereas a planetarium
would be a very different proposition. In the latter case the cost
plan would probably incorporate rather a lot of assumptions and
it would be necessary to check these in detail.
(6) The importance of the element. It would be a very self-confident
surveyor who would not bother to check the external walling, or
the roof of a single-storey building, even under the most ideal
conditions. On the other hand if time is pressing some of the
smaller elements can often be ignored.

Carrying out the cost check

Again this is a suitable occasion for using standard forms. Where the
architect is designing by elements the procedure will be considerably
simplified, but even if he is not doing so the check must still be done by
elements.
    The design of the cost check form may be left to the tastes of the firm
or other organisation. It should show at least the following information:
(a) Number of check. The checks on a particular project should be
numbered consecutively, starting at 1.
(b) Total estimated cost of project after completion of previous
check. (This amount will be got from the previous cost check
form, or if this is the first check it will be the unaltered total of
the cost plan.)
(c) Reference number of drawing or other information being
checked.
(d) Element being checked.
(e) Amount allowed in cost plan in respect of element (or as
amended by previous checks).
(f) Estimated cost of element as calculated from the drawing, or
other information, being checked.

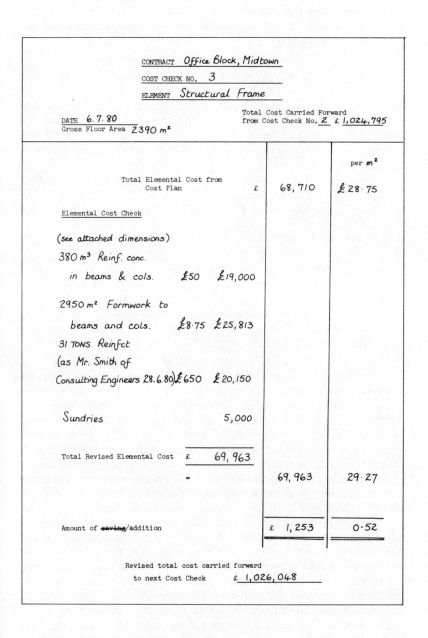

CONTRACT *Office Block, Midtown*

COST CHECK NO. 3

ELEMENT *Structural Frame*

DATE 6.7.80
Gross Floor Area 2390 m²

Total Cost Carried Forward
from Cost Check No. 2 £ 1,024,795

		per m²
Total Elemental Cost from Cost Plan £	68,710	£28·75

Elemental Cost Check

(see attached dimensions)

380 m³ Reinf. conc.

   in beams & cols.   £50   £19,000

2950 m² Formwork to

   beams and cols.   £8·75 £25,813

31 TONS Reinfct

(as Mr. Smith of

Consulting Engineers 28.6.80)£650   £20,150

Sundries   5,000

Total Revised Elemental Cost £	69,963	
=	69,963	29·27

| Amount of ~~saving~~/addition £ | 1,253 | 0·52 |

Revised total cost carried forward
to next Cost Check   £ 1,026,048

FIG. 12.9. *Example of cost check form*

(g) Difference (plus or minus) between (e) and (f).
(h) Estimated cost of project after (g) has been added to or deducted from (b).

A typical example of a cost check form is shown in Fig. 12.9.

As each cost check is carried out a copy of the cost check form should be sent to the architect so that he has an up-to-date running total of the project. If any check shows a substantial increase or decrease it would be as well to discuss the matter with the architect rather than merely sending the results of the check to him. Similarly he should be warned if the general standard of detailing appears to be more lavish than was allowed for.

If a drawing shows changes in more than one element a separate form should be used for each. The rough workings in connection with each check can be done on dimension paper and stapled to the office copy of the form.

A list should be kept of all drawings or other information received, with columns for marking:

(a) That cost check has been carried out.
(b) The reference numbers of the cost check form or forms.
(c) The elements involved. The purpose of this is to enable the checker, on receiving a drawing showing (say) part of the roof, to look back through the list to see whether any adjustments have already been made to this element.

If it appears that a detailed cost check of any particular drawing or information is not necessary the list can be marked accordingly. But all drawings and information (such as sub-contractors' quotations or replies to queries) must come to the cost checker in the first instance.

In connection with cost checking it is as well to remember the total cost of the project and also the inherent margin of error in cost planning; a surveyor whose estimates consistently get within plus or minus 5% of the accepted tender is doing well. In these circumstances it is obviously not worthwhile to spend much time cost checking isolated details of a large project, as the possible differences in cost are so small compared to the probable overall error.

Prices for cost checking may be obtained from the same sources as have been used earlier; although as there will be a tendency for the items to be more detailed than at cost plan or estimate stage the surveyor is likely to be using either built-up rates, price book rates, or actual rates from the Bill of Quantities from which the example analysis was prepared. Again it must be remembered that the builder's permission must have been obtained for this latter course.

It will be very tempting to lift prices from other Bills at this stage, but the errors that can arise from this practice have previously been pointed out.

If prices are built-up or obtained from price books the level of market prices on which the estimate is based must be remembered. It will also be necessary to include a realistic percentage for preliminaries and insurances; this will not necessarily be the same percentage as the builder used in the analysed example.

Cost reconciliation

When tenders have been received the tender which is most likely to be accepted should be reconciled with the cost plan. If, as should occur, there is little difference between the totals this is still worth doing; there are quite likely to be large compensating discrepancies in the various elements and these may provide information for future use.

The reconciliation is in fact a comparison of the final cost plan (as amended by cost checks) with a cost analysis of the tender. This also ensures the cost analysis getting done at the earliest possible moment instead of being left until "someone has time to do it".

There may be all sorts of explanations for a considerable difference between the cost plan estimate and the actual cost of a particular element; perhaps the cost planner made a mistake, quite possibly the builder's estimator made a mistake or did a deliberate price adjustment. But if there is a definite one-way divergence between cost plan and tender right through all the elements it is likely that either the surveyor misjudged market levels or that the tenders themselves are abnormally high or low. If the surveyor feels that the latter is the case then he could report accordingly.

Note that the contractor's permission is never required to analyse his tender for cost reconciliation purposes, it is only if the analysis is to be published, or if the individual prices are to be used for cost checking other projects, that the question arises.

Post-contract cost control

With the successful reconciliation of cost plan and tender the cost planning of the project is substantially completed. It will remain to control the cost during the progress of the works as described in the next chapter. If the tender is within the client's budget as a result of cost planning then variations ought not to be extensive, partly because the cost requirements will have been satisfied by the job as tendered for, and partly because the architectural pre-planning which should accompany cost planning will have produced workable solutions to the design and construction problems. Thus the extra time spent in cost planning may enable the total time spent on the job by the surveyor to be actually reduced.

Office organisation

With regard to the amount of work involved in cost planning, any sensible person would want to keep this to a minimum. The surveyor will soon learn from experience which items are of cost significance, where short cuts can be taken, where cost checks can be avoided. Experience will also show that the use of standard forms and procedures speeds things up as long as the cost planning staff are familiar with them. For this reason, and also because of the acceleration in working brought about by familiarity with cost and prices it may be found worthwhile in a large office to concentrate cost planning in a separate department rather than leaving it to be done by the takers-off on each project.

In coming to a decision on this point a powerful argument in favour of cost planning by the takers-off concerned must be considered; that it will give them familiarity with the project and thus make the actual preparation of the Bill much easier. Whether this proposition is as valid as it sounds is open to question; certainly a number of authorities who originally used this method subsequently changed over to separate departments. There is scope for experiment here, but if the cost planner and the taker-off are two different people there must obviously be a close and friendly liaison between them.

A critical assessment of elemental cost planning procedures

It has been suggested that elemental cost planning techniques will be justified if they consistently succeed in forecasting cost within a margin of 5% up or down, and indeed recent research suggests that even this target may be over-optimistic, given the variability which exists in tender levels. It might well be asked whether all this work is worthwhile if at the end of it all the tender is liable to differ from the estimate by such an amount. Traditional and much easier methods of estimating have often come far closer than this.

The answer is threefold; firstly that most budgets are flexible by at least this percentage or that if they are not it is simple enough to make the requisite modest alterations in the scheme. Secondly it must be emphasised that traditional single-rate methods cannot be *relied* upon to achieve anything like this standard of accuracy, and that for every "spot-on" square metre estimate there is another instance of such an estimate being up to 50% out. It must be made quite clear that where an estimate, however prepared, forecasts the cost to within 1 or 2% under traditional competitive tendering conditions, then luck as well as skill has played its part in the result. Thirdly, elemental cost planning achieves a balance and economy in the building which cannot be attained by any other method using traditional tendering procedures.

The author remembers an instance concerning a technical school which was estimated on a square metre basis and where the difference between estimate and tender was much less than 5%. Satisfactory though this was nobody was able to answer a very simple question from the architect during the design stage as to whether that estimate would cover a certain type of wall cladding. There was nothing in the estimate with which it could be compared.

In view of the alleged unreliability of estimates prepared by single-rate square metre superficial area methods it is as well to explain why these methods can safely be used for the preliminary estimate before the cost plan is prepared. It is because the cost plan will show up any error in the estimate before working drawings or Bills of Quantities have been prepared and the necessary adjustments can be made before any of the detail work is started. This is a very different situation to discovering the error at tender stage when time and money have been spent designing an impossible scheme in detail.

While elemental cost planning has made an outstanding contribution to the study, forecasting, and control of building costs, it nevertheless suffers from a number of basic limitations which have prevented it from developing much beyond the stage which it reached within the first few years. One might wonder whether it is doomed to be like the lead-acid electric battery which, although very useful, will never be capable of development into the kind of power-storage that the world is waiting for.

These limitations are:

(1) Nobody has yet produced a set of elements each of which performs a single function but which can be easily cost-related, nor are they ever likely to. This means, amongst other things, that it is not really possible to compare the cost performance of the same element on two different buildings, nor, within one element, to compare two different technical solutions concerning one building. In order to attempt this task (which the surveyor is often asked to do) it is necessary to consider all sorts of extraneous matters, some of which are difficult to quantify.

It might be thought that it would be possible to overcome this limitation by the use of complex computer programs which would enable the interaction of the elements to be worked out exhaustively. This might well be possible, but it would be very expensive and at the present time is not worth doing because of the next limitation.

(2) As we have already seen, but as is worth repeating here, the "costs" which are being manipulated may bear no relation to fact; they are not really "data" in any scientific sense. It is a waste of time and money to use sophisticated methods to manip-

ulate inaccurate data, as is recognised in the computer world where the maxim "Garbage in, Garbage out" is well known. In fact, such processing is worse than useless, because the fact that sophisicated analysis methods have been employed leads people to attach some importance to the results. They would immediately recognise the original data as unreliable if it were presented to them in unprocessed form.

It must be remembered that there is no pressure on the contractor to insert rates in his Bill of Quantities which represent carefully estimated production costs for each of the items, but there are many reasons (as set out previously) why he does not. The rates in the Bill of Quantities are not "retail" prices for which the contractor is offering to execute individual pieces of work in isolation, but are merely a notional breakdown of his total offer. However, even if it were possible to compel the contractor to show true cost estimates, and to enforce standard practice in defining and allocating overhead costs, there would still be the difficulty of setting production cost against square metres of design elements, as so many of these costs (e.g. the tower crane) are not directly related to element unit quantity.

(3) Even if the two previous limitations could be overcome the whole system suffers because under normal conditions there is no contractual commitment to the cost plan. The quantity surveyor has no responsibility for the tender amounts and the contractor has no interest in the cost plan.

The exercise thus has a good deal in common with weather forecasting. The surveyor is able to draw on a considerable body of past experience and can consider present trends, but he is in no position to guarantee the result. He will often be right, but if any unusual circumstances manifest themselves he can still be badly wrong.

The comparatively crude methods which have been set out in this chapter are usually adequate for forecasting within the wide limits of market pricing; any attempt to get much closer in these conditions is unlikely to be worthwhile. Therefore if the surveyor cannot offer any kind of guarantee to his client the latter is unlikely to agree to expenditure on expensive and sophisticated methods of "control" which are not in fact controlling anything but are just hopeful forecasts. If a higher standard of cost control is required than is provided by the reasonable development of these traditional methods then it will be necessary to sacrifice some measure of market freedom to obtain it, for example by involving the contractor at an early stage. There is just no way round this.

Finally:

(1) Elemental cost planning should ensure that the tender amount is close to the first estimate, or alternatively that any likely difference between the two is anticipated and is acceptable.

(2) Elemental cost planning should ensure that the money available for the project is allocated consciously and economically to the various components and finishes.

(3) Elemental cost planning does not mean minimum standards and a "cheap job"; it aims to achieve good value at the desired level of expenditure.

(4) Elemental cost planning always involves the measurement and pricing of approximate quantities at some stage of the cost plan or cost check.

Chapter 13
Real-time Cost Control

Cost planning and control as described so far is concerned with planning and monitoring costs during the investigation, planning, and design stages, and finishes at the point where tenders are received, or a contract entered into. During this stage nothing is irrevocable—drawings can be redone, the scheme can be reduced in size or its configuration altered, the whole thing can be started again from scratch or postponed or even totally abandoned at what will be (from the point of view of the total project) a negligible cost for abortive professional work. Even if the project has got as far as the submission of tenders by contractors, the scheme can still be radically changed or abandoned without any commitment to the tenderers or any need to recompense them for their trouble.

Whilst the accurate forecasting of a tender amount and the signing of a contract for that sum (or an amended one where the forecast hasn't quite worked out) is of considerable importance, the matter does not end there. The final agreed cost, after both the job and the various financial negotiations arising from it have been completed, is rarely the same as the original contract amount, and it is this final figure which the client actually has to pay and which will be the building cost for which he has to raise and service the finance. In many cases the "contract sum" may be merely an intermediate stage in arriving at this final cost, and a system of cost planning and control which stops at this halfway point will only be of limited use (and possibly not worth the money which it costs).

It is important, therefore, that the cost control process continues to the point of completion and hand-over of the project, and this continuation is often termed "post-contract" cost control for obvious reasons. It differs from design cost planning in many ways, and these will depend upon the exact contractual arrangements, but two differences will be inescapable, firstly that the interests of a contractor or contractors now form an important addition to the considerations involved, and secondly that major expenditure is currently being incurred and future options proportionately reduced. It becomes increasingly difficult to make major alterations of any kind at the stroke of a pen, once drawings and specifications are being translated into an expensive organisation of resources and finished work, and even delay caused by hesitation or reconsideration may involve the client in heavy costs. It is to emphasise this similarity with real-time computer control systems, and because in some circumstances there may not even be a contract, that we have chosen to use the term "real-time" rather than "post-contract" to describe this type of control.

The basis of real-time cost control is reporting at regular (often monthly) intervals or on a special occasion when a major decision has to be made. This cost control report will set out the client's likely final cost commitment in some detail and also the cost consequences of any remaining major options. In some instances this report may be made to the architect or other professional project controller but it is preferable that it should be made direct to the client. This service should be envisaged when the quantity surveyor's fee is being negotiated, and written into the agreement. Its purpose is to enable the client to budget for his likely expenditure, to enable the cost effect of any major changes to be seen in the context of the project as a whole, and to enable avoiding action to be taken if the total cost appears to be escalating unduly.

One of the problems attached to this service is the extent to which sums of money should be kept in hidden reserve by the underestimation of savings and the overestimation, or at least the pessimistic evaluation, of additional costs. There is a natural tendency towards this type of caution, which in its most extreme forms may be taken to the extent of inflating the projections sufficiently to cover without disclosure any mistakes which may be made by the architect or quantity surveyor and which will still leave the client with a pleasant surprise when the final account is inevitably settled at below the forecast amount. Such conduct would be as unprofessional and unhelpful as inflating the quantities in the Bill of Quantities for similar reasons.

Nevertheless, caution dictates that *some* allowance be made for things going slightly wrong, particularly where final costs will be subject to negotiation or where the full consequences of decisions or events cannot be exactly foreseen. The reasonable judgement of these allowances, avoiding both excessive pessimism or optimism, is one of the major factors in making this a truly professional task. In particular, the quantity surveyor who is successful in this role will develop a feeling for the average project, where not *everything* is going to go wrong, and for the occasional project where it would be wise to assume that it might.

In carrying out real-time cost control it is essential for the quantity surveyor always to be fully informed as to what is happening and what is intended, and ensuring this may well be one of the more difficult parts of the operation. Ideally he should be part of the decision-making process, in which case the difficulty will not arise, but this is not usually the situation. However, merely sitting in his office waiting for information to come to him is not going to be good enough. Most contracts contain no requirement for communication to and from the builder to flow through the quantity surveyor's office. He is likely to be informed eventually of everything necessary for him to play his part in the final settlement of accounts, but this information may be far too late to be of any use for real-time cost control purposes. It must be remembered that cost control requires not a record of costs incurred to date but of likely eventual cost commitments arising from current proposals or from acts of commission or neglect. The quantity surveyor must, therefore, instigate his own "current awareness" procedures, not only seeing that he gets immediate copies of all official orders, drawings, and letters, but also attending all site meetings and generally looking around the site to see what is going on and what verbal instructions might have been given. It has often been alleged that on many projects the "official" documentation is merely trying to catch up with the real but informal communications system. The preparation of interim valuations for payment purposes provides an excellent opportunity to monitor what is actually happening and should always be used for this purpose. The maintenance and updating of real-time cost control records is an ideal application for micro-computer spreadsheet systems such as "Visicalc".

Although, as shown above, many of the factors in real-time cost control are common to any type of contractual situation, it will be most convenient to look at the detail in the context of each of the different types.

Real-time cost control of lump sum contracts based on Bills of Quantities

In the real-time cost control system for this type of project the starting-point will be the contract sum, and the provisions which the contract makes for amending it.

The provisions will usually cover:

(i) The adjustment of "provisional" sums of money or quantities of work, which are embodied in the contract, in the light of the actual cost or quantity of work carried out. This type of provision is often made for work such as foundation excavation which cannot be foreseen exactly.

(ii) Payment for variations and for additions to, and omissions from, the work.

(iii) The adjustment of amounts included in the contract for work to be carried out by nominated sub-contractors and others, in the light of actual cost.

(iv) Correction of errors in Bills of Quantities and other contract documents.
(v) Adjustment for the effects of inflation.
(vi) Adjustment for the effects of new legislation.
(vii) Compensation to the contractor for the cost of delays in the work caused by circumstances for which the client is responsible (or, in more generous contracts, by circumstances for which the contractor is not responsible). These circumstances may include delays caused by the ordering of variations or by delay in the provision of drawings, etc., or where the more generous provisions apply, delays caused by bad weather or industrial action.

In addition to the likely revised contract amount the quantity surveyor's cost projections should include updated additional amounts for professional fees, furnishings (unless it has been agreed to exclude these), and also any other items which the client wishes to consider as part of the total cost.

An item which can give rise to controversy is the adjustment of the provisional contingency sum. This is an amount included in the contract sum by the architect to cover unforeseen expenditure, and the controversy centres around whether it is at his disposal to cover design development (or more bluntly, mistakes) or whether it is at the disposal of the client to spend on extra items. Some public authorities hold the latter view so strongly as to demand the omission of the contingency sum as the first variation on the contract, and to treat it as a saving. Except where the client holds such extreme views it is probably best to show the contingency sum separately in the cost control report, deducting any incidental extras of the appropriate kind and carrying the balance forward to cover further similar extras which can occur at any stage of the project. In any case a provision of *some* kind must be made for contingencies during the remainder of the project.

A general difficulty which faces the quantity surveyor is that although the contractor is required by most contracts to give written notice to the architect of circumstances having arisen which will give rise to an extra cost, he is usually only required to give this notice within a "reasonable time" of the occurrence, which in contractual terms has to be interpreted fairly generously, and which may well be too late for cost control purposes. The remarks already made about current awareness therefore apply strongly. A further difficulty under the British JCT Standard Form of Contract (although not always overseas) is that there is no requirement for the financial effect to be stated or agreed at the same time, and in fact this is positively discouraged both by the contract clauses and by traditional practice. The quantity surveyor's estimates, therefore, have to bear in mind that his figures may be subject to negotiation, and if the builder also suggests a figure at this stage (which he is not bound to do) the quantity surveyor will have to guess the point between them at which a deal is likely to be made. For this reason the quantity surveyor's real-time cost projections on this type of contract should never be shown to the contractor, since the quantity surveyor may have prudently assumed a higher figure for extras than he is prepared at that stage to concede.

Although the contract usually contains a similar provision for notification of reduced or omitted work by the contractor there is obviously less incentive for this to be done, and the duty is easily "forgotten". The quantity surveyor again is in a position to see that omissions are duly notified and adjusted.

The adjustment in respect of an amount included for a nominated sub-contractor's work may require to be done on several different occasions. The first adjustment will be done when a sub-contractor's tender is accepted for the work; this tender is likely to contain the same type of provision for further adjustment as the main contract and similar subsequent changes in cost are likely to occur which will have to be reflected in the cost-control report.

The adjustment of the cost-control report for inflation is a difficult one, particularly at an early stage of the project, since it involves not only a forecast of rises in building costs over the contract period but also an estimate of the likely progress of the work in cost terms so that the forecast increases can be applied to an appropriate proportion of the cost. There are three different figures to be calculated for inflation, and this will apply whether the contract adjustment is on the basis of the difference between ascertained actual costs of resources and costs at the time of tender, or whether it is done on an index-linked basis.

(i) Increased cost incurred to date.
(ii) Estimated additional cost for remainder of contract of increases announced to date.
(iii) Allowance for effect of future increases.

The figure which the client will require for budgeting purposes is the total of the three, although the total should be split into the three categories to emphasise the progressively more conjectural nature of the estimates. (Although it is theoretically possible for there to be a decrease in cost through the operation of this clause of a contract there has been no known instance of a reduction in the contract sum from this cause in the UK during the forty years prior to 1979.)

A most important point regarding cost control of lump-sum contracts is the perennial conflict between tight budgetary control and getting the best deal from market forces. The best budgetary control is achieved if a firm contractual commitment can be obtained at the earliest possible moment—in the case of extra work, for instance, before the order is given to go ahead. Even the British JCT Standard Form of Contract makes some provision for this in its use of the words "unless otherwise agreed" in its set of procedures for valuing variations. But, as previously mentioned, the contractor is under no obligation to agree a firm figure beforehand, with its attendant risk of underestimation, and may prefer to leave negotiation until he has all his final costs available. It is up to the quantity surveyor to advise his client on the advantages and disadvantages of agreeing extras at an early stage in the light of the client's particular budgetary problems and the apparent willingness or otherwise of the contractor to do a reasonable deal on this basis.

As an example of a system of cost reporting, two consecutive monthly cost reports on the early stages of a job are shown in Figs 13.1 and 13.2. There are many possible ways of setting out such reports, and the reader may well be able to devise what he considers to be a better format. What is most important is that any changes since the previous report should be clearly highlighted, either by the use of asterisks and notes as in the example or else by simply giving the previous figures as totals. Using this system the figures in the second example for "Net additions" could simply have been shown thus:

Net additions	£
As before	22,500
Extra work to entrance vestibule and staircase (V.O. 6)	3,000
	£25,500

Points where other people's tastes might differ include the rounding-off of estimated figures (a figure of £18,577 implies a standard of accuracy which £18,600 does not), and the item of "sundry minor variations" which could have been shown in detail. It is the authors' view that this document is prepared to assist budgetary control, not to start a premature witch-hunt against the architect. Consideration of such matters can usually be better left until the final account, when minor problems can be seen in the context of the finished job.

It will be noted that the report takes account of the variations ordered, and quotations accepted, for work which is not yet done, or even started. The possible claim for delay has been taken out of the contingency fund, which will not be able to stand many such demands upon it.

```
                        OFFICE BLOCK, MIDTOWN

Cost Report No. 2    10.6.80
                                                            £
                                           Contract Sum 1,003,638

Net Omissions                               £
Partial substitution of 'Conglint'
panels for Portland Stone (V.0.3)         14,800
* Saving in foundations and piling         4,000
                                          18,800              18,800
                                          ------             984,838

Net Additions                               £
Decoration and partitions in
offices (V.0.1)                           18,600
Carpeting in offices in lieu of
wood block flooring (V.0.2)                3,900
                                          22,500              22,500
                                          ------           1,007,338

Adjustment of P.C. Sums       Omit        Add
                                £          £
Heating Installation
(Midland Heating Co.)                     4,098
Electrical Installation
(Sparkes & Co.)                             532
* Curtain Walling
(The Curtain Walling Co.)     1,130       -----
                              1,130       4,630
                              -----       1,130
                                          3,500
Profit and attendance                      275
Net addition                             3,775               3,775
                                         -----            1,011,113

Adjustment for Fluctuations
(including sub-contractors)                 £
* (i)   Increase on work to date          5,100
* (ii)  Allowance for effect of current
        increases on remainder of work   60,000
* (iii) Allowance for possible future
        increases, say                   50,000
                                        115,100             115,100
                             Total estimated cost  £ 1,126,213

Amount included for contingencies           £
Contingency sum in contract              15,000
* Sundry minor variations (net extra)      530
                     Balance remaining  £ 14,470

Note * indicates changed or addition item since previous cost report
Professional fees not included in above figures
```

FIG. 13.1. *Real time cost report, June*

OFFICE BLOCK, MIDTOWN

Cost Report No. 3 . 12/7/80

£
Contract Sum 1,003,638

Net Omissions		£	
Partial substitution of 'Conglint' panels for Portland Stone (V.0.3)		14,800	
Saving in foundations and piling *(revised figure)		3,640	
		18,440	18,440
			985,198

Net Additions		£	
Decoration and partitions in offices. (V.0.1)		18,600	
Carpeting in offices in lieu of wood block flooring (V.0.2)		3,900	
* Extra work to Entrance Vestibule and Staircase (V.0.6)		3,000	
		25,500	25,500
			1,010,698

Adjustment of P.C.Sums	Omit £	Add £	
Heating Installation (Midland Heating Co.)		4,098	
* Additional Thermostats (V.0.7)		300	
Electrical Installation (Sparkes & Co.)		532	
Curtain walling (The Curtain Walling Co.)	1,130		
* Lifts (Ascenseurs Ltd.)	1,091		
	2,221	4,930	
		2,221	
		2,709	
Profit and Attend.		225	
Net addition		2,934	2,934
			1,013,632

Adjustment for Fluctuations (including sub-contractors)		£	
* (i) Increase on work to date		13,800	
* (ii) Allowance for effect of current increases on remainder of work		65,000	
* (iii) Allowance for possible future increases, say		40,000	
		118,800	118,800
	Total estimated cost	£	1,132,432

Amount included for contingencies			£
Contingency sum in contract		£	15,000
* Sundry minor variations (net extra)		1,320	
* Likely claim for delay in connection with Ground Floor walling layout (Site meeting 5/7/80)		5,000	
		6,320	6,320
	Balance remaining	£	8,680

Note *indicates changed or additional item since previous cost report
Professional fees not included in above figures

FIG. 13.2. *Real time cost report, July*

Finally, it must again be emphasised that under normal contractual arrangements the contractor has no duty to participate in any cost control (or cash flow control) scheme of the client, and there are sound commercial reasons why he may not wish to do so. Any such requirement, to be binding, must be written into the Form of Contract with legal advice and cannot simply be stated in the preliminaries of the Bill of Quantities.

The question of cash flow control has been raised in the last paragraph; this will be dealt with shortly.

Real-time cost control of negotiated contracts

A negotiated contract provides excellent opportunities for cost control, indeed this is one of its principal advantages for which, as usual, some measure of market-force benefit may have to be sacrificed.

From the moment he is drawn into the scheme the contractor should be committed by the architect and quantity surveyor to participate in the cost control process both during the design stage and subsequently.

This requirement should be made clear during the early stages of negotiation and duly written into the contractual arrangements, together with a provision for prior negotiation and agreement of extra costs.

Real-time cost control of cost reimbursement contracts

The situation here is quite different. There is no contract sum as a starting-off point and no possibility of contractual commitment to estimates of original or extra costs, so that real-time cost control by the quantity surveyor becomes of fundamental importance. On the other hand there is no price mechanism to cloud the issue, and thus no valid commercial reason why the contractor should not be willing to make all his own estimates and costings fully available to the client's representatives. It is preferable that cost control of the project should be carried out by the quantity surveyor co-operatively with the contractor since two heads will certainly be better than one and full advantage can be taken of the absence of commercial secrecy which is one of the main benefits of this type of contract.

At any point in the project the quantity surveyor's cost control report is likely to be based upon:

  (i) Quantity surveyor's original estimate of cost, which should have incorporated an allowance for inflation.
 (ii) Quantity surveyor's estimate of cost of variations, ditto.
(iii) Adjustment of estimated cost for actual cost of work completed or expenditure committed.

(iv) Any adjustments to the estimated cost of current or future work in the light of this experience.

Towards the end of the project he may switch to a simpler system involving the ascertained cost of work completed and the estimated cost of remaining work required.

The quantity surveyor's original estimate is likely to be based upon approximate quantities, as are his estimates of variations. In both cases, and especially the latter, he may instead adopt a "resource-based" approach in co-operation with the contractor. Even where approximate quantities are used, however, all estimates should be discussed with the contractor before being given to the client. The purpose of this co-operation is twofold; to ensure that the quantity surveyor has not made any false assumptions and also to enable a positive contribution to be made where the quantity surveyor finds that the contractor is proposing to use methods or equipment which he feels are unnecessarily expensive or inefficient. It must be remembered that the contractor's usual incentive to cost-cutting will be absent, it is not his own money which he is spending. In such an event there may have to be a meeting between architect, quantity surveyor, and contractor to decide what is to be done; this could in some instances involve minor redesign to enable something to be built more easily. This aspect of cost control is an important part of the quantity surveyor's contribution.

A most difficult part of the whole task will be the adjustment of estimated costs for actual ascertained costs. Under some forms used for cost-reimbursement contracts the contractor's responsibility for costs is limited to providing a periodic statement of total labour and plant costs, and invoices received, to date. Such a document is totally useless for cost control purposes both in format and in timing since invoices are often not available until weeks or even months after the cost commitment has been incurred, and the quantity surveyor must, therefore, ensure that the contractual arrangements provide for:

(a) Facilities for the client's representatives to participate in the contractor's estimating and work planning procedures and in the appointment and control of sub-contractors.

(b) The use of the contractor's own detailed costing system for the benefit of the client's representatives, or alternatively the installation of a suitable system where the contractors' system is unsuitable or non-existent.

(c) Early disclosure of all papers concerned with ordering, costing, delivery, or pricing.

It must be made clear prior to the contractors' appointment that these requirements exist, and they must be incorporated in the contract. The arrangements must not rely entirely upon goodwill, since at the least they are inconvenient to the contractor and are certain to involve him in some expense. This will need to be reflected in his fee.

The costing system will have to separate the costs in respect of specific parts of the work which correspond to identifiable portions of the quantity surveyor's estimate, otherwise any form of reconciliation between costs and estimate will be impossible until the whole job is complete. This means in turn that the surveyor's estimate will need to be structured suitably, an elemental basis being quite a good one. However, work executed by different trades at different times should not be telescoped into a single priced item (for example roof carcassing and tiling). A further point to watch is delay in reporting; cost of plant and materials may take some time to work through the contractors' office system and a method has to be devised for overcoming this delay. For example, materials can be priced off delivery dockets which should be instantly available. Reconciliation of delivered materials with measurements of major items of work should also be carried out to ensure that there are no unexplained differences up or down due to theft, excessive wastage, or clerical error.

Reconciliation of allowances for inflation poses some further problems, since these will often not be separately identified in the ascertained costs of resources. In most cases some form of approximation will be adequate in showing how much of the cost of some particular operation should be set against the allowance for inflation, since expensive and complicated book-keeping arrangements which do not affect the total to be paid are unlikely to yield any commensurate benefit to the client. Allowances for future inflation may need to be revised from time to time, as was the case with lump sum contract cost control.

It is necessary to watch closely the arrangements for sub-contractors. It may often be possible to appoint these on a price rather than a cost basis, as the work may be more clearly defined by the time they are involved. (For example, the structural items to which finishes are to be applied may actually have been built.) Competitive tendering might well be possible; again if the quantity surveyor does not look after this then nobody else will. It is much easier just to ring up a friendly sub-contractor and ask him to come round and start.

Finally, great care is necessary when work on a price basis and work on a cost-reimbursement basis are both comprised in the same contract. This is only likely to be satisfactory where one or more of the following circumstances obtains:

(i) The cost-reimbursement work is only a negligible proportion of the whole (e.g. incidental dayworks on a lump sum contract).

(ii) The two types of payment apply to two separate organisations (e.g. the main contractor and a sub-contractor).

(iii) The cost-reimbursement work is carried out by a separate gang of people using special materials.

(iv) The two types of work are carried out at different periods or at different sites.

Unless one of these conditions is fulfilled there will be a tendency for labour and/or materials used in the price-based work to be charged to the cost-reimbursement work, thus being paid for twice, and this is almost impossible to check without continuous monitoring. An example of the type of project where this could happen would be a small extension to an existing building where the extension was to be paid for as a lump sum but the alterations in the existing building were done on a cost-reimbursement basis. It would be very difficult to ensure that men's time was charged to the correct part of the work if it was all proceeding simultaneously, and even more difficult to check afterwards that this had been done. Such hybrid arrangements should therefore be avoided.

It will have been seen that the real-time cost control of cost-reimbursement contracts involves the skilful combination of builders' costing systems and client budgeting and cost strategies, and is likely to be expensive. There is no halfway house, however; cost control of this type of project can only be done properly or not at all. The client must make up his mind about this at the beginning. The internal cost control of a package deal contract would have many features in common with the above procedures.

Real-time cost control of management contracts

In many ways the procedures would resemble those on a cost-reimbursement contract, but probably at a more strategic level since the work will be undertaken using a number of different contracts, any of which in turn will require its own cost control procedures of the appropriate type already discussed. Nevertheless, the general pattern set out in items (i) to (iv) on pages 234–5 will also apply to the project as a whole.

Control of cash flow

So far in this chapter we have ignored the phasing of expenditure, except insofar as the effect of inflation on costs is concerned. However, in practice the client is usually very concerned about the sums of money he will be called upon to pay at any given time, and may require a cash flow estimate from the quantity surveyor before signing the contract, rather of the type shown on page 62 of Chapter 4 in respect of the block of flats. He will need this in order to make adequate arrangements to raise the money, whether he is operating in the profit sector or in the social sector. Quite clearly he is unlikely to be able to place the whole contract amount in his bank trading account at the beginning of the project, ready to be drawn upon as required over the contract period, and even if he were theoretically in a position to do this he would still have more profitable uses for the money in the interim, which would probably mean that it would not be instantly available.

The cash flow estimate will require to be revised by the quantity surveyor from time to time, preferably at the same intervals as the real-time cost control reports, and these revisions will take into account not only any changes in total cost but also the extent to which some aspects of the programme are running faster or slower than anticipated, or indeed whether the whole programme has slipped.

In many cases, a periodic report of this kind may be all that is required, giving the client an updated warning of cash requirements. (As well as performing this function it may also be very useful in monitoring programme slippage, because the level of cash flow required to complete on time may be seen to be quite impossible in the light of experience to date.)

However, in some instances a client will need not merely a report of what is likely to happen but some positive form of control. In the case of a cost-reimbursement contract it should be possible to order an increased or decreased tempo of work, and few problems arise. In management projects, also, the placing of contracts can be deferred or work accelerated, but serious difficulties occur in the case of lump sum Bill of Quantities contracts on the Standard Form.

Once a contract has been signed using the British JCT Standard Form of Contract the builder is not answerable for the phasing of expenditure. He does not have to provide an estimate of client's cash flow, and even if he agrees to do so as a favour he cannot be held to perform in accordance with it. His only duty is to proceed "regularly and diligently" and to complete by the appointed date or a later date which may be agreed upon because of delays; it is in the contractor's interest to obtain high level of payment in the early stages of the job in order to finance the later stages and he may inflate the prices for earlier parts of the work, and arrange early deliveries of materials, to achieve this.

Therefore if a positive form of cash flow control is required, a suitable provision will have to be made in the actual contract, and not merely in the Bill of Quantities or in correspondence. The contract might state a month-by-month cash flow programme with a provision that the contractor would not be reimbursed ahead of this programme if the work was carried out faster than scheduled, and that if expenditure fell behind the programme there could either be a provision for damages to be ascertained or, more constructively, for the difference between the programmed amount and the actual expenditure to be paid into a trust fund. It might be thought that there would be no damage to the client's interests if expenditure fell behind programme (provided the job was finally completed on time), but in the public sector and in some large private corporations construction is often funded on an annual basis and amounts unspent at the end of the financial year may be permanently lost to the authority or department concerned.

In the profit sector, however, quite apart from his general wish to reduce the cost of financing his cash flow, the client may find it difficult to raise the total cost of construction until nearer the time when the building will actually be producing an income. He might then have arranged for the contractor to bear part of the building cost during construction or even to take a share in the risk of the development. In such cases it would be essential for the arrangements for funding during the progress of the works to be formalised in the contract.

Cash flow control of major development schemes

Major development schemes may extend over many years and may include a large number of building contracts entered into at different times.

Cash flow control is necessary in the running of public development schemes to ensure that money is available to meet outgoings. If a project, or a development programme, is funded on an accrual basis (that is, unspent funds which have been allocated to it can be carried forward from year to year), and if it is not possible to lend out money at a profit (perhaps because the authority has not got the necessary powers), then nothing more than a "passive" control of cash flow will be required. The authority will simply need to order its financial affairs to suit what is happening.

However, most public funding is on a yearly basis, in which unspent funds in one sector are not carried forward for the benefit of the project or authority for which they were allocated, but are used to meet overspending in other sectors or applied to a reduction in government expenditure. In addition, most major building projects involve an unavoidable commitment to expenditure for some years ahead, although the authority's budget for these years may be unconfirmed when the commitment is entered into. Trouble may occur if major construction projects have fallen behind schedule, moving much of the expenditure which should have taken place in the current year into future years, and leaving a cash balance which will be lost to the authority with no certainty of picking it up again. It is, therefore, necessary to manipulate cash flow in the light of changes so that the year's allocation of funds is completely but productively spent and so that a realistic revision can be made of cash requirements for ensuing years. Similarly, if funds are reduced in any particular year, perhaps because of economic problems, the on-going programme may have to be amended. This could be called "active" or "positive" control of cash flow.

In any authority's development budget the expenditure will fall into three categories:

(1) Old projects.
(2) Current projects.
(3) New projects.

With each category the discretionary factor in expenditure is increased.

(1) *Old projects.* These are projects which have been completed, but for which full payment has not yet been made (possibly depending upon the outcome of litigation, arbitration, or negotiation). Once payments are due they will have to be met.

(2) *Current projects.* It may be possible for an authority to order a speed-up or slow-down of current projects in order to change its cash commitment during the year, even at the expense of an eventual increase in total cost. What more usually happens however is that circumstances beyond the authority's control cause such changes, and the cash flow budgeting has to be revised to suit. Almost invariably, expenditure tends to fall behind estimate because of delays in progress, although this may sometimes be counterbalanced to some extent by extras and by inflation. It might be thought that if an authority had a large number of projects on hand (such as a programme of 10 schools) the differences would tend to average out, but this does not happen in practice because the causes of delay are often national or regional in character—weather, industrial disputes, labour shortages, etc.

(3) *New projects.* It is these which offer the greatest scope for control. If the start of a two year project worth £10,000,000 is brought forward or put back by one month the effect will be an increase or decrease of £400,000 in the current year's cash flow, and correspondingly greater for longer periods than one month. There are two major difficulties however—the starting of a major project may have a comparatively small effect in the year in which the go-ahead is given (but it will then join the ranks of the current projects and will be an inescapable and major commitment for the following two years or more), and expenditure on projects tends to follow the well-known "S" curve where the

rate of spending is at its greatest in the middle period of the project with a comparatively slow build-up in the early stages See Fig. 4.1 on page 46). In many ways the best way to control the cash flow situation is by having a number of smaller short term projects ready to roll, and these can be largely completed during the financial year in question even if the order is not given until the year is quite well advanced.

A method of disbursing funds on a project which is falling behind programme is to pay for the work, or for materials, ahead of the legal liability to do so. There are obvious dangers in doing this and a public auditor would be unlikely to accept a straightforward attempt to do it. It might, however, be possible to pay money into a joint trust fund.

Up to now we have been considering cash flow as though we are simply concerned with the year as a whole, but this is rarely the case. Funds are not normally paid across to an authority in a single sum at the beginning of the year, nor are they paid as each cash commitment arises, but are usually paid in quarterly instalments or something of the kind. Quite clearly, therefore, the authority must avoid too much cash expenditure in the early part of the year since funds will not be available, whilst if it is empowered to lend surplus short-term money profitably it may be able to arrange matters so that it can do this. Even where there is a smooth monthly outgoing throughout the year, the money for the third month of any quarter will be available for the first two months.

Although this section has been written in the context of public or social development much or it is equally applicable to profit schemes, except that the problem of "spending all the money by the end of the year" is not so likely to occur and the pressure is likely to be in the opposite direction; the question of interest on money borrowed becomes of paramount importance so that any pushing back of payment dates will be welcomed, so long as final completion is not held up.

It is not unknown for this to happen in the public area; an overseas regional government, which was anxious to minimise the effects of a slump in the building industry, but had spent all its funds for the year, let contracts on the basis that no payment would be made until the following financial year, so that for the first six months or more the contractors were totally financing the programme. However, as would be expected, the tenders reflected this additional burden.

Chapter 14

Resource-based Cost Planning and Control

In Chapter 3, "How Building Costs are Incurred", we looked briefly at the cost of actual building operations, and it might be worthwhile to re-read pages 28–32 before starting on this chapter. The detailed cost models which we have been examining so far have largely been based upon the measurement of finished work in place, and its valuation from Bills of Quantities or other market-price-orientated data. Quite apart from the general fallibility of Bill rates, these models have embodied two major fallacies:

(i) That the production cost of a building element is proportional to its finished quantity.

(ii) That the cost of a building element has an independent existence which can be considered separately from the rest of the building.

We have been aware of these drawbacks almost from the start and have been able to come to terms with them through the exercise of professional skill. But it is worthwhile considering whether it would not be better to base our estimates and cost control procedures on production cost criteria, as is done in most (perhaps all) other industries.

One major reason why we do not normally adopt this approach has already been given, which is that under lump sum contracting arrangements it is the market price, rather than production costs, which concerns the client and his advisers. This reason, however, is not valid if we are considering a cost-reimbursement or management type of contract, or if we are looking at a situation where the cost planning is being carried out inside a design-and-build organisation.

There is, however, another and quite different ground on which resource-based cost planning can be criticised. Much of the resource cost of modern building is attributable to plant and organisation, and both initial estimating and the subsequent refining of the estimate require the envisaging of technological solutions. Whether the building will be steel-framed, precast concrete frame and panel, or in-situ concrete, will demand totally different approaches with probably significant cost differences for any particular configuration and set of user requirements.

This last paragraph in fact sounds like an argument in favour of a resource basis rather than a criticism, but the big disadvantage is that it moves the design considerations of a building into the production field much too early in the process. An economical structural system may be postulated and the configuration of the building developed, for example, to suit the radius of action of the tower crane (or cranes) placed in the most efficient positions, or to suit the repetition of precast units. The architect's traditional approach, as we have already seen, is the opposite one—the form of the building is evolved primarily as a set of inter-related spaces, and the best technological solution for that configuration is then investigated. Quite clearly, in both cases, some compromises may have to be reached, but the basic issue is whether user needs and environmental considerations come first and the construction follows, or whether production efficiency should be the consideration from which design develops.

There are too many existing buildings which remind us that construction optimisation lasts for months but the consequences last for years (although not always as many years as the designers intended). Unfortunately production managers are no less lazy than the rest of us and prefer to postulate easy solutions rather than applying themselves to devising an efficient way of building a use-orientated design. It ought to be possible to do this provided the details of construction have not been developed too far before the builder is called in.

Whilst it is true that the quantity surveyor's traditional elemental cost planning approach does enable the early design process to proceed with some semblance of cost control prior to construction decisions, nevertheless these decisions have to be faced sooner or later. Once this point is reached a resource-orientated approach has much to recommend it in cases other than the competitive price-in-advance situation, particularly where the builder who will be undertaking the work is a party to the cost planning exercise. If this is not the case, then the method is of dubious advantage; there are many different ways of organising a building site and each builder has his preferred methods and equipment, so that there is unlikely to be a "best" solution that any builder would automatically accept. Since so much of the advantage of a resource-based estimate is that it can be used for real-time control purposes, this will be lost if the chosen builder throws it out of the window.

A resource-based estimate will deal quite separately with the different cost components of labour, plant, materials, and subcontractors, rather than amalgamating them into a series of "all-in" rates as is the quantity surveyor's custom. It will also require the site organisation to be determined and priced.

The estimator's main concern will be with the structure of the building, including excavation, and also the integration of engineering services with the structure, since these will largely determine the site organisation and the contract period. He may well be looking at alternative configurations as well as alternative means of obtaining the same configuration.

Materials present few problems, since unlike labour and plant their cost is reasonably related to the quantities of finished work. Anybody preparing a resource-based estimate will, therefore, have to start off by measuring (or assuming) quantities of finished work in order to determine material requirements and also as a first step in looking at the scale of the project and the distribution and inter-relation of its parts. The person doing this will tend to work in bulk quantities (e.g. cubic metres of concrete) split into categories and locations which seem to him to be organisationally significant. Before he can proceed much further however, he will need to prepare an outline programme for the works.

Resource programming techniques

The estimator, in respect of each different estimate, will need to decide the principal operations to be undertaken and their methodology and duration. The operations cannot be considered in isolation since they will be inter-related by two factors:

(i) The need to use labour and plant effectively, so that neither men nor machines stand idle for long periods between tasks, nor are required to be working in two different places at once, nor spend too much time moving from one part of the site to another.

(ii) The inescapable sequence of building, so that, for example, the walls and columns cannot be built until the foundations are completed, and the first floor cannot be placed until the ground floor walls and columns have been built.

There are various techniques in common use to assist him in this task, which tend to rely in the first instance upon graphic methods.

The traditional method is the "bar chart". On this chart a horizontal time scale is used, often divided into weeks, and the various operations comprising the project are listed vertically down the left-hand side. The timing and duration of each operation is then indicated by a horizontal bar spanning the relevant period of weeks and shown on the same line as the operation it refers to. An example is shown in Fig. 14.1 and it will be seen that the bars follow the classic pattern of moving diagonally from the top left-hand to the bottom right-hand of the chart.

The bar chart is simple and easy to follow. It gives quite a good

WEEK	1	2	3	4	5	6	7	8	9	10	11	12	13	14	15	16	17	18	19	20	21	22	23	24	25
Site preparation	▬																								
Excavation		▬	▬																						
Concrete in foundations				▬																					
Brickwork					▬	┅	┅	▬	▬																
G.F. concrete								▬																	
Ist F. concrete						▬	▬																		
Roof trusses & carcassing										▬	▬														
Roof coverings												▬	▬												
Joinery 1st fixings					▬	▬	▬	▬	▬	▬	▬														
Joinery 2nd fixings															▬	▬	▬	▬	▬						
Plastering												▬	▬	▬	▬										
Floor finishes																▬	▬	▬	▬	▬					
Plumbing										▬	┅	┅	┅	┅	┅	┅	▬	▬							
Elec.					▬	┅	┅	┅	┅	┅	┅	┅	┅	┅	▬	▬	▬	▬	▬	▬	▬				
Painting																	▬	▬	▬	▬	▬	▬	▬		
Drainage					▬	┅	┅	┅	▬	▬	┅	┅	▬	▬											

FIG. 14.1. *A bar chart*

picture of the way in which the various operations fit into the total contract period and is very popular on building sites for the purpose of monitoring progress and forward ordering. It is, however, a better communication tool than a planning tool; it does not help in determining the duration of operations (it cannot be drawn until this is decided) nor does it bring their interdependence, or otherwise, to the notice of the planner. It tends to show the results of planning which has been undertaken by other means.

At one time these other means were usually informal, but in present-day practice the network diagram is commonly used. "Network diagram" is a generic term and also includes "precedence diagrams" and "critical path diagrams", which are special uses.

The network consists of a series of nodes joined together by lines or arrows, and normally moves from a start at the left-hand end to a finish on the right. In one system (Fig. 14.2), the lines or arrows represent

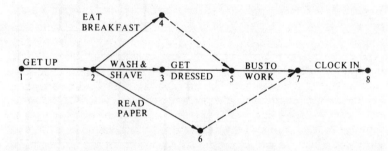

FIG. 14.2. *Simple "arrow = operation" network to illustrate going to work in the morning. Each node represents the beginning or end of an operation. Note the need for dummy (dotted) arrows. You cannot catch the bus to work until you have dressed and had breakfast. The paper need not be read until the bus ride.*

operations (or activities) and the nodes represent the interdependencies which occur at their start and finish; a network prepared in this manner has the advantage that it may be drawn to scale with the lines or arrows of a length proportionate to their time requirements, and can develop into something that is almost as easy to read as a traditional bar chart. However, this option is open to the same objection—that it cannot be drawn until the durations are known, and that once drawn, it is very difficult to amend if durations change during the progress of the work. It is really a bit of a halfway house. The system generally is open to the objection that it can be difficult to follow, particularly as it is usually necessary to draw a number of "dummy" arrows in order to close the network, and there is always a tendency to see the length of the arrows as having some significance even if they are not drawn to scale.

FIG. 14.3. *The same "project" on the "node = operation" system. The arrows simply indicate precedences. Note that in neither case does the diagram mean that breakfast is eaten whilst washing and dressing, simply that it is not essential for you to be dressed before eating—you might have your breakfast first. Similarly, the paper need not be opened until you get on the bus, but you have the option of looking at it at any time after you rise.*

For planning purposes, the alternative approach is to be preferred (Fig. 14.3) in which the nodes represent the activities and the lines or arrows joining them simply illustrate dependencies. The nodes are usually drawn in the form of sequentially numbered circles which are large enough to contain some numeric information; the length of the lines joining them is of no significance and is chosen arbitrarily to suit a clear layout of the diagram. The diagram can thus be drawn without any idea of the length of time which any operation will take and in this form reflects the earliest planning stage, in which the planner is identifying those operations which fundamentally depend upon each other and those which do not. Once this has been done it will never need to be redrawn (unless the project itself alters); any changes will be made only to the numeric information within the nodes.

A simple network in an unquantified form is simply a "precedence diagram", showing which operations must precede which. No operation can take place until all operations arrowed into it have been completed. Remember, on a building project, it is fundamental construction dependence which counts and not convenience or the efficient use of resources, which are considered at a second stage.

Two important points are worth noting. Firstly, the network can be expanded to include not merely the construction but also the whole of the planning and design process and can thus become a tool in the hands of the client's professional representatives, particularly useful where overall time requirements are important or where design and construction are to run in parallel on a management, design-and-build, or fast-track contract.

Secondly, the operations may be shown at a strategic level ("build walls") or at a much more detailed level ("build ground floor external walls", "build in sills and lintels", and so on). For eventual control purposes a fully detailed network may be used, but this is expensive to prepare and would be inappropriate at planning stage, before the actual detailed design has been finalised. On the other hand, a simple "planning" network cannot show the interdependence of meshing operations. For instance, if erection of precast beams can commence after only some of the columns have been completed this would require the work to each group (or even pair) of columns to be shown as separate operations. This problem occurs throughout the project, but at planning stage is only likely to be considered in those parts which the planner feels to be of crucial importance—probably major structural work rather than finishes.

Once the network has been drawn and the precedences and dependencies settled it is time to quantify the problem. The procedures are sufficiently standardised for there to be a number of computer packages available, and the work then entails filling in the estimated durations on a schedule, but if manual methods are being used a suitable method is to mark durations in the node circles which are divided into four quadrants for the purpose of quantification (see Fig. 14.4). In the

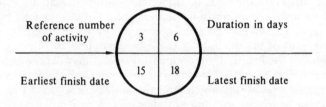

FIG. 14.4. *Activity node (showing division into quadrants for reference)*

top left-hand quadrant is written the reference number of the operation concerned (full description of the operation probably being written out in a numbered list) and in the top right-hand quadrant the estimated duration in days, weeks, or whatever unit is being used.

When all the individual durations have been inserted the total project time can be calculated. Beginning at the "start" and working along the arrows the shortest possible elapsed time to the completion of each operation is inserted in the bottom left-hand quadrant. This is arrived at by adding the duration of the operation concerned to the highest elapsed time of any of the other operations which precede it and are therefore arrowed into it. By the time "end" is reached the total time for the project will have been calculated.

In respect of each operation, we will now know the earliest time at which it can be completed. Where the operation concerned is a crucial one this will also be the latest time at which it can be completed if the project as a whole is to be finished on the calculated date. However, many less important operations may be able to be delayed without delaying the completion of the whole project.

In order to identify the crucial operations the bottom right-hand quadrant of each node may be used to show the latest possible date at which the operation can be completed without causing delay. This is calculated by working backwards from the finish and in the case of each operation calculating from the earliest elapsed time of any of the operations which immediately follow it.

When this task is completed it will be found that for some operations the earliest and latest dates for finishing are the same. These are the critical operations, and the sequence of arrows which joins them forms the so-called "critical path" through the project. In the case of a non-critical operation the difference between the earliest and latest finishing date represents the "float", or the period for which that operation can be delayed without affecting the completion date for the project. All these figures can of course be set out in the form of a schedule, instead of on the diagram itself.

It should be noted that if part of the "float" for a particular operation is actually utilised this may affect the float available for succeeding operations. If all the float is used up then the operation, and its successors, will have become critical and the critical path will have changed. It is, therefore, necessary for the project controller throughout the progress of the job to keep a close eye on operations with a very small float, as well as those which are already on the critical path.

Resource smoothing

There may well be two or more operations in a network which do not depend upon each other in the construction sequence—for example, foundation excavation and drainage trenches. It will not matter which is done first, and they could in theory be done simultaneously (whereas the foundation excavations and the concreting of them could not). However, their relative timing may depend upon resource utilisation. To dig the foundation and drainage trenches simultaneously would involve bringing an unnecessary number of diggers to the site, whilst to leave several weeks between the two operations would either involve machines standing idle or else taking them away and bringing them back. If both operations were on critical or near-critical paths then the additional expenditure would have to be accepted (or the time for the job altered), but otherwise their floats would be adjusted to give a more economical end-on sequence. The adjustment of a programme in this way to make the best use of expensive plant, and to give gangs of men a consistent and balanced work pattern, is an important part of the exercise, and is often called "resource smoothing".

Use of techniques in relation to design cost planning

As already explained, the cost planner who is intending to use resource-based methods will need to start off with some idea of the configuration of the proposed building—its size, shape, height, and preferred technology. He may well suggest a suitable combination of these requirements, based on systems already rationalised in his organisation and which he knows can be built quickly and efficiently, and for some types of development (e.g. industrial premises) this could be a valid approach. Alternatively, he may begin with a solution proposed by the architect, test it in terms of resource use, and then investigate alternatives.

At this stage he will be principally concerned with those things which he can identify as major time constraints and production cost constraints, by using the skills derived from his experience. He will be looking for a solution which gives effective use of labour and equipment by providing smooth and continuous work-flows, and which enables the most economical type of plant to be used. For example, if one single heavy component has to be lifted at the extreme reach of the tower crane this will dictate a much heavier and more expensive type of crane to buy and run, probably for the whole duration of the contract. The crane "cycle" will also dictate the intervals at which components, or skips of wet concrete, can be lifted into position, which in turn may determine the size of gang and the method of working. Alternatively, an efficient method of working may require a different cranage configuration to that first thought of. In turn, formwork usage will have to be considered and the concreting programme planned to allow for optimum reuse, with sufficient time allowed for any necessary alterations. This is where the builder may look for savings, for example, by keeping column sections constant all the way up the building, as he may decide that the cost of the extra material required in the upper storeys will be more than saved on labour, plant, and formwork. Decisions of this kind can often only be made in the light of the actual construction programme which is envisaged, and whether site-mixed or ready-mixed concrete is to be used.

The Property Services Agency of the DOE in the UK has produced an inter-active computer system (COCO) on an experimental basis, which is intended to assist a cost planner in making the right cost decisions on some of these matters, although this does not appear to have emerged from the experimental stage.

A further matter to be considered is the staffing of the site, and the number and type of supervisory and control staff.

The builder will also be very concerned, even at an early estimating stage, with the integration of the engineering services work with the construction programme. Some of this integration concerns the way in

which the various contractors will have to work together, as the installation of pipes, conduits, and components may be incorporated into
the design in a way which means that they will interfere with the
builder's own work sequence. He will also be on the look-out for major
items of equipment whose placing may cause difficulties. Equally he
will want to know whether, and if so when, he can use the permanent
engineering facilities for the purposes of his own work—lighting,
toilets, and passenger and goods lifts in particular. The duration of the
complete project, and of major stages in it, will have a most substantial
effect on plant, supervisory, and establishment costs, and this duration
may in the end be determined as much by service sub-contract requirements as by his own work. In highly serviced buildings in fact these may
be the prime determinant.

Resource-based estimates of this kind are certainly no cheaper to
prepare than a quantity surveyor's elemental estimate. Much the same
sequence will therefore be employed:

(1) Strategic estimates taking account of major factors only, often
those which are of importance in a comparison between alternative schemes. A resource-use plan at this level may also be
used in the preparation of a competitive tender based upon Bills
of Quantities.

(2) A detailed production plan and estimate, probably incorporating a full critical-path network. This would be intended for use
as a production control document, and would be unlikely to be
prepared until the design itself had been finalised and until the
builder was expecting to be chosen to construct it. It would
almost certainly involve consultation with major sub-
contractors, and the use of a computer package.

(3) Real-time cost control based upon the detailed estimate.

Cost control on a resource basis

As with real-time cost control on any other basis this fundamentally
depends upon swift and reliable reporting of what is actually happening, and the rapid reconciliation of this with the control document.

The cost controller will be concerned with two different aspects:

(i) The overall time programme for the project. The preparation of
the network will have involved a large number of assumptions
about the time to be taken by the various activities, and revisions must be made in the light of actual progress. In this
context it is only the activities on the critical or near-critical
paths which have to be considered, but any subtantial change
(for better or worse) may cause a change in the critical path
itself and in the duration of the works. Decisions will then have

to be made as to whether a different duration is acceptable, or whether the time for remaining activities must be adjusted somehow. In both cases cost will be substantially affected.

(ii) Cost of individual activities. A costing system has three objectives:

    (a) To measure actual expenditure against estimated cost.
    (b) To indicate whether performance needs to be improved.
    (c) To provide feedback which will improve future estimating performance.

Costs are recorded under "cost centres". These can be anything from the whole job to a tiny part of it, but to meet the above objectives costs need to be recorded under headings which can be identified with sections of the estimate, and the estimate in turn needs to be prepared in a suitable format to achieve this. There is a need to establish a level of breakdown which is neither so fine as to make the recording and allocation of labour and material costs unduly detailed, nor so crude that the "cost centres" are too broad to mean anything. Individual Bill of Quantities items are normally at too fine a level, a whole Trade Section would be too crude. A single activity, or a group of activities, from the network is usually a suitable basis.

Costing of site work has two main difficulties which distinguish it from normal production costing as practised in factories and as described in most text-books on costing, and they both spring from the one-off nature of most of the work (both in terms of the finished product and the conditions under which it is produced).

The first is that the usual system of "standard costs" does not really apply. A standard cost is an ascertained cost of carrying out an operation which can then be built into an estimating system, and which should normally be achieved in future—any substantial deviation requiring to be investigated. Machining operations in a wood-working shop can be costed on this basis—once a standard sequence of events has been carried out on a machine a number of times (inserting the work, operating on it, withdrawing it) there is no reason why the same operation should not always cost exactly the same in the future. Site operations are not only less standardised than this, but the position of the work, weather conditions, etc., varies continuously. It is very difficult to get a sufficient run of identical work to establish standard costs and still have enough similar work ahead to make it worthwhile to apply them. Certainly it is not usually possible to apply such data from job to job, as a joinery works or engineering works would do.

The second problem concerns the difficulty of actually recording and processing costs of labour and materials. When men are dispersed about the site it is almost impossible to record accurately what they are doing except in fairly general terms, unless a quite unacceptably expensive staff is engaged for the purpose. Many sophisticated costing systems have failed through the time sheets being filled in on a Friday afternoon in the foreman's office from memory.

Materials to some extent are an equal problem, as nothing like a factory control system is operated on most sites when materials are drawn from stock. The invoice is often the main weapon in materials cost control, so it is convenient if the cost centres are sufficiently large and identifiable for particular purchases to be identified with them. However, some contractors' systems do not bother overmuch about materials, since as we have already seen, these are much less liable than labour and plant costs to deviate from estimate, given a reasonable level of management. This is another advantage, from the contractor's point of view, of not using "all-in" rates.

This may sound very defeatist—difficulties exist to be overcome, not to be excused. They can indeed be overcome, but except in some limited circumstances (such as repetitive house-building) nobody has found that the cost and trouble of doing this has produced economically worthwhile results, because of the difficulty of deriving "standard costs" from the data for reuse. All one is likely to get is an expensive post-mortem report.

A further point to remember is that some of the people on a site, particularly labourers, are doing work which has to be done but which may not have been identified as an operation in the network—sweeping up, carrying odd materials, attending on the Clerk of Works.

It is, therefore, preferable to use fairly broad cost-centres "fixing formwork to second-storey", and devote one's attention to getting the feed-back rapidly and with a fair degree of reliability. It should then be possible to measure actual expenditure against estimated cost with reasonable accuracy, and also to a somewhat lesser extent fulfil the other two objectives of a costing system.

In the reconciliation of costs and estimate, the difficulties concerning inflation, and alterations to the scope of the work, which were mentioned in the previous chapter will again be encountered, although the former problem can be minimised by working in man-hours and machine-hours, rather than money, for comparison purposes. A contractor's costing system will in any case need to highlight the cost of alterations, because very often they will form an extra to be charged to the client. It will also be necessary to ensure that the cost performance of sub-contractors is kept up-to-date in order to arrive at the projected total for the job, complicated by the fact that these may often be on a price, rather than a cost-reimbursement, basis.

Chapter 15
Further Cost Modelling Techniques

Introduction

In Chapter 7 the concept of a building cost model was introduced and we looked at the way in which simple traditional cost models had developed, which allowed the quantity surveyor to improve his forecasting ability. At the same time their deficiencies were noted and we put forward a list of criteria for judging cost models. In this chapter it is intended to take this idea a step further and look at the possibilities of adopting other models, now being extensively used in other disciplines in the search for better cost information. Some of these models involve the use of statistical terminology, and these terms are defined in Appendix C for those readers who may not be familiar with them.

When we refer to better cost information what do we really mean? There are probably four major ways in which it is possible to advance. We can:

(i) Provide cost information *quicker.*
(ii) Provide *more* information so that a more informed decision can be made.
(iii) Provide *more reliable* cost information which will introduce more assurance into the decision-making process.
(iv) Provide information *at an earlier stage in the design process.*

By harnessing the power of modelling techniques it is hoped that each of these objectives can be achieved, or at least a step will have been taken to improve the chances of achieving them. However, the techniques on their own are unlikely to provide a very great advancement. The time involved in manual calculation and organisation inevitably means that only a very few alternative possibilities for a design can be explored. If a giant leap in cost knowledge is to occur, then it would appear that non-manual methods are essential. Of the methods available to us today the micro-processor appears to hold the major potential for advancement. For a lower cost than that of employing one man for a month in an office, it is possible to purchase a machine that will perform vast quantities of calculation a great number of times, and thus explore situations and possibilities which would be quite inaccessible if we were restricted to using manual methods. Future development is likely to make the above cost comparison even more favourable.

However, these machines have their own language and organisation and it is essential for any proposed use of the machine that its structure, constraints, and communication are well understood. These factors will affect its efficient use and, therefore, its profitablity. In the context of modelling, the model itself should be constructed in such a way that unnecessary calculations are not undertaken, and the memory store of the machine is not overloaded with unnecessary word information. Strings of alpha characters can gobble up store, and slow down processing, at an alarming rate.

It is envisaged in this chapter that some form of computer will be used with the models to speed the calculations. The traditional models evolved in the way that they did because it was expected that manual labour would be employed to do the calculations, which resulted in an over-simplification of the models, at all levels, for the sake of expediency. A new view of what is needed in terms of cost information, without reference to the constraints of manual computation, is required if the full potential of the new technology is to be tapped for the benefit of the design team.

It is not possible to explore every type of model in a book of this nature. The approach will be to look at the classification, the principles behind the construction of the more important types, and the potential use, of models.

When should cost models be used?

The simple answer to this question is that models should be used at all stages of the design and construction process. However, the particular interest of this book is in the cost planning of buildings and, therefore, the early forecasting and subsequent control of building cost. In Chapter 6 it was noted that probably 80% of the cost of a building had been committed before even the sketch design had been produced. This suggests that the major scope for modelling is to improve the flow of cost information at the stage prior to production of the scheme design. It is interesting to note that John Southwell, when a RICS Research Fellow at Bath University, suggested that an extra stage be introduced into the RIBA Plan of Work (see Chapter 6, page 83). Between "Inception" and "Feasibility" stages, he saw the need for what he called a "Viability" stage. This was defined as "that period when a cost forecast may be required, but where no sketches of the building layout are available". Feasibility is then defined as "that stage when some form of elementary sketch layout is available, and the design team are therefore evaluating a definite proposal". This is a useful concept as it allows a separate category for those techniques which attempt to give information based on abstract hypostheses (from which a cost strategy for design may be developed), and those techniques which take the result of a strategy in the form of a tentative proposal, and carry out an evaluation of that specific suggested design.

When a cost model is being developed it is nearly always constructed to be as universal as possible, so that it can be applied to a large number of cost situations and building forms. The basis of the model is therefore nearly always an abstract hypothesis which is made real or firm by the application of quantities and costs to its parameters.

Parameter can be defined as "a quantity which is constant in a particular case considered, but which varies in different cases". Each hypothesis, therefore, may involve the application of different quantities to a set of parameters which will themselves probably remain the same. It can be argued that the basic principles of any building cost model should be found in the simple models constructed before a design has been produced, and that any further development is merely a refinement of those principles into a more detailed model. To simplify this introduction, the models will be kept as straightforward as possible without detailed refinements, and will be orientated towards giving advice at the very early stages of the design process.

Classification of models

There are a large number of ways of classifying models. For example, classification may take place according to the function they perform, e.g. evaluating, descriptive, analytical, optimising, etc. On the other hand it may be according to the form of construction, e.g. iconic (physical representation of the item under consideration), analogue (where one set of properties is chosen to represent the properties of another set, for example, electricity to represent heat flow), or symbolic (where the components of what is represented and their interrelationships are given by symbols). The last is perhaps the more useful structure, but the definition lacks clarity as all models are to some extent symbols of the actual commodity under consideration.

In some ways it matters very little to which system or set the model belongs so long as the overall purpose and construction are well understood. Perhaps the most important knowledge concerning any model is an understanding of its limitations within the context of its use. Every model user should have a very clear idea of what the model is measuring, the data upon which it is based, and the factors that need to be applied to the results before a decision can be made.

A useful system for representing the role of models in the decision-making process is given below:

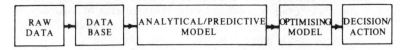

RAW DATA	DATA BASE	ANALYTICAL/PREDICTIVE MODEL	OPTIMISING MODEL	DECISION/ ACTION

The process is as as follows:

(i) Raw data is collected on cost and its relationship to design variables.

(ii) The data is analysed and synthesized according to the requirements of the cost models that are to be used. The data is also arranged for quick access, updating, and use.

(iii) Analytical and predictive models are then used to explore cost situations and changes in the design variables.

(iv) Optimising models are used to select the best alternatives from the results of the previous models, based on criteria determined by the design team. It is extremely difficult to optimise in building design for reasons already given in Chapter 6. Even the optimisation of future and initial costs based on static assumptions of use is difficult because of the problems of cost prediction. To take into account aesthetics, comfort, efficiency, flexibility, etc., as well would be impossible (at least in any meaningful way) at the present time.

For this reason the models included are largely of the analytical type, which allow comparison between alternatives from a cost point of view. It is not proposed to deal with models that attempt to forecast the effect of, say, government and international decisions on the construction market, and, therefore, upon its price levels, as these are not yet sufficiently developed.

Three examples of primarily analytical models have been chosen which, it is felt, are likely to be typical of the major applications of models of the immediate future. These are as follows:

(1) *Causal or empirical models.* These are symbolic models which, in our case, are based on relationships between the design variables and cost, and which have been derived from observation and experiment. In previous chapters we have already seen that the quantity surveyor has been using a symbolic language to represent a building for a number of years, even from the very beginning of his professional existence, namely dimensions and descriptions. In the process of time this language has been refined and standardised and has allowed subsets of the language to be developed such as cost per square metre, elemental unit rates, etc. It is a small step therefore to translate

this language into a general algebraic form relating to the morphology of the building and its components, to which cost factors can then be applied. By changing the value of the algebraic terms according to the requirements of a particular building, the change in cost related to the design variables such as shape and height can be discovered.

(2) *Regression models.* In the empirical model it is usually assumed that there is a fixed relationship between the design variable and cost, and that the cost factor applied to the algebraic formula is constant. However, in the social sciences, and particularly where human performance is involved, exact relationships are not generally observed. Instead statistical relationships prevail, and only average relationships may be observed among the variables. Trends may be detected through the data that has been analysed and it may therefore be possible to determine a trend algebraically, and allow an estimate of cost to be made, knowing one or more of the design variables. A regression model is a method of determining the relationship between variables by the "method of least squares" which seeks to minimise the sum of the squares of the difference between the observed values and the predicted values. For example by knowing the shape, height, or other variable of a particular building type we may, through this technique, be able to forecast the cost of the building more reliably than by using one of the traditional single-price methods.

(3) *Monte Carlo simulation.* The problems that exist in forecasting the future or even investigating the enormous number of combinations of shapes, specifications, and use of buildings make it a task that cannot be completely solved by a simple mathematical expression. Some other technique is almost certainly required that will allow us to sample a large number of possible solutions to discover the best solution in that sample, and the range of costs that could be expected given the known probability of an event or cost occuring. The Monte Carlo technique is simply a way of sampling from a distribution, or distributions, in a random manner to provide a range of solutions which may be directed to finding the best solution (or simply to establish the range of possible solutions available). What is attempted by the method is to simulate a series of future events (production on site, maintenance characteristics of components, operating costs of buildings) or the design of a number of buildings. In doing so it may use causal or regression models to provide the forecast of cost for the sample it has chosen.

Causal or empirical models

In terms of building cost causal models are in some ways just a refinement of traditional estimating techniques. If instead of measuring up a building and applying a unit rate to the derived quantities of each component we express the building in algebraic terms, then we can give values to those algebraic terms, apply cost coefficients and arrive at a cost estimate.

Let us take a very simple rectangular building as one example. We shall only look at the major structural elements and to retain simplicity we shall ignore the thicknesses of walls and slabs. (In a working model these would need to be accounted for if they are cost significant.) Figure 15.1 shows the physical form of the model, but of course any realistic value can be given to each of the buildings dimensions. Let us approach the model in elemental form and deal with each element in turn.

FIG. 15.1. *Physical form of causal model example*

(a) *Sub-structure*

To express this element in algebraic format we need to consider the cost significant components which need to be represented, together with their most suitable method of measurement. Let us assume that from our observation and experience these are discovered to be:

(i) *The ground floor slab.* The cost of this component can be considered to be a function of the ground floor plan area. The algebraic equation is therefore:

$$\text{Area of slab} = l \times w.$$

To this equation must be applied a cost factor (CF_1) related to the cost per square metre of ground floor slab including additional items such as reduced level excavation and hardcore, which relate to this particular horizontal measurement. Already it can be seen that approximations and assumptions are creeping in to prevent the model becoming too complex.

$$\text{Cost of slab} = l \times w \times CF_1.$$

(ii) *The perimeter strip foundation.* The cost of this component is a function of its total length. The cost factor (CF_2) for this item would include for excavation, concrete, brickwork, etc.

Length of strip foundations $= 2 \times (l + w)$.
Cost of strip foundations $= (2 \times (l + w)) \times CF_2$.

(iii) *The bases for the frame.* If an average bay length (B_L) is assumed together with the average bay width (B_w) then a formula can be given as follows:

$$\text{Number of bases } (k) = \left(\frac{l}{B_L} + 1\right) \times \left(\frac{w}{B_w} + 1\right)$$

The value of the expressions (l/B_L) and (w/B_w) would probably be taken up to the next whole number to achieve an integer number of bays. This could easily be done by the machine if the model is computerised. The cost factor (CF_3) to be applied would include for soil conditions, loading, etc., that would affect the size of each base and would allow for excavation, concrete, reinforcement, etc., that would relate to this size.

$$\text{Cost of bases} = \left(\frac{l}{B_L} + 1\right) \times \left(\frac{w}{B_w} + 1\right) \times CF_3.$$

The total cost of foundations would therefore be the sum of these three expressions.

This type of build-up is summarised below for the remainder of the major components; these are taken in an unfamiliar order because some elements are dependent on the results from the calculation of another, e.g. area of solid external wall is dependent on area of windows. In a real computerised system a more familiar order could be adopted, either within the program itself or by simply printing the results in a different order from that used for calculation.

(b) *Window*

Height (h) $= (S_1 + S_2 + S_3) + d$.

Window area (WA) $= 2 \times (l + w) \times (h - d) \times (g/100)$.

Window cost $= WA \times CW_1$.

Where g $=$ percentage of external wall to be glazed.

CW_1 $=$ cost per unit area of windows.

WA $=$ window area.

(c) *External wall*

External wall cost $= ((2 \times (l + w) \times h) - WA) \times CE_1$.

Where $CE_1 =$ cost per unit area of external wall.

(d) *Roof*

Roof cost $= (l \times w \times CR_1) + (2 \times (l + w) \times CR_2)$.

Where $CR_1 =$ cost per unit area of roof.

$CR_2 =$ cost per unit length of perimeter detail.

(e) *Upper floor*

Upper floor cost $= (l \times w) \times (N - 1) \times CU_1$.

Where $N =$ the number of storeys.

$CU_1 =$ cost per unit area of upper floor.

(f) *Frame*

(i) Column cost $= h \times k \times CS_1$.

Where $k =$ number of column bases (see sub-structure).

$CS_1 =$ cost per unit length of column.

(ii) Beam cost $=$

$$N \times \left[l \times \left(\frac{w}{B_w} + 1 \right) \right] + \left[w \times \left(\frac{l}{B_L} + 1 \right) \right] \times CS_2.$$

Where (w/B_w) and (l/B_L) are rounded up to the next whole number.

$CS_2 =$ cost per unit length of beam.

(g) *Staircases*

Total rise in metres $= h - (S_1 + d)$.

No. of staircases $= \dfrac{l \times w}{f}$.

Where f is the maximum floor area to be served by each staircase and the result of ($l \times w$)/(f) is rounded up to the next whole number.

Staircase cost $= [h - (S_1 + d)] \times \dfrac{l \times w}{f} \times CV_1$.

Where CV_1 = cost per unit rise of staircase.
(*Note:* It has been assumed that there is no staircase from the top floor to the roof.)

The above elements have been given to illustrate the build-up of an empirical model in algebraic terms. The rest of the building would continue in a similar way. Services would present a major problem but heating cost could be made a function of external envelope, "*U*" value and building volume; lighting could be a function of lighted area; and plumbing and sanitary services could be a function of the number of sanitary appliances required. Preliminaries (i.e. supervision, plant, etc.) would be more difficult to forecast except as a percentage addition. However, with some research it may be possible to identify how these costs vary with changes in building, shape, specification, and area so that a simple model could be included.

Obviously a great deal of simplification has taken place and some very broad assumptions made. No account has been taken of the interrelationships between elements, and specification has been ignored except as a function of the cost factor applied to each formula. In practice, models of this type require fine tuning to ensure that they are sufficiently reliable for the point in the design process at which they will be applied. The cost information would probably come from the experience of the quantity surveyor, from an office data bank or from a manufacturer. The principles of the model would no doubt evolve over time as the user became more experienced in its operation and realised its shortcomings. It is also unlikely that a universal model for all building types could be achieved, as the quantity of various elements (e.g. stairs) would vary with the use and regulations pertaining to the particular type of building under consideration.

The great advantage of this particular model is the flexibility available in its use. By changing the length and width in our example it is possible to vary the area of accommodation of the building. In addition, different glazing ratios and different bay sizes can be assumed. If the cost data is held in the store of the computer used for modelling, the process of exploration can be automatic with the machine's program altering the design variables to suit the possibilities that exist. If instead of using length and width we convert this to a universal plan shape index (see Chapter 16) then we can explore irregularly-shaped buildings.

The problems associated with the model are largely those facing the traditional estimating methods, and in particular, elemental estimates using elemental unit rates. These problems have been documented elsewhere in this book but it is worth reminding ourselves that one of the major problems of elemental estimating is choosing which cost factor is to be applied to the elemental unit quantity. The problem still

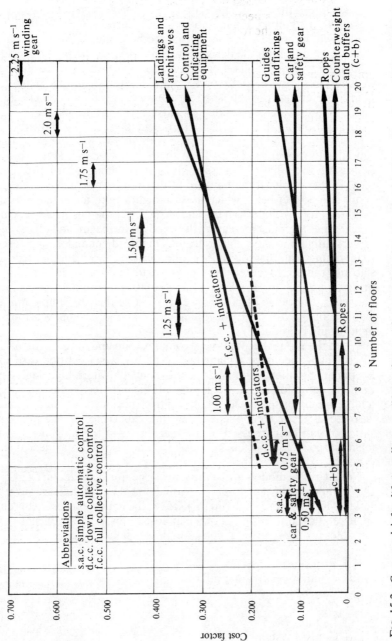

The Comparative Cost of Components and their Fabrication for a Given Number of Floors

FIG 15.2. *Cost model for lift installations. (Note: this graph was originally prepared in 1974 when the actual cost could be determined by multiplying the cost factor by £10000.)*

exists in this model. However, provided that the right cost relationship exists between the components, that the cost factors do not themselves change with quantity, and that the costs are fairly reasonable, then the model will allow realistic comparisons to be made. If these comparisons are made within the design constraints then it should be possible to identify (providing all other factors are equal) which of the alternatives tested by the model represents the least cost. In this manner a point of reference is established for comparison with any other selection, and a step has been taken towards providing better value.

In addition to the cost factor problem there is the difficulty of representing a building in algebraic format. In our example, large simplifications were made to keep the formula simple. However, in reality the size, shape, and assembly of the building is far more complex. For example, if the bay size of the frame was changed it might result in a deeper beam which in turn might result in a greater storey height, a larger volume to heat, and so on. The repercussions would be much larger than just increasing the depth of the beam, and this would be very difficult to show algebraically. On the other hand the increased span might mean that it is more economical to choose another type of slab or frame altogether! It is possible to build into the computer program a check to see whether an alternative is a better proposition. However, the range of possibilities is so large that the simple model would soon have difficulty in coping, and a far more complex arrangement would be required.

When the model becomes very complex then updating, particularly of cost data, becomes a giant task. There is a very strong case for keeping the model as simple as possible and allowing a high degree of human interaction with the computer. If the user acts as the data bank and manipulates the choice of alternative specifications, and in some cases the size of components, then the experience of the quantity surveyor can be harnessed to the machine, and the judgement that makes a good estimate is not lost or handed over to a mechanical process.

Not all causal models are of the same structure. Take for an example the lift model shown in graphical form in Fig. 15.2. In this case several tenders for lifts were analysed to discover the important cost items and their relationship to one another in cost terms. The significant cost variables for the type of lift considered were taken to be:

   (i) Rope cost.
  (ii) Counterweight and buffers.
 (iii) Car cost.
 (iv) Guides and fixings.
  (v) Landings and architraves.
 (vi) Control system.

Costs were allocated under each of these headings by Mr R. Wiles, a student at Bristol Polytechnic in 1974, who followed the pattern of Messrs Knight and Duck in 1962. The tendency was for each component of the model to be linear in respect to the major variable of number of storeys served by the lift. (The linear trends could be produced by using regression analysis as described later). Although the tendency was linear this did not mean that the trends were continuous, and if you look at the winding gear in particular you see "jumps" or "thresholds" where the cost rises disproportionately to the number of storeys due to the increased speed required for efficient operation. In the same way the linear relationships of the control system costs are only applicable over a certain range, and moving from one control system to another produces a dramatic rise or fall in cost. To operate the original model in order to discover the cost of a lift it was simply necessary to add up the component costs above the number of storeys shown on the x-axis. The car size was assumed to be for eight people but could be increased in size at a special "extra over" cost per person.

However, for this edition of the book we have translated these costs into comparative cost factors to show only the relationship. In a working model the actual costs would be used as in the original.

It is a simple matter to computerise the working of a model such as this. Each component can be expressed algebraically by the formula for a straight line $y = a + bx$ (a = intercept, b = the slope of the line, x = the number of storeys, and y = the cost of the component). If the program logic is used to select when a particular type of component is suitable then it is a simple matter for the computer to total the cost of all components it has selected and give the overall lift cost. If the prevailing National Association of Lift Manufacturer's index is then applied to the total, a reasonable current figure for the lift cost should be obtained.

However, there is a problem in using historic cost relationships to generate the equations, because the trends may change over time and the application of a cost index to the results may not reflect the current situation. A model of this type would need to be revised, by repeating the analysis procedure, about every three years, and this revision may well be a time-consuming procedure. In fact, if the model is not used very often the cost of writing and frequently updating the programs could exceed the cost of manual working.

In these circumstances it is a better proposition to express the relationships in terms of labour, plant, and material costs required for manufacture and fixing, in other words "resources". Any difference in the inflation rates will then be accounted for by the new resource costs that would be fed directly into a revised computer program. However, it is not always easy to find the resource costs, especially for engineering services, and in the case of the lift, historic cost data had to be used.

Regression models

Equations are used in mathematics to express the relationships among variables. Very often there are "exact" relationships from which "exact" values can be obtained when the equation has been solved. A familiar example is the formula for the perimeter of a circle which is normally given as twice the radius multiplied by pi. The results from this formula are considered to be accurate for any change in the value of the radius. In the symbolic model previously described, the derived formulae representing the building were assumed to be exact for the purposes of obtaining a result. However, it was recognised that broad assumptions had been made in the construction of the equations and that the unit costs to be applied were themselves subject to considerable variability.

This inherent variability is due in some measure to the fact that human performance has to be estimated to arrive at the unit cost, and this is not only very difficult to forecast but is unlikely to be consistent. In the social sciences exact relationships are not generally observed among the variables, but rather statistical relationships prevail. Average relationships may be observed, but these average relationships do not provide a basis for perfect predictions. For example the labour "constants" used in contractors' estimating are guides obtained from experience and do not represent the actual time for completing a particular job. The actual time taken to complete a specific operation may be the result of a large number of factors including the incentive scheme offered, the location of the task, the degree of supervision and even the problems in the operative's home! Where relationships exist between a known performance or cost, and the major variables that explain why that performance or cost has occurred, then it may be possible to explain those relationships in the form of a mathematical expression. This expression can then be used to forecast future performance or cost, knowing the values assigned to the explanatory variables. A large number of examples of relationships can be quoted which apply to building cost such as the relationship of the cost of preliminaries to time, the relationship of the cost of heating installation to envelope area and U value, and the relationship of the cost of windows to area and shape. It may not always be possible to produce a reliable mathematical expression, or indeed to identify all the significant cost variables, but an improvement in estimating technique may be available nevertheless.

Regression analysis is a method by which estimates are made of the value of a variable (e.g. cost) from a knowledge of the values of one or more other variables (e.g. height and shape of building), and the errors involved in this estimating process measured. In its simplest form it describes the relationship between two variables by computing a straight line through the data obtained. This is known as "two-variable linear regression". The factor whose value we wish to estimate (e.g. cost) is referred to as the "dependent variable" and denoted by y. The factor from which these estimates are made is called the "independent variable" and is denoted by x. (Cause and effect is not necessarily implied by the terms "dependent" and "independent".)

In two-variable linear regression the expression for the straight line is of the form

$$y = a + bx$$

where a is the intercept of the line with the y-axis and b is the slope of the line (Fig. 15.3).

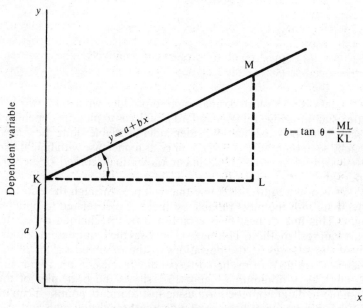

FIG. 15.3. *Formula for a straight line*

To illustrate the use of the technique a hypothetical example has been chosen. It is assumed that there is a relationship between building height and building cost per square metre of floor area. The first step is to establish whether or not a linear relationship exists and this is usually done in simple cases such as this by plotting the data on a graph to allow a visual examination. For the sake of simplicity, data from ten buildings of similar function and construction has been obtained and

this is summarised below. (N.B. In practice this would be an inadequate sample and at least 30 data points should be found for a reliable
result.)

TABLE 11. HYPOTHETICAL EXAMPLE

Building cost related to height

Building	Height in metres	Cost/m² (gross floor area)
A	4	500
B	20	544
C	17	580
D	10	570
E	7	504
F	23	560
G	24	600
H	6	524
I	10	530
J	15	542

This data is now plotted on a graph to produce what is known as a
scatter diagram (Fig. 15.4). Standard practice is to plot the dependent
variable long the y-axis and the independent variable along the x-axis.
It can be seen that there is a trend for costs to increase with height and
that this trend appears to be linear rather than curved or heavily
dispersed.

What is now required is a line that will pass through the data and
provide us with the most reliable estimate of cost related to building
height. This line of best fit is established by a technique called the
"least squares" method. The method imposes the requirement that the
sum of the squares of the deviations of the observed values of the
dependent variable from the corresponding values on the regression
line must be a minimum. Figure 15.5 shows the principles of the
technique in diagrammatic form using just four data points. It can be
seen that a number of lines can be drawn through the data and also
through the average value of x and y (a requirement of the technique)
but only position 3 provides the least squared deviation from the line.
Calculus is used to apply the condition that the sum of the squared
deviations from a straight line must be a minimum and this results in
two equations, one each for a and b in the straight line formula.

$$b = \frac{\Sigma xy - n\bar{x}\bar{y}}{\Sigma x^2 - n\bar{x}^2}$$

$$a = \bar{y} - b\bar{x}$$

where $\bar{x}$ and $\bar{y}$ are the arithmetic means of the x and y variables and n is the number in the sample.

FIG. 15.4 *Scatter diagram*

Position 1

Position 2

Position 3

FIG. 15.5. *The principles of least squares (Note: The smaller squared deviations from the regression line in position 3 makes this the line of best fit)*

Using our previous data in Table 11 the equations can be solved:

Building	x	y	xy	x^2	y^2
A	4	500	2,000	16	250,000
B	20	544	10,880	400	295,936
C	17	580	9,860	289	336,400
D	10	570	5,700	100	324,900
E	7	504	3,528	49	254,016
F	23	560	12,880	529	313,600
G	24	600	14,400	576	360,000
H	6	524	3,144	36	274,576
I	10	530	5,300	100	280,900
J	15	542	8,130	225	293,764
	136	5,454	75,822	2,320	2,984,092

$\bar{x} = 13.6 \quad \bar{y} = 545.4$.

Therefore:

$$b = \frac{75,822 - (10 \times 13.6 \times 545.4)}{2,320 - (10 \times 13.6 \times 13.6)}$$
$$= 3.5$$
$$a = 545.4 - (3.5 \times 13.6)$$
$$= 497.8.$$

Placing these values in the straight line formula ($y = a + bx$) gives us $y = 497.8 + 3.5x$ and, this can now be plotted on the scatter diagram (Fig. 15.6).

A test can now be employed to discover the measure of the degree of association between the two variables, i.e. how well they are correlated. The measure usually adopted for this purpose is the "sample coefficient of determination" (r^2) which is given by the following formula:

$$r^2 = 1 - \frac{\Sigma(y_E - y_A)^2}{\Sigma(y_E - \bar{y}_E)^2}$$

where y_A is the actual value of the sample data and y_E is the estimated value using the regression line.

The sample coefficient of determination may be interpreted as the proportion of variation in the dependent variable y that has been accounted for or explained by the variation in x. It is therefore a very useful assessment of how closely the regression equation fits the data. In our case this will mean how well it predicts the value of the cost per square metre of the building, given its height.

Calculation of this expression can be quite tedious without a standard computer package and, therefore, short cut methods have been devised for manual or self-programing use. One such formula using the values of a and b already calculated is:

$$r^2 = \frac{a\Sigma y + b\Sigma xy - n\bar{y}^2}{\Sigma y^2 - n\bar{y}^2}$$

[Source: Hamburg, M., *Basic Statistics* (Harcourt, Brace and Jovanovich Inc.)]

FIG. 15.6. *Scatter diagram (showing straight line of best fit)*

By using this formula very little additional information needs to be found which has not already been included in the table to find a and b. Therefore, using the previous data in the formula we get:

$$r^2 = \frac{(497.8 \times 5,454) + (3.5 \times 75,822) - (10 \times (545.4)^2)}{2,984,092 - (10 \times (545.4)^2)}$$

$$= 0.61$$

In other words approximately 60% of the total variation in the dependent variable is explained by the relationships between y and x expressed in the regression line.

The coefficient of determination estimates the proportion of the variation which the dependent variable shares with the independent variable(s). Another measure that is often used is the "coefficient of correlation", which is the positive square root of the coefficient of determination. This measures the probability that there is a genuine relationship between the variables and that it has not arisen by chance. The closer the value of r is to plus one or minus one, then the narrower the range of the predicted value of the dependent variable.

The relative importance of the independent variable(s) can thus be determined, and a decision made as to which should be included.

Whether a value of r or r^2 is considered high depends on the field of study. In estimating r^2, values of over 0.9 should be expected, which should preferably be higher still if a multiplier is to be applied to the resultant estimate. If the values are much lower than this, then either additional variables require to be introduced (as in the case of the crude cost/height relationship we have just looked at), or else the relationship is not a linear one.

The three major problems with the technique from the point of view of cost modelling are as follows:

(i) Where historic data is being analysed the resultant coefficients are "locked into time". By this we mean that no matter how comprehensive the data, and how good a correlation is achieved, the line of best fit will relate to that sample of data at that point in time. The weightings given by the coefficient may well change as new production methods are developed, new materials are marketed, or cost relationships change. Unfortunately, the technique will not accommodate these changes unless a re-analysis is undertaken incorporating these new factors. It therefore has similar basic problems to the storey-enclosure method in that the weightings given may be satisfactory at the time of publication but quickly become outdated. One method of overcoming this problem is to undertake the analysis on resource quantities (e.g. the regression equation would predict the amount of labour required to build a high building) rather than costs. The current cost of that resource can then be applied to the estimated quantity and a total cost for it established at current levels. Although this overcomes the problem of a change in the relationship between the unit costs of resources it does not provide an answer to changes in, say, productivity. However, construction processes tend to change more slowly than resource costs and therefore error is not likely to creep in so quickly.

(ii) Unless there is a regular building programme it may mean that at certain times, for example, when the construction industry is in depression, very little data will be available with which to undertake the analysis. The method may not therefore be available to the cost adviser at times when the effect of his cost advice is probably most beneficial due to the economic constraints. A further difficulty is that lack of input data at times of recession may distort the index itself, unduly weighting it towards boom conditions.

(iii) It is possible to place a line mathematically through any set of data even though no correlation exists. Care must be taken, therefore, to ensure that a linear relationship does exist, and other statistical tests such as correlation should be used to confirm the strength of that relationship. Checks to make sure that there are no cost thresholds are also important. For example, in practice the cost per square metre will probably fall for the first four to five storeys and then rise again thereafter. Two linear regression models will therefore be necessary to accommodate these two slopes. If this point is missed the fitted line may show a continuous rise right from the very first storey. This will tend to throw all the estimates out to some extent and in particular those for the first four storeys. A careful look at the scatter diagram and a graphical analysis of residuals (see later) will assist in identifying any problem areas.

So far we have been dealing only with two-variable linear regression, but in practice it is usual to find a large number of factors affecting the cost of a building or other major item. In the case of an office block, for example, they may include the height, shape, density of partitioning, standard of finish, level of services, and so on. In these circumstances it is possible to use an extension of the technique called multiple linear regression. Here the same principles apply but unless there are only three variables (where a two-dimensional plane can be placed through the data points) it is not possible to draw the resultant regression plot on a scatter diagram. It is usual for a computer package to be used to establish the coefficients (b) to be used in the regression formula. This formula now becomes:

$$y = a + b_1x_1 + b_2x_2 + b_3x_3 \ldots + b_nx_n$$

where x is the value of each respective independent variable.

The number of "b" coefficients included will depend on the number of variables chosen. Coefficients of multiple correlation can be determined which are similar in their interpretation to the simple expression used before. The technique now becomes very useful as an estimating tool, as all the major factors affecting cost can be included in the formula, although it still suffers from some of the defects previously described for two-variable regression. The technique has been applied reasonably successfully to reinforced concrete frames, simple building types and even service installations. One word of warning is that the choice of variables is left to the user, and he may leave out a most important variable because he does not know of it, or does not consider it worthwhile. Trial and error is required to establish which variables are significant, and commonsense should be used to ensure that silly correlations are not included even if they improve the model. (For example the height of the architect may be correlated in the sample to the cost of the building.) When choosing variables it is preferable to choose those which are well correlated to cost, and avoid those that are simply correlated with each other, and it is sensible to keep the number of variables well below the number of data points.

Finally, until now, we have been talking about linear relationships between the variables. In a number of situations the plot of the relationship may be curved or even broken. In the former case a curve will need to be fitted to the data (computer programs are capable of doing this) and in the latter, the regression model will need to be split into sections to cope with the thresholds apparent in the sample data obtained.

A useful visual guide to see how well any regression model fits the data is a graphical analysis of the "residuals". Residuals are the difference between the estimated value of the item using the regression model and its actual value taken from the sample. If the residuals are plotted against the fitted values and to the same scale, a very clear indication of the closeness of fit and any peculiarities in the model can be seen. Figure 15.7 shows a plot for fixed light aluminium windows where the variables chosen to predict the cost per square metre of glazed area were area and shape. There are in fact three models plotted, one for each area classification of window, and it can be seen from the sample data that the regression model is most reliable in the case of the larger windows.

Points to watch out for in graphical analysis are:

    (i) The existence of "outliers", i.e. a few of the residuals much

Cost per square metre of glazed area

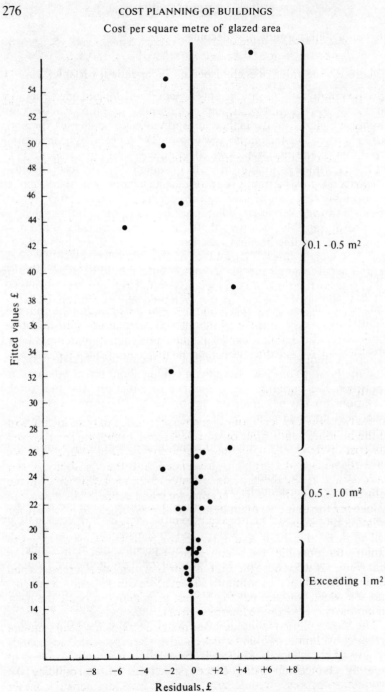

FIG. 15.7. *Graphical analysis of residuals. Fixed light windows with mill finish*

larger in magnitude than all the others. These should be investigated to discover the reason for the poor performance. In many cases it may be due to freak circumstances, in which case that particular item of data can be ignored.

(ii) The existence of a curved pattern of residuals which would suggest that a different model may be more beneficial.

(iii) A skew (or other non-normal) distribution. Non-normality can be detected more reliably by using normal probablity paper. This concept can be followed up by studying most elementary statistical text books.

(iv) A progressive change in the variability of the residuals as the fitted values increase, indicating non-constant variance and a violation of one of the major assumptions in regression analysis.

This section on regression has been a very superficial introduction to a topic which will have its own section in any library of statistics. Before attempting to use the technique it is important that the model builder becomes fully conversant with the method of construction, the tests to be applied to ensure reliability, and the limitations within the context of forecasting cost. A number of elementary statistical text books cover the basic principles in much more detail than it has been possible to achieve in this subsection and these should be read in detail.

Monte Carlo simulation

In the two previous techniques we have attempted to describe the cost of the building in algebraic or statistical terms so that we can estimate the cost effect of changing one or more of the design variables. We have recognised the problems associated with the variability of our basic data, and also the difficulties in predicting what will happen in the future. It is probable, however, that we could define a likely *range* of values for the unit cost of an item, and also the likely *range* of say the inflation rate over the next few years. What we need is a technique that will allow us to use this assumption of the probable range of values to explore the possible cost solutions available using the values within that range. If we repeat the exercise for two or more alternatives and obtain a distribution of solutions for each, we can compare the results and see which solution has the highest probability of being the most economic choice over the likely range of circumstances.

The Monte Carlo technique is one method by which we can simulate activities over time, of a kind which could not be represented adequately by any of the theoretical models. Simulation is simply a means of creating a typical life-history of the system (e.g. the total building, the production process, maintenance, costs-in-use) and activities under given conditions, working out step-by-step what happens during each unit of life of the system. In order to do this we need to know the detailed characteristics and operation of the system and its relevant measures. The effect of variability on the system as a whole is reproduced by sampling from the relevant distributions.

Whilst the example chosen will be in the field of costs-in-use, the same principles can be applied to any other problem where values are not constant. The building of a brick wall with its variability of labour times for the various operatives involved is an example of another field, this time production, in which the technique can be used. In production there is often a sequence of events which are "end on" to one another and which therefore form a "queue" of activities. These events are very often dependent upon one another and, therefore, an irregular performance in one part of the system will probably have an impact on the total performance. For example, if the labourer supporting the bricklaying gang is not up to scratch then the overall performance of the gang will be affected. It is also unlikely that any one member of a gang will work at a constant rate and, therefore, variability in the team's performance is bound to occur for this reason. The Monte Carlo technique will allow simulation of that "queue" of activities, or the special operations research technique of "queuing" can be applied direct. Queuing as a technique is not discussed in this book but it is worth following up if your interest lies in this area.

Perhaps the most difficult forecast to make with regard to buildings is the cost of running and maintaining the property, not only because there are so many factors affecting the way the building performs (maintenance strategy, standard of use, design detailing, workmanship, etc.) but also because of the long period of time over which the prediction must be made. The problems of using "costs-in-use studies" have been identified in Chapter 8, one of the major problems being the choice of assumptions that have to be made before a calculation takes place. The example of the "factory cladding" calculation will be remembered in this connection.

To illustrate the ability of Monte Carlo simulation to assist us in decision-making by giving us more information on the range of possible future costs, a simple hypothetical example has been taken. This concerns a building component that requires no routine maintenance or repair but which normally needs to be replaced several times during the building life. Taxation, inflation, disruption costs, and secondary maintenance have not been included, thereby simplifying the calculation. The variables dealt with are therefore:

    (i) Component life.
    (ii) Life of building.
    (iii) Interest rate.

At the heart of the technique are the distributions from which the sampling or the simulations will take place. These distributions can only be determined from data collected over a long period of time and will relate to the variables previously mentioned. Figure 15.8 shows the histogram for building life in our hypothetical example. Each class interval is shown with its frequency of occurrence for this type of building on a probability scale between zero and one, with the value of one being the absolute certainty that the event will occur. Thus in this histogram there is a 50% chance that the life of the building will be between forty and sixty years, and only a 10% chance that it will be within zero and twenty years (for the purposes of the exercise it is assumed that there is no chance of it exceeding eighty years). It has been known for some buildings to be knocked down almost immediately after completion, for one reason or another, and therefore this possibility is included albeit at a very low probability.

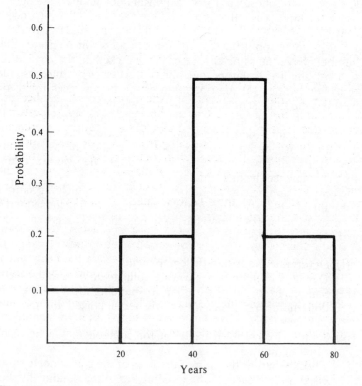

FIG. 15.8. *Histogram of building life*

The next step is to translate this histogram into a cumulative distribution curve or "ogive" from which we can sample the distribution. This is achieved by adding each probability to the previous one, in order, starting with the lowest class interval.

Building life	Probability	Cumulative building life	Cumulative probability
0–20	0.1	0–20	0.1
20–40	0.2	0–40	0.3
40–60	0.5	0–60	0.8
60–80	0.2	0–80	1.0

These points are then plotted on a graph as shown in Fig. 15.9, which we can sample from the distribution. Sampling is a simple matter of selecting a random number (from random number tables or a random number generator) and reading off the resultant life of the building. For example, if the random number 0.30 came up then the life of building would be chosen as forty years. Random numbers are figures between set limits (usually zero to 0.99 or zero to 99) which occur entirely by chance. For example, they could be generated by a roulette wheel or by some sophisticated electronic process which ensures that all numbers have the same chance of being picked on the next selection. Most small calculators and micro-processors produce pseudo random numbers and if the operation of selection is performed too many times the same sequence of numbers will begin to appear again. Statistical tables containing a selection of random numbers are available for manual simulation and a sample sheet is included as Appendix B. If the other distributions for component life and interest rate are treated in a similar way (as shown in Fig. 15.9) then we are almost ready to commence the first simulation.

The only remaining consideration is the order in which the simulation should take place, and a useful way of demonstrating the sequence of events is by means of a flow chart as in Fig. 15.10. This is a short cut way of saying the following:

(i) Determine the cost of the component.
(ii) Decide how many times you are going to do the simulation.
(iii) Sample from the distribution for building life by using random numbers. (This figure will remain fixed for the first simulation.)
(iv) Sample from the distribution for component life by using random numbers.
(v) Check whether the sum of the lives of the components simulated to date exceeds the building life. If the building life has been exceeded then store result of total discounted values to

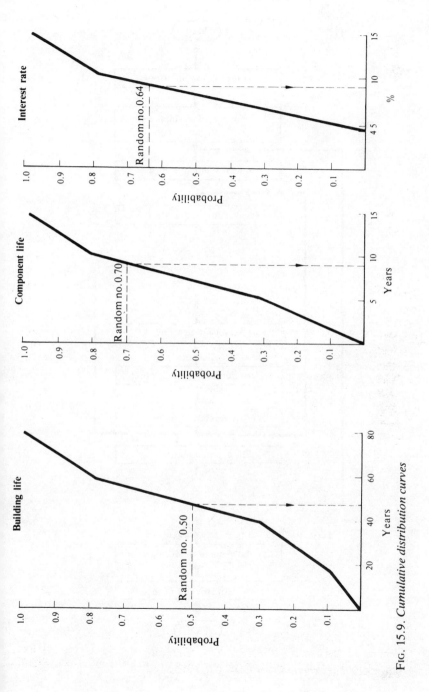

Fig. 15.9. *Cumulative distribution curves*

FIG. 15.10. *Flow chart. Monte Carlo CIU model*

date and check whether the required number of simulations has been made.

(vi) Sample from the distribution of interest rates by using random numbers.

(vii) Add the selected component life to any previous cumulative total of component lives for this simulation.

(viii) Calculate the discounted value of the component using the interest rate selected and the year when the component is replaced.

(ix) Add the resultant discounted value to previous total of discounted values (including initial cost) for this simulation.

(x) Repeat items (iv) to (ix) until the check in item (v) tells you that the component has been replaced a sufficient number of times for the building life of this simulation.

(xi) Record the total discounted costs of the component for this simulation and store.

(xii) Repeat items (iii) to (xi) until the required number of simulations has been made.

(xiii) Calculate the arithmetic mean and standard deviations of the stored results of the total number of simulations made.

(xiv) Prepare distribution of results.

The above simulation would be very tedious if the calculations had to be done manually, but by using a computer the whole process is speeded up and requires no effort by the user other than inputting a small amount of data. Figure 15.11 shows the results of such a program run for six hundred simulations with a component costing £25.00 and the distributions shown in our cost-in-use example. It should be stressed that the above example has been over-simplified for the purposes of communication and in practice many more variables and a smoothing out of erratic movements in the interest rate may be required. If the process is now repeated using another possible alternative component with different initial cost and different periods for replacement (i.e. the component life distribution is different) then a comparison can be made as to the probability of one component being a more economic solution than the other. Figure 15.12 shows this in diagrammatic form with the two distributions superimposed on each other. It can be seen immediately that component A is generally the better proposition but there is a point of overlap between the two. Within the range of values of the shaded area, either A or B could prove to be the better proposition. However, the chances of finding component A to be the least expensive solution is much greater even within this range. For example, the area of the distribution of component A to the left of, or lower than, a present value of £70.00 is much greater than the area below the same present value in the distribution

```
****************DEMONSTRATION PROGRAM******************

THE PROGRAM DEMONSTRATES THE USE OF MONTE CARLO TECHS.
FOR CIU MODELS. IT SELECTS THE LIFE OF BUILDING,COMPONENT
LIFE,AND INTEREST RATE FROM THREE SEPARATE DISTRIBUTIONS
PREVIOUSLY DETERMINED. THE RESULTS OF THE SIMULATIONS ARE
STORED AND ARITH. MEAN,STD. DEVIATION AND HISTOGRAM
ARE CALCULATED FOR THE NUMBER OF TRIALS REQUESTED.

MONTE CARLO SIMULATION ←CIU

WHAT IS INITIAL COST OF COMPONENT ?
←25
HOW MANY TRIALS DO YOU REQUIRE PER RUN ?
MAX. NUMBER = 999
←600
  ARITHMETIC MEAN      = £     65.0564
  STANDARD DEVIATION   = £     18.655
DO YOU WISH TO HAVE A HISTOGRAM OF RESULTS?
←YES


***********************************************************

        HISTOGRAM OF RESULTS FROM CIU SIMULATION

NOTE: EACH HORIZ'*'REPRESENTS A FREQUENCY OF FOUR

 >                      FREQUENCY


 0

10

20          ********
            ********
30          *****
            *****
40          ******************
            ******************
50          ***********************************
            ***************************************
60          ********************************
            *******************************
70          ****************************
            ***************************
80          *****************
            ****************
90          *********
            *********
100         *****
            *****
110         **
            **
120


ARITH. MEAN       = £ 65.0564
STD. DEVIATION    = £ 18.655
```

FIG. 15.11.

FIG. 15.12. *Comparison of distributions of results of simulations for alternative components*

of component B. As the area under the curve represents the probability of the cost falling within a certain price range (in our case, below £70.00) then it follows that it is much more likely component A will be a better choice than component B.

What the Monte Carlo technique has allowed us to do is to explore the future cost of a component within defined ranges which have been weighted from previous knowledge or experience by means of the distributions used. The steeper the slope in the ogive the greater the chance (class intervals remaining the same) that the values within a certain class will be selected by the random number. By repeating the exercise a number of times we have artificially "lived through" or simulated the lifetime of the building a similar number of times. The distribution of results gives us a very good clue as to the likelihood of a particular cost arising, whereas to obtain this sort of information by more conventional mathematics would be extremely difficult and probably impossible.

Although the technique has overcome some of the problems of variability of data it has not helped us with problems such as technological change. If a component were to come on to the market in future years which was a much more attractive proposition than the original component, then it is likely that this new material would be the replacement component. The model cannot predict this kind of variation and over the life of a building this type of change may occur several times—think back over the last sixty years! Another problem lies in the distributions. One method of constructing them would be to look back into history to see what range occurred in the past. However, this may not be reasonable; a distribution for inflation constructed in, say, 1965 based on rates over the past one hundred years would certainly not have been predictive of inflation during the 1970s and probably not for the remainder of the century either. The same would apply to interest rates. Materials which have just been introduced would have no record to build upon, and hypothetical distributions would need to be produced.

The subjective building of distributions may not be too much of a burden however, provided that they can be justified by reason and sound professional judgement. After all, giving a range of likely possibilities is surely a better proposition than pulling a single figure out of mid-air with very little chance of it being correct. At least the risk in the decision of choosing between the alternatives is reasonably identified, and it is at least recognising that estimates cannot be rigid, accurate, predictions. Of course, only a very simple example has been demonstrated here which would need considerable refinement if it were to be included in a working model—if all the variables effecting a solution were required to be sampled the model would probably involve a score or more distributions for a single component. As with all cost prediction techniques it would be very difficult to find sufficient data to produce the distributions required. However, not all assumptions are cost significant and therefore a concentration on the more important distributions will probably be sufficient for this kind of predictive, exploratory exercise.

Monte Carlo simulation can be adapted for other uses such as undertaking a random search for the optimum solution to a design problem within a computer. Random numbers are used to select alternative shapes of buildings, structural frame types, specification, etc., to build up a causal model of the building cost. The machine searches for an improvement on its original selections and when it finds it, holds the new solution and aborts the previous one. This process continues until after a specified number of successively more attractive solutions, the program finishes, and the last solution is presumed to be the best or optimum solution. (In fact it rarely is the optimum as the number of alternatives is for practical purposes infinite.) To assist in the search for the best alternative the computer program can guide the search by means of "rules-of-thumb" established from the practical experience of the author of the program, and it can also incorporate short cut methods of rejecting obviously abortive solutions earlier in the routine to avoid unnecessary calculations. Even with these aids and a powerful computer it can take several hours to achieve a successful solution with a complex model.

Generally

There is no doubt that if the full potential of the micro-processor is to be harnessed for the benefit of the cost adviser, the development of models must play a large part. In the past, the time-consuming task of calculating algebraic formula many times over has daunted even the keenest cost explorer, but with the computer and its ability to perform iterative processes without effort, a new generation of cost advice appears to be on the horizon. Unfortunately the construction of the models, the development of software for use by the computer, and the collection of the data to be applied, have not kept pace with the enormous advances in the electronic hardware of computing. In this chapter we have scratched the surface of an enormous area of potential knowledge which has yet to be developed for the benefit of the quantity surveyor. It has not been the intention to delve into the mathematical basis for these techniques but to show by simple illustration the opportunities available in just three model types. There are a very large number of books on operations research, statistics, and systems which the reader should follow up if his interest has been stimulated in this area of study.

Chapter 16
Building Morphology

Cost parameters

We have already defined parameter as "a quantity which is constant in a particular case considered, but which varies in different cases". It is now necessary to look at the factors that influence the quantity of components in terms of area, number, and size, and also their quantity in terms of cost. Unfortunately, insufficient research has been undertaken to date to give clear indications of the degree to which changes in the parameters of the building (or by implication its model) will have on the cost of that building. There is, however, a very great depth of knowledge gained by practitioners which provides us with some general "rules-of-thumb". In some cases we can be quite specific about how cost varies. For example, if we change the shape of a single-storey building so that the area of external brick cavity wall is increased, then we can be reasonably sure that, all other things being equal, the wall cost will probably have increased in direct proportion to the increased area. Similarly, if the standard of facing brick is increased and the shape of the building is fixed, then the wall cost will have increased by the extra material cost of providing the better specification. Whilst we can probably rely on this kind of simple wisdom for small brick buildings it may not be adequate for dealing with more complex multi-storey concrete clad structures. If we change the shape or height of the building, it may not be just the extra quantity and quality that we have to pay for, but indirect costs such as different lifting equipment, improved fixings to deal with increased exposure, access, and manoeuvrability and dispersal of plant on site and so on. Some very useful studies have been undertaken in areas such as this (COCO, the PSA computer program, has already been mentioned in Chapter 14) but anyone who has attempted research in the field of cost will tell you that every research project opens up a whole series of new research proposals! Cost research is still in its infancy and it may be many years, if ever, before we obtain a reliable body of scientific knowledge on which to base our judgements.

Using our existing knowledge we can, however, establish some starting principles which can be the foundation for any further cost research. We can view the cost parameters at two levels. Firstly at the level of the building form, or as it is sometimes called its "morphology", where we see the effect of shape and height on cost, and secondly at the level of its major components and the factors that influence their size, quantity, and cost.

(Note: The dictionary definition of morphology is "the science of form" and the derivation comes from "Morpheus" the Greek god of dreams. This suggests that the origin of the shape or form lies in the imagination and the word therefore appears appropriate for the source of building form.)

Building shape

The building shape has its major impact on the areas and sizes of the vertical components such as walls, windows, partitions, etc., as well as the perimeter detailing such as ground beams, fascias, and the eaves of roofs. It would seem obvious that the building that has the smallest perimeter for a given amount of accommodation will be the cheapest as far as these items are concerned. However, the shape that has the smallest perimeter in relation to area, is the circle and this does not very often provide the cheapest solution for the following reasons:

(i) The building is more difficult to set out for the contractor.
(ii) Curved surfaces, particularly those incorporating timber or metalwork (e.g. in joinery or formwork) are very expensive to achieve.
(iii) Circular buildings seldom produce an efficient use of internal space, as inconvenient odd corners between partitions and external walls are generated. There is a tendency for them also to generate non-right-angled internal arrangements.
(iv) Standard joinery which normally envisages right angles will not fit against curved surfaces, nor into acute-angled corners.
(v) The circle does not usually allow efficient use of site space.

In these circumstances it would appear that the right-angled building which has the lowest perimeter will provide the best answer. This shape is of course the square. Now, although a compact square form is generally recognised as the most economic solution because of its reduction in the cost of the external vertical elements and as it has the lowest area of wall for heat loss calculations, there are some very important qualifications to be made:

(i) Where the square plan produces a very deep building requiring artificial ventilation, air conditioning, and lighting, the shape usually becomes uneconomic. It is only the single-storey building with its opportunities for natural top-lighting and ventilation which may be regarded as a partial exception to this rule, although even here, really satisfactory arrangements for roof-lighting and venting are likely to be expensive both in cost and in maintenance.

(ii) Where there is a high density of rooms, the use of the external wall as a boundary to the room may compensate for the amount of partitioning required. It is, therefore, sometimes preferable to elongate the building in some way so that rooms can be serviced from either side of a spinal corridor rather than have a deep building resulting in a complex network of corridors to service all rooms plus the possibility of artificial ventilation to those that are internal.

(iii) A given amount of accommodation housed in a square, but multi-storey block, may be much more expensive than the same accommodation housed in a less compact two-storey block for reasons we shall discuss later.

(iv) On a sloping site involving cut and fill, it may be more sensible to provide a rectangular building with the longer side running with the contours than a square building which would cut more extensively into the slope.

These are just a few of the qualifications which need to be made when talking about the efficiency of shape. In any case, the shape of the building is often dictated by the site boundaries, topography, and orientation, and the choice is, therefore, rather limited.

There have been a number of attempts to measure the cost efficiency of a building shape and some simple examples are listed below:

(a) $\dfrac{\text{Wall}}{\text{Floor}}$ ratio
This is perhaps the most familiar of all the efficiency ratios but it can only be used to compare buildings with a similar floor area and does not have an optimum reference point such as those below.

(b) $\dfrac{P - Ps}{Ps} \times 100\%$

(J. Cooke)

This simple formula relates any shape to a square which would contain the same area thus providing a reference point for shape efficiency.

Where P = perimeter of building

  Ps = perimeter of square of the same area

(c) Plan compactness or POP ratio (Strathclyde Univ.)

$$\frac{2(\pi A)^{\frac{1}{2}}}{P} \times 100\%$$

In this case the point of reference is the circle (a square would have a POP ratio of 88.6% efficiency and yet it is probably the best cost solution in initial cost terms).

Where P = perimeter of building
A = area of building

(d) Mass compactness or VOLM ratio (Strathclyde Univ.)

$$2\pi \frac{[(3V/2\pi)^{\frac{1}{3}}]^2}{S} \times 100\%$$

This formula chooses a hemisphere as the point of reference for considering the compactness of the building in three dimensions.

Where V = volume of hemisphere equal to volume of building

S = measured surface area of the building (ground area not included)

(e) Length/Breadth Index (D. Banks)

$$\frac{p + \sqrt{(p^2 - 16a)}}{p - \sqrt{(p^2 - 16a)}}$$

Where p = perimeter of building

a = area of building

In this index any right-angled plan shape of building is reduced to a rectangle having the same area and perimeter as the building. Curved angles can be dealt with by a weighting system. The advantage here is that the rectangular shape allows a quick mental check for efficiency. As these formulae are only for guidance purposes this index is probably sufficient for early design advice.

(f) Plan/Shape Index (D. Banks)

$$\frac{g + \sqrt{(g^2 - 16r)}}{g - \sqrt{(g^2 - 16r)}}$$

Where g = sum of perimeters of each floor divided by the number of floors

r = gross floor area divided by the number of floors

This is a development of the previous index to allow for multi-storey construction. In effect, the area and perimeters are averaged out to give a guide as to the overall plan shape efficiency.

While the above indices are useful, they obviously have severe limitations as they consider only those elements that comprise the perimeter of the building, or in the case of VOLM the perimeter and roof. However, the repercussions of shape on many other major elements are considerable. For example, wide spans generated by a different plan shape may result in deeper beams which may result in an increase in storey height which in turn may affect nearly all the vertical elements. These implications should be represented in any advanced model of building form and an awareness of their cost effect should be part of the cost adviser's knowledge.

Size of building is another factor of importance in cost efficiency. The larger the plan area for a given shape, the lower the wall to floor ratio. For example, a square building of 100 m² and 5 m high would have a wall/floor ratio of 2, whereas a square building of 1,000 m² and identical height would have a wall/floor ratio of 0.63. However, the previous points that have been made, with regard to artificial ventilation and lighting in particular, may counteract this saving in envelope area. The savings that result from larger buildings make the grouping of buildings cost-attractive. External walls and their finishes need to have a high performance, as they are exposed to the weather, and they therefore tend to be expensive, so that if the area of external wall can be reduced then a considerable saving should ensue. Terraced housing is a good example of cost savings due to grouping; by taking three detached houses and making them into a terrace you save two brick faced flank walls, two lengths of foundations for these walls, two roof verge details, downpipe, drainage, and so on. You would also replace two other faced brick walls with party walls which would almost certainly be cheaper. Extra savings could be made by having narrow fronted terraces rather than broad fronted. However, the social disadvantages of such terracing may easily outweigh any advantage in cost terms.

Another advantage of large buildings containing grouped accommodation is the greater sharing of common facilities. If in a residential block there is a central service and circulation core then the more accommodation units which can be clustered around, and thus serviced by, this core, the less will be the cost of the service facility for each unit. However, too many flats per floor may result in long circulation routes and corridors, and additional fire precaution problems. In speculative office buildings it may be unwise to over-centralise circulation and services as this may create problems in dividing up the office space for letting. It is in these circumstances that the experience and knowledge of all members of the design team will be most beneficial in determining the best solution.

Height

Here it is possible, and desirable, to be dogmatic. Tall buildings are invariably more expensive to build than two- or three-storey buildings offering the same accommodation, and the taller the building the greater the comparative cost. The only exception to this rule is that the addition of one or two storeys to the design of a tall building for the purpose of making the best use of the lifts or other expensive services may slightly decrease the cost per storey, but this is a limited exception and does not invalidate the general rule.

What are the reasons for this?

Firstly, the cost of the special arrangements to service the building particularly the upper floors. Apart from the necessity of providing sufficient high-speed lifts it is necessary to pump water up, and break the fall of sewage and other rubbish coming down, and sometimes complete service areas may have to be provided at intervals of ten or fifteen floors to deal with these problems. Special ventilation and lighting arrangements may be needed because of the impossibility of providing adequate light wells in a tall building, and also a very high standard of fire resistant construction and escape arrangements.

Secondly, the necessity for the lower part of the building to be designed to carry the weight of the upper floors, which obviously makes it more expensive than if it was carrying its own weight alone. Also the whole building will have to be designed to resist a heavy wind loading, a factor which would hardly affect a low building at all. This factor became even more important with the introduction of rigorous design standards following the Ronan Point collapse.

Thirdly, the cost of working at a great height from the ground when erecting the building. Apart from the cost of hoisting all materials and operatives to the required level, and of the time spent by operatives going up to their work and down again at the beginning and end of the day and at break times, there is the extra cost of working at high altitudes and of all the safety requirements which this entails.

Fourthly, the increasing area occupied by the service core and circulation. As the height of a building increases so it needs more lifts, larger ducts, wider staircases and corridors, etc., and these installations take up more and more of the area of the lower floors, so cutting down on the usable area. It is possible to imagine a building so tall and thin that the whole of the ground floor is occupied by vertical services; adding additional floors to such a building would produce no increase in usable area at all!

Many of the above factors will also influence the running and maintenance costs—such items as window cleaning, repainting, and repairs to the face of the building will all cost more than similar work to a low structure.

Therefore, high building should never be considered favourably on cost grounds unless the savings in land cost due to the smaller site area will pay for the considerable extra building cost. Land values must be high for this to occur, since a tall building needs a good deal of space around it and the reduction in land requirements is not proportional to the reduction in plan area.

Just as high building is not usually economic neither is single-storey building. The exceptions here are rather more numerous and important, for instance where large floor areas free from obstruction by walls or columns are required it is more economical to build horizontally than vertically, since to provide a loadbearing floor over such areas would be far more difficult and expensive than a roof. Similarly where very heavy floor loadings are required it would be cheaper to build floors resting on the ground than suspended floors over other storeys. The third instance where single-storey construction is economical is for temporary or sub-standard buildings where the foundations and structure cannot easily be made capable of supporting a further storey.

The reason for the relative economy of two- or three-storey buildings compared to single storey is that one roof and one set of foundations will be serving two or three times the floor area, and that the walls or frame will be capable of carrying the extra load with little or no alteration. In domestic construction it will be possible to use cheap timber upper floors which will help the comparison still further.

Once the building exceeds this number of storeys various factors contribute to higher building costs. It is less often possible to dispense with a separate frame, the frame itself must be more substantial, and the necessity for lifts, fire-resisting construction, and other expensive measures makes it difficult to attain the low costs possible with two-storey construction.

Optimum envelope area

The "envelope" of a building, that is the external walls and roof which enclose it, is an important factor in the cost of a building. We have already seen that a square building is inherently economical in wall area, but the total envelope cost will depend upon the number of storeys that are chosen for the accommodation.

For example, imagine a large single-storey building. If we arranged the same accommodation on two floors we should reduce the roof area by more than the consequent increase in wall area, so that total envelope area would be reduced. The same thing might happen if we arranged the same accommodation on three floors, but if we continue the process, making the building higher and higher but retaining the same gross floor area, the process eventually reverses and the increase in wall area is greater than the roof saving. This reversal happens quite slowly, so that the envelope area changes very little over a range of several possible storey arrangements close to the optimum. We can use a formula to calculate this optimum for a square building thus:

$$N\sqrt{N} = \frac{x\sqrt{f}}{2s}$$

N = optimum number of storeys
x = roof unit cost divided by wall unit cost
f = total floor area (m^2)
s = storey height (m).

If the desired width in metres (w) of the building is known the formula becomes

$$N^2 = \frac{xf}{2sw}.$$

More complex formulae involving several elements have been developed to optimise the shape of the whole building, but these often result in over-simplification which renders them of little practical help.

Elemental cost studies

Cost research or cost studies are usually called for in the earliest design stages of the project, when the architect is considering design alternatives. It is at this stage that cost models such as those described earlier will be most effective. However, at the present time these studies would normally be done by means of approximate quantities, about which sufficient has already been said.

Cost studies if done properly are expensive in professional time, and therefore cannot usually be undertaken in respect of the majority of items in the project. They should therefore be reserved for comparisons of important components, or for projects which are themselves unusual and for which ordinary elemental cost data are of little use. Large-scale cost studies are inappropriate where the component is not a significant part of the cost structure, or where the difference in cost between the alternatives is obviously going to have little effect on overall costs.

Where there is little cost difference between one solution and another the decision should be taken on grounds other than cost and not on the possibility of a marginal saving; if the contract is to be awarded in the traditional manner with competitive tendering on Bills of Quantities no surveyor can possibly forecast which of two alternatives with a marginal cost difference would actually be priced the cheaper by the (unknown) successful contractor. In connection with this the surveyor must remember the natural tendency of the contractor to play safe when pricing work involving unknown or experimental materials and techniques.

Another point to bear in mind in connection with cost studies is that all constructional systems have certain optimum conditions (of loading, span, etc.) in which they are at their most economical. There is usually a reasonable spread of conditions on either side of the optimum in which the system remains reasonably economic, but once the conditions get outside this range costs will start to rise steeply. Even though the particular system may still be perfectly feasible in these unsuitable conditions it is likely that there will be a cheaper and better solution.

It is also worth noting that a high standard of fire resistance, thermal insulation or sound insulation normally costs money, and that it is usually wasteful to employ methods of construction or materials which offer these advantages if they are not required.

We will now look at some of the principal elements in the building, and the particular aspects of design costs which affect each.

Foundations

The type of foundations required will normally be influenced by the type of structure which they are to carry; obviously a structure which imposes heavy point loads cannot be carried on conventional strip foundations. Piling is almost always a very expensive solution and is normally employed only where conventional foundations are impossible because of the depth at which a bearing formation exists, combined sometimes with the waterlogged nature of the ground. Different systems of piling have particular advantages and disadvantages but the specialist piling firms are usually more than ready to offer their services in connection with early cost investigations. As previously noted the cost of the piling itself will usually be a complete extra, because the complex of pile caps and ground beams associated with this form of construction is often as expensive as conventional foundations.

Frame

Cost studies may be necessary to determine the type of frame to be used or indeed whether there should be a frame at all. External walls of habitable buildings need certain qualities of weather resistance and heat insulation, and such a wall capable of bearing quite substantial loads cost no more than a non-loadbearing wall with similar weathering and insulation performance. In conditions where normal external walling would be capable of carrying the weight of floors and roof the cost of a frame is a complete extra, and it follows that for small buildings of not more than three storeys a frame is likely to be an expensive solution, even though it may be desirable for other reasons. A frame for small buildings only becomes economically justified where it is necessary to have a very high proportion of the external walls glazed, or in farm sheds and the like where the walls do not need good insulation or aesthetic qualities and cheap non-structural materials such as asbestos-cement sheeting can be used.

A frame, if required, is likely to be of steel or reinforced concrete, with light alloys and timber as recent and rather specialised competitors. As with other material comparisons, if either steel or reinforced concrete held all the cost advantages the other would long since have disappeared. For multi-storey construction there is a general tendency for reinforced concrete to be cheaper in normal conditions of loading, although the difference may often be small. The structural steelwork industry is continually improving its techniques of design and construction, particularly when the cost competition from reinforced concrete becomes severe. One such technique is a composite structure in which a steel frame is erected with beams of tee section instead of heavier joist section, the flange of the tee taking tensile stresses and the *in situ* concrete beam casing dealing with the compressive stresses in the upper part of the beam. This, by the way, highlights the worse cost difficulty that structural steelwork has to face, that although it is inherently cheaper than reinforced concrete the saving is completely wiped out by the measures necessary to give the structure an adequate fire-resistance (usually in-situ concrete cladding to beams and columns).

Steel therefore gives its best comparative cost performance as a frame to single-storey buildings or in roof framings where fire resistance is not normally required by the building regulations and where the steel may be used without any protection other than paint. For such applications reinforced concrete is not usually competitive, except in some proprietary systems for constructing factories or sheds out of standard precast units.

It is worth noting that some contractors (particularly small or medium sized firms) prefer working with a steel frame to erecting a reinforced concrete structure of their own, and this preference would be reflected both in tendering enthusiasm and in completion time for the project.

Most constructional steel firms and specialist reinforced concrete contractors are very helpful in giving cost information for a new

FIG. 16.1. *Alternative grid layouts*

project. If a consulting structural engineer is appointed for the project the surveyor would obviously work with him in providing cost information; in many cases the consultant would provide most of the cost information himself but as alternative frame designs may affect other elements as well he may not be able to ascertain the full cost implications without assistance.

As well as a choice of materials, frame design will involve a choice of frame shapes and spacings. The most uneconomical solution will occur where heavily loaded beams have to span long distances expecially if they are also restricted in depth. The spacing of columns and beams will have an important effect on cost, particularly if the columns are expressed on the elevations and covered with expensive cladding. If the frames are spaced too closely the savings in sections will not pay for the additional frames, since although frames spaced at 2.5 m centres will each be carrying two-thirds of the weight of frames spaced at 3.75 m centres they will cost much more than two-thirds of the latter. This is because the choice of section for a beam is affected by its own span as well as by the load it carries, and the span of the beams will not have been changed (see Fig. 16.1).

Since the most economical spacing will depend upon the span and upon the loading it is necessary to consider each case individually. For normal floor loadings however it is unlikely that spacing as close as 2.5 m will give the most economical solution, while spacings much in excess of 5 m will begin to produce additional costs on the floors and roof owing to their increased span, even though the frame design itself may still be economical.

Staircases

Since the structure of a concrete staircase represents less than a third of the total cost (the remainder being caused by finishes and by balustrades) and since the whole elemental cost is only a minor one it is doubtful whether the staircases of a building are the most fruitful field for cost studies. However, the true total cost of a staircase would include the surrounding walls of the staircase together with foundations, windows, wall finishes, doors, roof, etc., and would be quite considerable. The most rewarding approach is therefore likely to be the reduction in number of staircases rather than in the details of their design.

Upper floors

In contrast to staircases upper floors are an important element and require comparatively little work in the evaluation of alternative designs, which may therefore be well worth doing. As with some other elements, it is difficult to arrive at true cost comparisons without considering the "frame" element as well.

Roofs

The architect may require cost studies of alternative roofs, to which most of the preceding remarks apply. In addition the comparative costs of flat roofs and pitched roofs may be involved; these will depend more upon the level of the comparable specifications than upon the basic difference in roof type. However, for medium to large spans a satisfactory pitched roof is likely to be rather cheaper than a flat roof of comparable quality, partly because of the simplicity of spanning large areas with roof trusses rather than deep beams.

Pitched roofs also tend to be more durable than flat roofs which are sensitive to poor workmanship and poor design detailing, unless very expensively built.

Rooflights

Rooflighting is not normally the most economical method of lighting rooms where windows are a possible alternative, and individual dome-lights or small lantern lights are probably the least satisfactory from a cost point of view. However, there are many reasons why the architect may choose this means of lighting and the element is not important enough for this to affect the total building cost very considerably.

External walls

This may be the most important structural element, particularly in a multi-storey building, and being one in which a tremendous range of constructional methods and finishes may be used is a suitable element for cost studies. In the type of building where the external walls comprise a series of repeating panels it will be sufficient to study a single panel in detail. It will often be difficult to consider this element in isolation from windows, internal finishes, and frame. Note that ordinary brick or concrete block walls finished with facing bricks externally are likely to be far cheaper than any other construction of comparable performance and durability; so that a considerable area of plain walling on a building may enable smaller areas of luxury construction or finish to be used while still keeping the overall elemental cost quite reasonable.

Internal walls and partitions

The comparative costs of traditional partitioning methods are well enough known for cost studies to be unnecessary, but if it is proposed to use a special type of partition on a large scale then a cost investigation would be worthwhile. Comparative costs of small areas of special partition or glazed screens on the other hand would not have much effect on the total building cost and would not usually be worth investigating.

If *The Architects' Journal* or similar list of elements is being used it is important to remember that the cost of finishings to traditional partitions are included in other elements, but the complete cost of self-finished proprietary partitioning is included in the "partitions" element, so that in this instance elemental costs will not be strictly comparable.

Windows

These are often a major element of modern buildings and have a very large cost range. Cost differences will normally be due to performance requirements rather than the actual materials used in manufacture; standard metal or timber windows for housing schemes are competitive in cost as are high class metal or hardwood windows for prestige buildings, but the latter category may be four or five times dearer than the former. Apart from the actual material and section of framing the cost of windows is substantially affected by:

(a) *Size of window*. Small windows tend to be high in cost per square metre, both because of the greater intricacy of the window itself and the cost of forming the opening in the wall; these two costs vary according to perimeter rather than area.

(b) *Size of panes*. Very small panes increase the cost per square metre, so also do panes which are so large that it is necessary to glaze them with stout float glass instead of sheet glass. It is unlikely that any saving on window frame or glazing bars would counterbalance the cost of plate glass unless an extremely expensive type of window was being used.

(c) *Opening lights*. This is probably one of the most important factors in window cost, particularly where a high standard of weather resistance is required. The heavy comparative cost of opening portions of windows (as against areas of fixed glazing) makes it very difficult to compare window costs on an overall square metre basis unless the pattern of opening and fixed areas is very similar. Unfortunately it is not even possible to compare the costs of opening portions on a square metre basis as so much of the cost (hinges or pivots, fasteners, framing to angles) varies according to the number of sashes rather than their size.

Because of the above factors it is often necessary for any cost studies of windows to require individual consideration of all the window types in the building, rather than being confined to a typical window and the results being applied to the remainder on a square metre basis.

Doors

Except on buildings which are divided into a large number of very small rooms, such as hostels or flats, the doors are not usually a significant element. Because of this, because they are one of the components most subject to heavy mechanical wear, and because they are also one of the most noticeable features of the building it is probably a mistake to be excessively concerned with cost when designing this element.

Floor, wall, and ceiling finishes and decorations

Cost studies of these elements are likely to be comparatively simple, and where large areas are involved are certainly worth doing.

Joinery fittings

Of all minor building components single joinery fittings involve the most work in arriving at a cost, and so cost studies of such fittings should not usually be attempted. Where a fitting has been designed for repetition (such as a bedroom fitting for a large hostel, or a typical bench to be used as a basis for furnishing a set of laboratories) the position is of course different.

Services

Where the services of a building are a major factor and cost studies are required it is likely that a consulting engineer will have been appointed. However the surveyor should be aware of the considerations involved, as he will have to co-operate with the engineer in arriving at cost comparisons. Apart from comparisons of material costs (such as copper or polythene tubing), the most usual studies are of alternative methods of heating and ventilation. As the required levels of heating will almost certainly have been already determined the comparisons usually involve different compromises between capital costs and running costs. The engineer will be able to give the requisite figures of installation costs and fuel costs, but the surveyor will be required to produce the various ancillary costs which will not be part of the engineering work. These include such things as different methods or standards of thermal insulation of the building generally, and also the provision of accommodation for heating or engineering equipment.

For instance, not only is heating by solid fuel or oil-fired boilers more expensive in first cost than an electric heating system but it will necessitate the provision of a boiler room, chimney stack, fuel store, ducts, and access and turning space for large delivery vehicles; these costs will be calculated by the quantity surveyor rather than the engineer, and have to be added to the cost of the system in order to arrive at the true capital cost.

The whole question of the cost of services has become of acute concern, because of their increasing importance as a proportion of the total building cost (sometimes over 60%) and the lack of effective cost forecasting and control techniques comparable with those relating to the building structure and finishes. There have been numerous cases where the careful cost-planning of the structural and finishing elements has been rendered useless because of the difficulty of forecasting the services part of the costs to any acceptable degree of accuracy.

Special services (lifts)

Some factors affecting lift cost have already been detailed during the discussion on causal models earlier in the chapter. Lifts are of course the province of the specialist engineer, although the surveyor will need to provide information on costs of shaft structure, motor rooms, etc. However, as lift costs are a critical factor in the economic design of some multi-storey buildings a few more general remarks will not be out of place.

As has already been seen much of the cost of a lift is determined by its performance in terms of speed and load, and by the sophistication or otherwise of the control arrangements. To a large extent the number of floors served is of minor cost importance, each additional landing involving only a few extra feet of wire rope, a set of gates, a further set of relays in the control boxes and some wiring. If there is a large increase in the number of floors these items will, it is true, add up to a considerable sum; it may also be necessary to improve the speed and capacity of the lift so that it can deal with the increased traffic which is likely to use it and because a lack of speed which is tolerable for a short journey becomes irritating when ascending a longer distance.

Nevertheless, even when these latter factors are taken into account the cost of the lift will be in no way proportional to the height of the building, and the only rise in cost per floor served will occur when the traffic arising from the increased height necessitates the provision of an additional lift. This will suddenly cause the cost per floor to double, but as further floors are added this cost will start to fall again until eventually a third lift is needed, and so on.

In some classes of building, notably multi-storey low-rental flats, the gross lift costs can amount to as much as 15% of the cost of the flats, so that the height or size of the block may be partly determined by the maximum number of flats that can be effectively served by a pair of lifts. (In tall buildings it is usual to have more than one lift owing to the consequences of breakdowns where only one lift is used.) Similarly, costs per flat will increase sharply when a building reaches such a height that the introduction of lifts to the design becomes necessary for the first time, and for this reason five and six storey blocks of flats are not very common.

Dangers of "rule-of-thumb"

At the beginning of this chapter, mention was made of "rule-of-thumb" cost knowledge, and some of the advice given in the chapter itself has been of this nature.

Rule-of-thumb guidance is always highly empirical, and tends to relate largely to conditions within an experienced range of normality. It is most important to distinguish between empirical rules, to which there may be a large number of exceptions, and natural laws, of which there are none. For instance, even the golden rules on optimisation of external wall area could prove quite false in a very mild climate with periods of very heavy rain, where the performance expected of the wall of a single-storey building is low, but the roofs must not only be of a high quality but also should preferably not be too large because of problems of run-off and maintenance. In these circumstances a series of free-standing pavilions could be a much better solution than the grouped type of building which has been generally recommended.

It is necessary, therefore, always to be on the look-out for conditions where normal experience may not necessarily be a good guide.

Summing-up

We have seen many ways in which cost studies can contribute to the design of a building. But it is important to realise that it would not be economically possible to employ more than a few of them on any particular building, as a complete cost study of every element, major and minor, would not produce savings commensurate with the amount of time expended. The only occasion where such a course might be practicable is where a large number of similar buildings are to be erected, as for instance a standard house design for a large housing authority.

Chapter 17

Models for Optimisation

Every day each member of the human race is engaged in one overriding common activity. That activity remains true, no matter what the geographical, political, religious, cultural and ideological climate in which the individual is found. It is common to all peoples and yet the choices made will vary almost as much as the number of individuals. Even when the same person is monitored, the activity remains the same, but the choices made will vary with time for the same individual making the same decision.

This common activity is the search for what the individual considers to be the "best" solution. Whether it be selecting a chair in front of the television set or the quickest route from A to B; the choosing of the most compatible member of the opposite sex for a spouse or voting for a new government; the human mind is searching for what, in a given set of circumstances, is 'the most appropriate solution. The choice will be tempered by the mind's own perception of the problem, its own prejudices and preferences, and the many constraints, both physical and cultural, within which it has to work.

This search for the "best" is known as the process of optimisation. It is this task that is set the design team at the beginning of every building contract and yet it is an almost impossible goal to achieve. Some of the reasons for this difficulty are common to many optimisation problems, such as:

(i) what criteria are to be used to judge the alternative choices? Is the utilitarian principle of "what solution will bring the greatest happiness to the greatest number of people" to be applied? If so, this is an extremely difficult criterion to satisfy, particularly with a long-term and complex asset such as a building.

(ii) what time is available to make the choice? We have already seen in Chapter 6 that one of the differences between design method and scientific method is the extra constraint of time. Thus we often have to be satisfied with optimal (i.e. close to the best) solutions rather than the optimum even when the criteria are clear.

(iii) do objective measures exist for measuring the best solution? For a simple reinforced concrete framed column it may be possible to design the minimum size of cross section, but to determine the most pleasant internal arrangement of building space would be a problem of different magnitude altogether. The former has a well-established and formalised method of calculation and measurement. The latter will involve social issues, aesthetics, efficiency, lighting and so on, many of which have no means of accepted measurement.

(iv) do we optimise for now or extend into the future? Buildings are not judged at a single point in time. Assessments are made by the owners, the occupants and the community throughout its life as to its quality and performance. Some decision as to what time scale it is reasonable to plan for, needs to be made.

(v) who will assess the optimum solution? In building design should it be the client, the architect, society (through legislation on space, quality, cost, etc.) or the occupants? Naturally, the assessment of these members or groups will overlap, but who arbitrates in the case of conflict?

It is these issues and others like them which have made the authors of this book rather reluctant to enter the optimisation arena in previous editions. While it is quite possible to come to an apparent "best" solution at sub-problem level, it is much more difficult to optimise between the results of the sub-optimisations. Very often there will be conflict between two optimum solutions at the sub-problem level, e.g. optimum cost and optimum comfort. There is, however, a danger that the hard tangible nature of a cost figure will carry more weight than the more subjective nature of a description of comfort. It is not until after the decision has been made that the error becomes apparent.

Those aspects of design which can be quantified have an unfair advantage over those which rely on "word models" such as a description or even visual models such as drawings. The advantage is even more unfair where the figures convey an apparent accuracy and confidence which conceal the assumptions and guesswork which lie behind the results presented. In life cycle costing we have already made the point in Chapter 8 that unless there is a strikingly obvious difference between alternatives in cost-in-use terms then the decision is probably best made on other grounds.

The same also applies to a lesser extent with initial cost. The use of unit prices for a data base abstracted from a model which does not always reflect cost occurrence on site (the Bill of Quantities under SMM.6 and before) does not give confidence in establishing an optimum design which will set the parameters for the production process on site.

The counter argument to these concerns must be that it is an obligation placed on the cost adviser and the members of the design team to try and achieve the best solution. This "ideal" must be tempered with a recognition that our processes are imperfect but capable of improvement. By seeking to use and develop models that provide a single best solution, we begin to establish a pattern of enquiry which will give us greater understanding of small parts of the building system and eventually the whole.

Whether it will ever be possible to provide the optimum total design, even for a simple building at a single point in time, is extremely unlikely. Bob Phillips of the School of Architecture at Bristol University has shown that to optimise a spatial layout with twenty spaces and a different activity in each so that the spaces were arranged to provide the best solution for internal circulation would take 6×10^{17} iterations if every possibility were tested. Even using a powerful computer which could make one total building evaluation of spatial arrangement every second would take over 2,000 years! Most clients are reluctant to wait that long!

If all the other design possibilities and options are included it can be seen that the lifespan of the earth is unlikely to be sufficient for an exhaustive evaluation of one building. Now this is a rather comforting thought for it means that perfection is still an ideal to be sought after, but with little chance of being achieved. We can however, get somewhere near it through a combination of knowledge, experience and technique.

Over the years a conventional wisdom has developed which acts as a screening process for likely solutions. We do not consider some options because we "know" (through education or experience) that they are generally unsatisfactory in this situation. The human brain develops its own search processes for seeking a solution and it is only in the detail (e.g. how much extra would an increase of 0.2 in the wall/floor ratio cost) that it needs the assistance of technique. Most evaluative computer programs are handling the detail rather than the major issues. Most designers will be able to provide a reasonable stab at a building form and specification that will satisfy the client's requirements for support and enclosure. It is the marginal improvement of that solution, but which may appear to the client quite large, to which most design aids are aimed.

One way of approaching the design problem could be to search for the minimum cost and then move away from this cost through the minimum acceptable level of design to the client towards the optimal solution. Figure 17.1 shows this possibility diagrammatically and is a development of the graph shown in Fig. 6.2. Building "B" is likely to be a simple building with a smaller range of options and therefore higher percentage commitment at the start (e.g. a warehouse). Building "A" is likely to be a more complex building with few constraints and many more options.

The problem is posed of course as to how far we should go beyond the mere satisfying of the client's requirements before we stop "improving" the design. A parallel exists in aircraft design where one approach is to find the "least weight" solution and then add on the extra items which will add to passenger comfort and managerial efficiency until the anticipated benefits of these additions balance the extra cost both in initial and future (fuel, maintenance. etc.) terms.

FIG. 17.1. *Hypothetical accumulative expenditure over time for two building types A and B.*

This balancing of the marginal benefit with the marginal unit cost introduces the concepts of utility and value. Utility is a concept which is well defined in economics and is sometimes defined as "the amount of satisfaction a person derives from some thing or service without any reference to its usefulness". This degree of satisfaction tends to decrease as the consumption of the good, benefit or service increases in amount. With successive new units of a good the total utility will grow at a slower and slower rate. The extra utility added by the addition of the last unit of good is known as marginal utility and the law of diminishing marginal utility states that this decreases as more units are added. This is because there is a fundamental tendency for our psychological ability to appreciate more of the good, to become less keen. Attempts have been made to measure utility but even when considering consumer demand theory for less complex situations than buildings the majority of economists would prefer to rank the comparative utility rather than measure it.

There is another law—the law of equal marginal utilities per pound or dollar, which says that each good is demanded up to the point where the marginal utility per pound spent on it is exactly the same as the marginal utility of a pound spent on any other good.

This equilibrium condition is a useful concept for it provides a clue to the theoretical upper limit for improvement which will be related to the resources at the client's disposal which he could use for other purposes should he so wish. At the point where the marginal improvement in benefit or utility equals the marginal increase in cost then a search for improvement should stop. In practical terms this benefit will be hard to measure and even the marginal increase in cost is by no means certain.

However, this balance of benefit to cost is close to a more general definition of value that is sometimes given. Value can be defined as the balance between the client's wants (i.e. shelter, security, income, etc.) and the resources at his disposal (i.e. finance, time, etc.) and the constraints within which he works (planning, site, technological, etc.). On some occasions the constraints on resources will be so great that the theoretical balance of utility and cost will not be able to be met. However, this will not affect an assessment of value as constraints are accepted within the definition. If these concepts are accepted then it will be realised that it may be possible to have "quality for money" but not "value for money" as money is already part of the value assessment in projects where it is a criterion.

The purpose of the above discussion has been to lay the foundation for the introduction of optimising techniques. Our techniques should be searching for this theoretical balance between benefit and cost or where the constraints are tight should be attempting to provide the best satisfaction of wants (i.e. design quality) within the resources available. We must also realise that some, probably the majority, of benefits derived from a building are difficult to measure and as we have seen in Chapter 9 costs themselves are by no means certain. However, a step can be taken if we make some simplifying assumptions such as:

(i) assume certainty (e.g. as to cost) when in reality there is variability.
(ii) insert human search processes to reduce the number of options considered (e.g. where the human brain can draw associations much more quickly than a computer—as in spatial layout).
(iii) assume simplified mathematical relationships (such as linear) between variables, providing there is a close approximation to reality.
(iv) assume "rules-of-thumb", which may be based on experience, for the evaluation of the building. For example, the number of lifts may be related to the plan area of a building and its speed to the height. A large number of these empirical rules would allow the internal contents of a building to be costed with reasonable accuracy once a building shape had been determined.

In the techniques that follow simplifying assumptions such as these will need to be made and together with the qualifications already discussed, it is apparent that these techniques will only lead to optimal rather than optimum economic solutions. We can get within an approximation of the best solution but cannot guarantee to have found it. In choosing the techniques for this chapter the authors have concentrated on three processes which provide a representative sample of approaches and which have all been used in building cost experiments. It is too early to say whether one or more of the techniques is likely to become a lasting and common technique for the cost adviser. The development of computer systems will no doubt encourage the use of more mathematical techniques mainly because the chore of calculation will have been removed and data will be readily accessible. It has not been possible to go into detail within the space available, but it is hoped that sufficient information has been given for a clear appreciation of approach.

Structured search approach

This is perhaps the simplest of the possible optimisation methods. An outline of the procedure has already been given on page 98 related to the design process. In that procedure it was suggested that if a table of possible solutions were produced then one of these solutions could be chosen and form the basis of a design strategy. The problem is how to arrive at the table and what variables should the table consider.

An appreciation of the objective is given in Fig. 17.2. This simple diagram illustrates the point that there are a number of constraints acting on the solutions available and these form a boundary to what is possible. (Some of these boundaries will not be clear and will depend on other constraints.) Within the boundary will be found those solutions which are feasible, providing that the constraints do not rule out every possibility. Within this zone of feasible solutions, which in practice usually contains an infinite number of building shapes and combination of components, there will be "better" economic solutions. To avoid trying to search through a

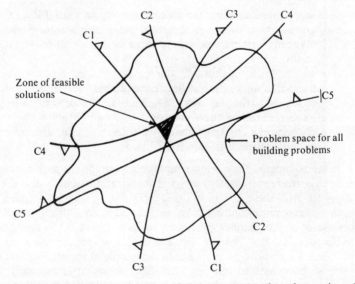

FIG. 17.2. *Diagrammatic representation of how constraints reduce the number of solutions available*

wide range of possibilities in order to find a good solution the zone could be "mapped" at regular intervals in order to establish a trend and if possible a least cost solution. From this "least cost" reference point other alternatives can be considered which may be better from other design standpoints and their cost compared with the "least" cost already calculated. It can then be seen whether it is worthwhile to pay this extra amount of money to achieve the improvement in design. If a similar table were produced for future costs then it might be possible to narrow down the number of solutions still further.

Since there are different objectives and constraints for initial and future finance, the separation of the two will enable the client to apply his own weighting to the importance of each. This will no doubt be influenced by a number of factors including the interest paid on capital as shown in Fig. 17.3.

Some of the building shape variables will be discrete (i.e. whole numbers) such as the number of storeys and therefore the chances of missing the "best" solution in the "mapping" process will be reduced for these variables. Others will be continuous and if these are used to generate other costs, e.g. plan area may be used to determine the number of staircases, then there is always a danger that a cost threshold has been missed.

However, as has already been stated in this chapter, it is not possible to

FIG. 17.3. *Annual percentage spent on capital and future costs for a sample of Crown office buildings (DOE, R & D Bulletin Building Maintenance, Report of the Committee 1970)*

consider every possible combination of specification and shape. The opportunities are infinite and human experience must be brought to bear on the problem to act as a filter to avoid those options which are most likely to yield an unsatisfactory result. Even with this initial screening the possibilities are still enormous and some search strategy must be applied which will enable the information to be handled in a meaningful way. If a number of options are to be evaluated, it is essential that a computer is used. The danger here is that the operator will be swamped with paper, and confusion caused by over-kill of information will be the order of the day. Those projects which have the widest number of choices will be those found on "green field" sites with no planning constrictions or heavily constrained internal environments. An infill site between two adjacent buildings in the centre of the city will be severely constrained by shape and probably specification.

One possible procedure is that shown in Figs 17.4 and 17.5. It consists of a two-stage affair. The first stage involves the design team choosing certain specification options from an analysis of the brief for each of the major cost-significant components of the building. These are "explored" from the point of view of cost as if they were independent of any building. Models such as the lift model in Chapter 15 or cost models for the comparison of different structural frames could be used for this purpose.

FIG. 17.4. *Design model*

FIG. 17.5. *Cost model related to above*

From this initial exploration, the specification and parameters of components for a building can be chosen which are then taken into the second stage. This next evaluation involves the use of these chosen specifications, which would be checked for compatibility, in another model which calculates the whole building cost for a number of building geometries.

It is anticipated that this kind of optimisation process would take place prior to design and therefore the level of detail required for the geometric model would be rather coarse. This would be essential in any case, if we were to allow the designer to use his own particular skills of spatial organisation and aesthetics to full advantge. The geometric variables could be:

   (i) Number of storeys.
  (ii) Accommodation area.
 (iii) Plan shape index (see page 291).
 (iv) Plan compactness ratio (see page 291) to circumscribe the building plan.
  (v) Average storey height.
 (vi) Glazed area.
(vii) Density of partitioning.

These are probably the minimum number to obtain some useful quantitative information for cost evaluation and at the same time "trigger" the cost thresholds that exist, say, for the number and speed of lifts. There is no reason why these variables should not also interact within themselves. For example, the glazed area could vary with the assumed depth of plan. Alongside these parameters would be a series of "rules-of-thumb" which would generate the requirements for other aspects of the building and these could include rules for circulation areas, staircases, toilet accommodation, service cores, etc. Constraints such as site area and shape, minimum plan area, etc. would also be included to avoid unnecessary evaluations.

The presentation of the final series of cost maps could be similar to that shown in Fig. 17.6. In this case the change in cost related to the plan shape index and number of storeys is shown for a commercial building. (Cost is in thousands of pounds.) All other variables and specifications have been kept constant and the "map" contoured for ease of comprehension. It can be seen that for this set of constants the "least cost" solution is at six storeys with a square plan shape. We can now ask the question "how much extra will it cost to go for a four-storey building and more external modelling with, say, a plan shape index of 1:4" and then probably more importantly "is it worth it?" The difference in cost must be balanced by the additional benefit to be derived from the improvement in the form of the building. The "guide" costs (and the results should be put no higher than this) will give a clue as to extra cost and the client will have a datum for measuring value. The argument has been put forward rather simplistically and there are all

	Number of storeys									
Plan shape	1	2	3	4	5	6	7	8	9	10
1.0	2874	2031	1926	1804	1768	1720	1827	1865	1897	1933
1.5	2877	2035	1931	1810	1775	1727	1835	1874	1906	1942
2.0	2883	2043	1941	1822	1788	1742	1850	1890	1924	1961
2.5	2890	2053	1953	1836	1803	1758	1868	1909	1944	1982
3.0	2897	2063	1965	1850	1819	1775	1887	1929	1965	2004
3.5	2904	2073	1977	1864	1834	1793	1905	1949	1986	2026
4.0	2911	2083	1989	1877	1850	1810	1924	1969	2007	2048
4.5	2917	2092	2001	1891	1865	1826	1941	1988	2027	2070
5.0	2924	2102	2012	1904	1880	1842	1959	2006	2047	2090
5.5	2930	2111	2024	1917	1894	1858	1976	2025	2066	2111
6.0	2937	2120	2034	1930	1908	1874	1993	2043	2085	2131
6.5	2943	2128	2045	1942	1922	1889	2009	2060	2103	2150
7.0	2949	2137	2055	1954	1935	1903	2025	2077	2121	2169
7.5	2955	2145	2066	1966	1948	1918	2040	2093	2139	2188
8.0	2960	2153	2075	1977	1961	1932	2055	2110	2156	2206
8.5	2966	2161	2085	1988	1974	1945	2070	2125	2173	2223
9.0	2971	2169	2095	1999	1986	1959	2085	2141	2189	2241
9.5	2977	2176	2104	2010	1998	1972	2099	2156	2205	2258
10.0	2982	2184	2113	2020	2009	1985	2113	2171	2221	2274
10.5	2987	2191	2122	2031	2021	1997	2126	2185	2236	2290
11.0	2992	2198	2131	2041	2032	2010	2140	2200	2252	2306
11.5	2997	2205	2139	2051	2043	2022	2153	2214	2267	2322
12.0	3002	2212	2148	2060	2054	2034	2166	2227	2281	2338
12.5	3007	2219	2156	2070	2065	2045	2178	2241	2296	2353
13.0	3012	2225	2164	2079	2076	2057	2191	2254	2310	2368
13.5	3016	2232	2172	2089	2086	2068	2203	2267	2324	2382
14.0	3021	2238	2180	2098	2096	2080	2215	2280	2337	2397
14.5	3025	2245	2188	2107	2106	2091	2227	2293	2351	2411
15.0		2251	2196	2116	2116	2101	2239	2306	2364	
15.5		2257	2203	2124	2126	2112	2250	2318	2377	
16.0		2263	2211	2133	2135	2123	2262	2330	2390	

FIG. 17.6. *Cost map of permissible solution space within natural and legal constraints (costs in thousands of pounds). Blank evaluations exceed constraints.*

sorts of qualifications that would need to be made. There is a danger, particularly in government circles, for the least cost to be chosen irrespective of the other benefits. It is incumbent on all members of the design team to strengthen the quality argument whilst at the same time developing more explicit quantitative models.

The cost maps are relatively easy to produce (although the models are more difficult) and it is therefore easy to loop back through the system and select a different specification for components, or undertake a different analysis of the brief, to see what impact this would have on the final output. (The maps of course would also look at other combinations of geometric variables and future costs as well.)

At the end of the day, from the wide selection of cost alternatives, a design strategy would be adopted which took into account cost, form and specification levels, albeit at a very coarse level. It may not be optimum cost but it may be a step towards optimum design. In essence the quantitative and qualitative issues are being made explicit to aid the approach to design. This is shown diagrammatically in Fig. 17.7. Once a strategy has been taken on board (the computer can reel off the assumptions made in the chosen solution) then more formal budgetary control mechanisms such as elemental cost planning can be used as drawn information becomes available. There is in fact no reason why the computer should not produce the first broad outline cost plan from its evaluative routines. It is interesting to note that the cost patterns do not always conform to conventional ideas and indeed when "future cost" contours are superimposed, may open the way to more adventurous design possibilities.

The procedure outlined above is one developed into a pilot model by the authors some years ago and is now being improved. This is, however, only one approach to the structured search for optimisation and simpler or more

Quality 1

Quality 2

Quality 3

FIG. 17.7. *Diagrammatic representation of cost map profile with different quality levels* complex models could be derived. In the above system most of the models were empirical although there is no reason why a variety of different types should not be used, particularly in the first stage of the process.

A simpler form of one-stage model could be developed from a regression equation where a table is produced from a systematic evaluation of the major variables. At the other extreme a multi-stage model could be devised which relates to the various "entry points" into the analysis and synthesis stages of design. This more complex model would allow more flexibility for the designer and would make assumptions based on "rules-of-thumb" with regard to information which is not available at the time. This is a small step towards the development of what is known as a "knowledge base", necessary for the development of a computerised expert system. Currently the knowledge base is held in the human brain and accesses the data base to make a decision.

As time goes by more of the experience of the cost adviser will be able to be made explicit in the machine and there will be less need for human intervention in the search. This has a number of serious ramifications for the profession and introduces a number of ethical questions and it may be that future editions of this book will return to this issue.

Lastly, it should not be thought that the structured search approach will provide a panacea for all our problems, or that the theory behind the models is well developed. However, with the increase in computer power there is no reason why it should not provide a substantial step forward in providing better cost advice.

Monte Carlo "hill climbing" approach

In the above approach to optimisation all the steps along the path to finding a solution were made explicit. At the end of the day cost comparisons could be made alongside other design criteria. There was a good deal of human interaction to sieve through the wide range of possibilities and it was recognised that better solutions may lie between the points identified in the cost map.

Another approach might be to say—let the computer do all the work and select from the options that are available, trying out every combination that is possible. If this was done randomly rather than in a structured way as before, it would amount to a "suck it and see" approach controlled by chance processes. The machine would select at random the geometry of the building comprising, say, a plan shape index, a certain number of storeys, an average storey height, a specification for each element, etc. and then evaluate it from a cost file to obtain a total cost. It would hold this figure until it undertook an evaluation which was less than the previous lowest cost. The process would continue with all higher costs being discarded until no further improvement could take place. The final solution would then be considered to be the optimum.

Now it is obvious that even with the powerful computers we have today it would take several thousand years (as noted earlier in the chapter) to calculate a cost for every combination of shape and specification that is possible. Once again for large problems some sort of strategy must be employed to get to the end solution more quickly and it must be accepted that we will only get near to the optimum, not on it.

The technique for random sampling is quite straightforward and is identical to that outlined in Chapter 15 page 277. Where discrete variables are concerned, e.g. the number of floors, then random numbers within a certain range can be allocated to each number in the range. Even with continuous variables these can be classified and included as discrete variables to speed up the operation. For example, supposing the machine had to select the span and bay size of a reinforced concrete framed floor, then the options could be structured as shown in Table 12.

TABLE 12. COST PER SQUARE METRE

Span \ Bay size	20 m²	25 m²	30 m²
3 m	38	36	35
5 m	40	38	39
7 m	44	45	47

To select a bay size and span the discrete distributions would be set up as shown in Fig. 17.8 in which a span of 5 m and bay area of 20 m² have been chosen. The cost of £40 per square metre would now be included in the cost evaluation. On the next selection a different set of random numbers are likely to be generated and therefore probably a new bay area and span.

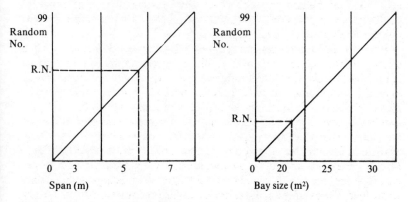

FIG. 17.8. *Random selection of span and bay size from tables*

This kind of sampling would be undertaken for all building components.

The important question now is, how do we impose a strategy on this process to avoid the selection of the expensive solutions? In other circumstances (e.g. an external wall component with U-value provided and the final cost represented in present value terms) it may be less self-evident which solution or combination would be the cheaper.

This is where the "hill climbing" aspect comes in. Imagine an undulating plain dotted with hills. The high points are the least cost solutions and the plain represents the higher costs. The strategy to be adopted is metaphorically to find the highest mountain and climb it. One approach that could be taken is

(i) Take the mean of all the options as a starting point for the first evaluation (i.e. the random number on the first round is therefore fixed at 50).

(ii) Assume that better solutions will be found near to previous good solutions.

(iii) Start with a fairly wide area of search around the "good" point and as improvements continue to be found gradually narrow the search area (by restraining the band of random numbers available to be used).

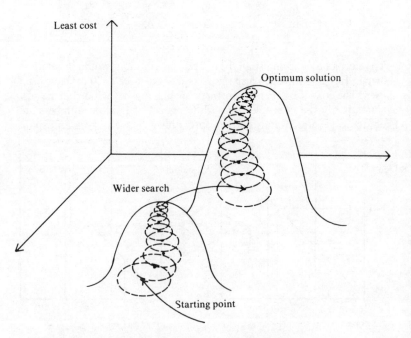

FIG. 17.9. *Diagrammatic representation of "hill climbing" approach*

(iv) When, after a specified certain number of evaluations or trials e.g. 200, no improvement has taken place, then the search area should be widened considerably to see if there is a higher mountain.

(v) If no higher mountain is found after a specified number of trials assume that the optimum has been found. This is shown diagrammatically in Fig. 17.9.

The process is shown in a procedural form in Fig. 17.10. Note that in this example the centre point for the new search radius is the value of the variable as found in the latest improvement.

A number of experiments have been undertaken with this method although once again it must be said that the complexity of a building makes it unlikely that complete structures can be effectively optimised by this technique. The closest to a useful model using this procedure for the

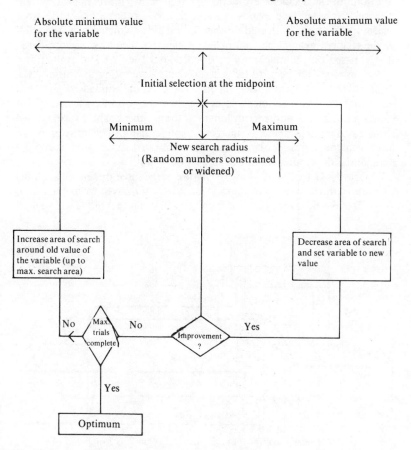

FIG. 17.10. *Possible approach to "hill climbing" model*

cost of a building expressed in annual equivalent terms was that devised by Dr Clive Bastin of the Wyvern Partnership, Swindon. In his research at Bristol University he developed a model called AIM which moved accommodation units (e.g. rooms or compartments) around in three dimensions until the cost of movement between spaces, heating and ventilating and physical elements were in the optimum relation to each other. The rooms were rectangular but were able to be expanded or contracted within certain constraints. Simplifying assumptions were made on structural requirements, costings, etc. and even so the optimisation of six or seven spaces took several hours starting from scratch with each space independent of the others. An additional search strategy was adopted to speed things up whereby an elemental cost profile was used to abort an evaluation in the early stages if it did not look like producing a good solution. If the element evaluation proved to be more than a certain percentage above the previous "good" solution for that element then that trial stopped. A sophisticated routine was included which moved the order of the element evaluation to make sure the critical costs were considered first— based on the machine's experience after the first few evaluations.

The process has been tested with students attempting to optimise the same number of spaces as the machine, using annual equivalent costs, but on a manual basis. In most cases the machine produced a better cost solution but it took appreciably longer. If the number of spaces is increased then the time requirements increase exponentially. The answer to an improvement in time probably lies in an improved search process and the anticipated developments in the speed of computing.

Figures 17.11 and 17.12 show the nature of the three-dimensional model together with the pattern of improvement in cost derived from one run of AIM. Despite the experiments it is unlikely that this technique will be used

FIG. 17.11. *AIM partial completion of optimisation process using "hill climbing" method*

FIG. 17.12. *Graph showing number of improvements and reduction in cost for one run of AIM*

in practice in the near future except for fairly simple, well-structured and constrained problems. It has been used for optimisation of circulation space and for selection of cladding panels on an envelope but is rather cumbersome.

The advantages of the technique, such as the fact that it can cope with non-linear and discontinuous variables (i.e. those where there are one or more thresholds and costs do not change in direct proportion to quantity), are outweighed by the over-simplification of large problems to overcome the time problem. The two major criticisms voiced are, however, that the technique may miss the very highest "mountain" altogether and consequently not find the best solution, and the considerable time involved in defining and structuring all the design possibilities.

Linear programming

The problem of how to utilise limited resources is a familiar one to the cost adviser. He faces it in a variety of circumstances. For example, when attempting to get the best "mix" of houses on a site, when trying to arrange the best use of plant and labour in construction or manufacture, and when trying to select the optimum arrangement of different cladding panels.

A range of mathematical techniques has been developed to tackle this particular type of problem and includes linear, non-linear and dynamic programming. Of these the simplest and most widely used is linear programming. In a book of this nature it is only possible to introduce the concept of the technique leaving the reader to tackle the mathematical basis and development by further study.

To keep the approach simple we will deal only with linear programming and then only with a problem which has two unknowns so that it can be solved by graphical means.

To be able to use linear programming five conditions must be met:

  (i)   the problem must be capable of numerical formulation.

  (ii) a number of alternative courses of action (solutions) must be possible.

 (iii) there must be one or more constraints on the alternative courses of action.

 (iv) some criterion must be available to optimise the various courses of action, e.g. least cost.

  (v) the relationship must be linear, although it is possible to deal with some non-linear relationships by simplifying or, for example, by transposing a curve into a straight line by taking the log.

The technique is used to maximise or minimise the objective of the exercise. For example, we may wish to maximise profit or minimise cost. A solution can only be found by graphical means for up to three variables; beyond this number mathematical routines are available such as the "Simplex Method" involving a manual iterative process or more commonly computer programs are used to handle the complexity of the problem.

To introduce the technique a very simple example will be taken which first appeared in a similar form in *Building Magazine* in March 1969. It nevertheless illustrates the basic principles very well and has a long history of use in some academic establishments!

Suppose the design team wished to clad a modular factory wall with two different cladding panels comprising different proportions of glazed to solid area. Each panel would have different U-values and costs. The problem is to determine the number of each type to provide an external wall of at least 3.5 $w/m^{2o}C$ and a glazing area of at least 140 m^2 for a minimum cost. Both panels are 4 m high $\times$ 3 m wide and are able to be substituted by each other in every situation. The attributes of the two panels are as follows:

Panel	Glazed area in m²	Solid area m²	U-value w/m²° C	Cost £	Number of each
A	7	5	4	500	x
B	2	10	2	400	y

The total area of cladding surface is to be 480 m² and therefore the total number of panels required is $\frac{480}{12} = 40$ panels.

To solve this problem graphically it is necessary to go through a number of stages which identify the constraints and objective function and express them in a numerical form before plotting them on a graph and reading off the optimum figure.

Stage 1: Formulate the constraints and objective functions:

U-value constraint

$$U\text{-value} = \frac{U_A.x.12 + U_B.y.12}{x.12 + y.12} \leqslant 3.5$$

Transposing this equation and including the known U-values we get

$$\frac{12\,(4x + 2y)}{480} \leqslant 3.5$$

$$2x + y \qquad \leqslant 70 \tag{1}$$

The glazing constraint is represented as

$$7x + 2y \geqslant 140 \tag{2}$$

In addition the total number of panels must not exceed the cladding area and this can be expressed as:

$$x + y = 40 \tag{3}$$

Since we cannot have a negative number of panels then it follows that

$$x \text{ and } y \geqslant 0 \tag{4}$$

The "objective function" is the expression which describes the line along which the maximum or minimum solution for which we are searching must lie. In our case we are trying to minimise cost and therefore the solution will lie along the line expressed by z.

$$500x + 400y = z \tag{5}$$

Our objective is to find the minimum value of z within the constraints given.

The formulation of these equations concludes the numerical formulation or mathematical model of the problem.

FIG. 17.13. *Non-negative:* x,y $\geqslant 0$

Stage 2: Plot the constraints on a graph.

As this problem only has two unknowns, i.e. the two different types of cladding panel, the constraints and objective function can be plotted on a two-dimensional graph. If there were three panels a three-dimensional graph would be necessary and beyond this a graphical solution would not be possible and other approaches would need to be taken. The object of the "plot" is to identify the range of feasible solutions and then find the minimum (as in our case) or maximum according to the criterion chosen, e.g. least cost. The area of feasible solution before constraints are included is shown in Fig. 17.13. As x and y are equal or greater than zero then any part of the shaded plane satisfies our constraint (4).

Thermal constraint
The first constraint to be plotted is the thermal constraint and the intercept with the two axes can be found by setting x and y to zero in the equation (1), thus:

when $x = 0$
$$0 + y = 70$$
$$y = 70$$
when $y = 0$
$$2x + 0 = 70$$
$$x = 35$$

The fact that the constraint requires the total of x and y to be less than 70 means that all values below the line AB in Fig. 17.14 (i.e. the shaded area) satisfy this condition. All values above this line are not valid.

FIG. 17.14. *Thermal constraint:* $2x + y \leqslant 70$

FIG. 17.15. *Glazing constraint:* $7x + 2y \geqslant 140$

Glazing constraint
The equation for the glazing constraint was

$$7x + 2y \geqslant 140$$

Again we plot the equality condition to give the line CD shown in Fig. 17.15.

When $x = 0$
$$0 + 2y = 140$$
$$y = 70$$
when $y = 0$
$$7x + 0 = 140$$
$$x = 20$$

In this case the "greater than" condition means that all values above the line CD are feasible.

The combined effect of these two constraints is represented by the shaded area ACDB in Figure 17.16 which identifies the range of feasible solutions so far.

FIG. 17.16. *Glazing and thermal constraints*

Number of panels
The final constraint specifies that the total number of panels must be equal to 40.

$$x + y = 40$$

This condition is satisfied by the line FG in Figure 17.17. As this is an equality condition only those values of x and y which lie on FG satisfy the condition. However, only the part of this line crossing the area identified by lines ACDB will conform to all constraints. This is shown by the thicker line HJ.

FIG. 17.17. *Glazing + thermal + area constraints:* $x + y = 40$

Stage 3: Plot objective function.
The reader will recall that the objective function is represented by the line

$$500x + 400y = z$$

In order to find the minimum value of z it is necessary to plot the *slope* of the objective function and to move it parallel to itself away from the origin (intersection of x and y axis) until it meets the line HJ. The intersection with HJ will be the correct arrangement of x and y which will satisfy the constraints and provide minimum cost.

To plot the slope of the function

$$ax + by = z$$

it is necessary to take any point on the x axis and a point on the y axis so that

$$\frac{y}{x} = \frac{a}{b}$$

and join the two points.

The objective function is $500x + 400y = z$ so that points on the x and y axes must be chosen so that

$$\frac{y}{x} = \frac{500}{400}$$

This is satisfied by taking for example $y = 10$ on the y axis and $x = 8$ on the x axis since

$$\frac{y}{x} = \frac{10}{8} = \frac{500}{400}$$

The line ab shown dotted in Fig. 17.18 is the plot of the slope of this line. We now move this line parallel to itself towards HJ until it touches it. (Note that if we were maximising cost we would be moving ab from above HJ towards the origin.)

FIG. 17.18. *Glazing + thermal + area constraints cost:* $400x + 500y = z$

Stage 4: Calculate results.
The point of intersection is with point H and this is therefore the optimum solution to the problem. Reading from the graph at point H we obtain the following values for x and y:

$x = 12$ representing 12 of panel A
$y = 28$ representing 28 of panel B

The shell U-value is

$$\frac{4 \times 12 \times 12 + 2 \times 28 \times 12}{12 \times 12 + 28 \times 12} = 2.6 \text{ w/m}^2 \,^\circ\text{C}$$

which satisfies constraint (1).

The glazing area is

$$7 \times 12 + 2 \times 28 = 140 \text{ m}^2$$

which satisfies constraint (2).

The total number of panels is

$$12 + 28 = 40$$

which satisfies constraint (3).

The total cost is

$$500 \times 12 + 400 \times 28 = £17,200$$

which is the minimum cost.

Although this example shows clearly the principle of the technique it will also be observed that the whole problem has been over-simplified in that many other design factors, e.g. aspect, noise, aesthetic values, would need to be taken into account. In addition not all problems could be specified so clearly in numerical and linear terms; other problems would arise if the result had not been an integer (whole number) as we would not have known instantly whether to round up or down. In more complex examples this can be a real problem and integer search techniques would need to be applied. Also many constraints are subject to thresholds, e.g. the number of lifts required for a given number of storeys or floor area. Providing the relationships still remain linear it is possible to overcome this problem although it complicates the process. Computer programs are available to undertake much of this work and this becomes almost essential when dealing with a large number of unknowns. Although manual iterations are possible (but beyond the scope of this book) it becomes a very time-consuming business. The stages of structuring the problem are however very similar, no matter what the method, and starting in a simple way will assist in developing the reader's knowledge for the complex problems.

Linear programming has been used for several different types of building optimisation problems including:

(a) Hotel design (INVEST from ABACUS, University of Strathclyde).
(b) Housing development mix. (See article by Terry Pitt in *Chartered Surveyor BQS Quarterly* Vol 4, No 3 Spring 1977, pp 40–42.)
(c) Site management. (See R. Oxley and J. Poskitt, *Management Techniques Applied to the Construction Industry*, Granada, 1980 and J. F. Woodward, *Construction Management and Design*, Macmillan, 1975.)

The reader is recommended to follow up this simple introduction with some reading of introductory textbooks in Operations Research. If it is possible to gain access to one of the many computer programs available for the technique even greater speed of comprehension will result providing the underlying structure is understood.

Generally

The purpose of this chapter has been to introduce some concepts in optimisation which it is hoped will be of benefit to the reader. A number of warnings have already been given but a final parting shot may not go amiss. There is always the danger with any new process, and particularly those which are computerised, that the inexperienced user will become so engrossed with the technique and its methodology that he loses sight of the overall main objective and the limitations of the tool he is adopting. By all means encourage the use of numerical techniques where they will enlighten, improve and assist in the development of design. However, they are not an end in themselves and the danger is that used unwisely they will give too much weight to a part of the design problem, which though important may be less significant than is first supposed.

Chapter 18
The Future and the Cost Adviser

It is always difficult to make predictions about the future with regard to the changes that may occur. The nineteenth-century prediction that the population of London would be waist deep in horse manure by the middle of the twentieth century is a useful reminder that situations are not static and, therefore, extrapolations of existing knowledge are always liable to error! One thing we can be sure of, however, is that change will occur and our ability to adapt to that change will determine our ability to survive. In his book *Future Shock,* Alvin Toffler diagnosed a new disease, with both social and physical symptoms, caused by the future coming too fast. He identified a wide range of areas where the rate of change that the current generation was expected to absorb was probably greater than all the changes in the intervening period since the invention of the wheel.

The response of the professions to these rapid changes has been to follow cautiously behind the rest of society. Even today there is still a rather negative professional reaction to many of the technological advances to be seen in industry and commerce. In some cases this natural conservatism has been well founded, as the proposed change was subsequently discovered to be inadequate or inappropriate to its use in professional (or even industrial!) applications. In other cases, however, it has meant surrendering ground to commercial interests or a shifting of expertise from one profession to another.

The intention of this chapter is not to put forward any new hypothesis with regard to the forecasting, budgeting, and control of cost, but rather to look at those factors which it is considered will be of critical importance in the years ahead, and to hazard a guess at their impact in the field of design economics. Of course it is possible, and indeed probable, that the factors considered important now will be viewed with some amusement in thirty years time. However, an understanding of what the future might hold is essential to the planning and development of a profession. Bearing in mind that a generation very often passes between graduation and a senior executive position in a firm or office, the centres of education have a responsibility to prepare their students for any new role or technique that may emerge. This preparation is unlikely to be specific in its nature, but rather the creation of a flexible, adaptable, and analytical approach to problem solving which can respond to the new situation.

To help clarify the presentation the changes have been considered in two areas, firstly the techniques used by cost advisers and secondly the environment in which they work. It may seem strange to deal with the techniques first because they will surely be moulded by the prevailing economic and political climate. Whilst this is partially true, it is equally true that a major technological change may itself create an entirely new environment. Such a development is the production of the silicon chip, and in particular its application in micro-processors. There is no doubt that its use will have serious economic and social implications. Already political capital is being made of the way in which both government and opposition are preparing to deal with the matter, and both unions and management are looking over their shoulder to discover or defend their place in the new environment that will exist. At this point in time, therefore, the major motivator for change would in the short term appear to be technology.

The techniques

It would be impossible to look to the future development of cost advice without considering the opportunities afforded by the computer. The development of this machine is unparalleled in the history of mankind. An analogy quoted by one computer spokesman may give us an insight into the enormous strides that have been made over the last twenty-five years. He said that in the 1950s a Rolls Royce car would do 15 miles to the gallon, and 150 miles an hour, and would cost about £7,500. If the same development had taken place on the Rolls Royce as has taken place in the computer field, then the car would now do 150 miles to the gallon, 1,500 miles an hour and its purchaser would get change out of seventy-five pence! It is the incredible reduction in cost that now makes the computer's use in the office inevitable. There are two possible effects stemming from its use. Either it will replace labour because it calculates faster and more reliably than the human brain, or, with the same amount of labour (but perhaps of a different kind) it will provide more information in the time available to the benefit of the client and the industry.

The reduction in labour in the professions is probably unlikely while existing techniques are still adopted. The techniques of measurement (i.e. according to the SMM rules), and of forecasting using simplified forms of analysis, have evolved to suit human ability with due consideration to human limitations. These techniques are not very well suited to the potential of the machine. Many private firms of quantity surveyors have tried and rejected computers for Bill production because they have found them uneconomical. Those that persist very often argue their case, not on the merits of the machine, but on the severe lack of competent working-up staff at technician level. It would appear that a good "cut and shuffle" system is indeed hard to beat if well implemented. The major problems from the point of view of computer operation in these traditional techniques are the amount of data preparation and the lack of repetitive calculations. These constraints will not allow the machine to exercise its main attributes of an extensive, easily accessible data storage with an ability to "crunch numbers" at enormous speed according to a predetermined logic. Until the techniques change it is likely that the present cosmetic use of the computer will only have an impact on non-qualified staff.

The obvious next question is, of course—will the techniques change? There is no doubt that in the long term there are bound to be pressures to tap the potential ability of the machine. Already, as introduced in this book, there are developments in forecasting technique involving the use of models that will depend heavily on computer evaluation. As the models become more mathematical and analytical, so the need for machine support becomes essential. People in other disciplines, such as the economists dealing with demand management for the government, already build econometric models related to various scenarios of political, social, and economic action. The decisions based upon the results of these simulations will have repercussions for the building industry and, therefore, the industry itself will need to be simulated as a sub-model of the main program for forecasting purposes. The present stage of the art is, however, still at the embryo stage of development and most of these packages suffer from severe "tunnel vision". In other words they have great difficulty in coping with all the factors influencing change, and they, therefore, content themselves with dealing with what their creators consider to be the major factors involved.

Television coverage of a general election demonstrated some of the problems. After the first few seats were announced the computer purchased by the TV company severely overestimated the scale of a win by the Conservative Party, because it did not allow for an unusual regional difference in voting patterns which its programmers had not foreseen as a factor, whereas a humanly operated "swingometer" anticipated the country as a whole and forecast the correct result from the very beginning. It is in this area of the software (programming) that the next major advance is likely to be found. Hardware (the machine itself) has developed so fast that its potential is severely limited by lack of commensurate development in software applications. Considerable effort is being made to catch up with software development, and the use of computers for cost advice will largely depend on the progress made in this area.

For software to be effective, however, it must have some underlying basis, purpose, and theory in order to harness the ability of the machine. As the machine responds well to mathematical stimuli, it is likely that early developments will need to be expressed in mathematical format. Algebraic descriptions of buildings, their components and efficiency will need to be associated with a program logic that will deal with the interrelationship of these elements. In addition, the development of data bases to cope with the flood of technical information and cost will be essential for the models to operate efficiently and effectively. The work undertaken by the BCIS and CCPI may be a first step towards providing national and regional data banks, to which access may be obtained from a remote terminal in the office. Although this possibility sounds attractive, there may be many who would recoil from using data over which they had little control. The trend at present is away from large centralised "main frame" computers to small office based machines. If this trend is to establish itself then it is essential that universal office data handling systems are developed to cope with the rapid input, retrieval and updating of data that will be necessary for acceptance by the profession.

Some steps in simplifying handling problems may be taken by the construction industry itself for other reasons. The last two decades have seen a rapid increase in the standardisation of components, if not buildings. This standardisation tends to limit the number of alternatives, and certainly the number of sizes available, which in turn will mean a reduction in the amount of data to be held for costing purposes. If this is coupled with a trend towards dimensional co-ordination then it will be simpler to represent buildings and their components in the machine, and development should, therefore, be that much quicker.

Looking much further ahead it is difficult to see the limits to the computer horizon. Already simple programs involving voice recognition are available and one can imagine that the pen and typewriter might become redundant in giving cost advice! Even more remarkable are the advances being made in heuristic programing allowing the development of an artificial intelligence. This will have arrived, according to one researcher, when it requires a computer sociologist to analyse a result rather than a mathematician! Work is being undertaken by architects in this field, and attempts are being made to get the machine to "learn" from its mistakes when providing poor or incorrect solutions. At the moment the programs are too simple to be of any practical use, and human judgement provides the criteria built into the machine for good or bad solutions. Given time and a rapid advancement of these applications in other fields we may yet see the computerised architect and quantity surveyor. Of course social pressures may be so great that this kind of development will be severely restricted. The next century should provide an interesting study for the detached observer.

The environment

The pattern of events for the future will to some extent be moulded by the social effects of the developments in computer technology. If the decrease in labour requirements predicted in recent government reports takes place then we might expect to see some reduction in the cost of labour compared with materials, assuming that the forces of supply and demand were allowed to have full play. However, since labour is not merely the only resource that has a vote, but in its other guise as the human race is supposed to be the beneficiary of the whole system, any government would certainly artificially maintain the value of labour, at least in the short and medium term. Ironically, the matter will be made worse with the increasing scarcity of raw materials. Many building materials are for practical purposes irreplaceable and it is only the labour resource which is likely to be plentiful in the future. This must result in a very different view of what is economic in building.

It is against this background that any future view must be set of what will be the role of the cost adviser. At the very root of any economic planning the concept of scarcity is always to be found. We are now at the point where we can foresee the end of plentiful supply of our major world resources. These include arable land, fossil fuels, base metals, and mineral deposits; "greenfield" building land is already totally exhausted in some areas. As these commodities become even scarcer there will undoubtedly be social tensions at both national and international level, and demands for conservation and thrift will compete with selfish desires for consumption, convenience, and comfort. The design team can play a small part in diffusing these pressures by using and manipulating the available resources in the most effective way possible, perhaps having to think in terms of resource husbandry as well as money cost. Economics has been defined as "the study of human behaviour in the disposal of scarce resources" and it is the application of the knowledge gained from this study that will play an increasing part in determining the pattern for responsible design in the future

Just as we have spoken of "socially acceptable" cost so there is socially acceptable, and unacceptable, development. This notion incorporates, of course, economic considerations but is equally concerned with politics and the fashions of the times. It seems incredible to people in 1984 that, no more than fifteen or twenty years previously, comprehensive high-rise redevelopment was seen as the social and aesthetic (not just the economic) answer to urban living, and that local councillors who put forward the idea of low-rise high-density housing, or rehabilitation of old buildings, were laughed to scorn by their colleagues and the experts. (Certainly it is to the credit of many cost advisers in the public sector that they consistently opposed the fashionable high-rise mania.) It is possible that the praiseworthy trend towards preservation, conservation, and rehabilitation could in the end over-reach itself, and the cost adviser might again have to exert a modifying influence. (Perhaps, on the other hand, we have all grown up.) Nevertheless, as in the past, the cost adviser will have to be responsive to, but not carried away by, social pressures.

Already many architects are calling for a re-think on the priorities and philosophy of design. Professor McLoud and Alex Gordon have put forward the "3 L's" concept of Long life, Loose fit, and Low energy as being the key to good design in the future. Most buildings today do not last as long as the major components of which they are composed. If their economic life is to be extended their layout has to be more flexible allowing a multiple use of the internal space. This will allow future changes of demand for accommodation to be provided within the same structure. An example quoted by Alex Gordon is that of the multi-storey car park. Present designs are unable to be converted to other uses when the running cost of cars becomes prohibitive. He suggests that by spending an extra 5% in initial cost now (e.g. to increase the storey height), it may be possible to easily convert the building to another function when its use as a car park becomes uneconomic. Long life may also be the result of a better choice of material, improved maintenance, and more careful use.

If conservation is to be the theme for the future then the cost adviser will have to change his emphasis from initial cost to future cost control. This will inevitably present a call for the improvement of techniques such as costs-in-use, or the development of another method altogether which may be more acceptable to the client. Indeed if social stress is caused by the competition for scarce resources it is likely that clients may well divert their attention to short term investments and the building of well constructed long-term buildings may fall instead of grow. Prediction of the impact of the next fifty years is a perilous occupation and if political upheaval is added to the problem then the task becomes practically impossible.

Most forecasting, however, assumes that the political and economic climate will remain fairly stable, and that change will follow orderly patterns, in order that planning and decision-making can take place. Much of the responsibility for that stability will lie with the government of the day and it has been argued that an economic consensus on basic issues be agreed by all parties to retain stability of investment and resource planning in the medium and long term future. If this could be agreed, then this would improve the probability of making a correct prediction, although it would not exclude variations due to external sources.

The major example of external impact on the economy in recent years has been the energy crisis. As the Western World continued to increase its oil consumption at a rate which would in any case have exhausted the world's supplies in a few decades, the major producing nations precipitated the crisis by calling a halt to accelerated extraction and used a cartel to control the supply and price of this important commodity. The ramifications of this control have been felt throughout the Western World and have brought home the need for energy-saving measures and the development of other energy and raw material sources. There is no doubt that the cost adviser has an important part to play in evaluating alternative schemes in these new terms. Because of the importance of energy, research is being undertaken to evaluate buildings in terms of their energy equivalent, i.e. the amount of energy used in their production. As the world becomes more energy conscious it may be that this kind of evaluation will have more impact than a purely financial assessment.

Generally

In this brief discussion it has only been possible to focus on two major factors affecting the future of the cost adviser, and indeed mankind. The development of computer technology and the conservation of scarce resources are problems of enormous magnitude. However, it would not be right to end on too much of a pessimistic note. Man has proved himself resourceful in a number of difficult areas in the past and there is no reason why he should not use his ingenuity to harness and solve these particular concerns. The role of the cost adviser must be to adapt his techniques to suit both needs and the opportunities of the future, and to discover improved methods of comparing and forecasting the cost of alternatives. If he is to be effective in this task he must increase his awareness of design objectives, world resources, computer technology, mathematical modelling, and national and world affairs. A heavy responsibility is held by the centres of education to provide for this improvement in understanding, and it may be on their shoulders that the survival of the existing professions will depend.

Appendix A

List of Elements from Standard Form of Cost Analysis

This appendix contains the element definitions from the Standard Form of Cost Analysis, but not the full requirements for unit quantity costs, etc., for which the Form itself should be consulted. (Note: The amplified form (i.e. to the sub-element level) is no longer published by the BCIS but is provided here because some firms still use it within their offices.)

1. Sub-structure

All work below underside of screed or where no screed exists to underside of lowest floor finish including damp-proof membrane, together with relevant excavations and foundations.

Notes:
(1) Where lowest floor construction does not otherwise provide a platform, the flooring surface shall be included with this element (e.g. if joisted floor, floor boarding would be included here).
(2) Stanchions and columns (with relevant casings) shall be included with "Frame" (2.A).
(3) Cost of piling and driving shall be shown separately stating system, number and average length of pile.
(4) The cost of external enclosing walls to basements shall be included with "External walls" (2.E) and stated separately for each form of construction.

2.A Frame

Loadbearing framework of concrete, steel, or timber. Main floor and roof beams, ties and roof trusses of framed buildings. Casing to stanchions and beams for structural or protective purposes.

Notes:
(1) Structural walls which form an integral part of the loadbearing

framework shall be included either with "External walls" (2.E) or "Internal walls and partitions" (2.G) as appropriate.

(2) Beams which form an integral part of a floor or roof which cannot be segregated therefrom shall be included in the appropriate element.

(3) In unframed buildings roof and floor beams shall be included with "Upper floors" (2.B) or "Roof structure" (2.C.1) as appropriate.

(4) If the "Stair structure" (2.D.1) has had to be included in this element it should be noted separately.

2.B   Upper floors

Upper floors, continuous access floors, balconies and structural screeds (access and private balconies each stated separately), suspended floors over or in basements stated separately.

Notes:

(1) Where floor construction does not otherwise provide a platform the flooring surface shall be included with this element (e.g. if joisted floor, floor boarding would be included here).

(2) Beams which form an integral part of a floor slab shall be included with this element.

(3) If the "Stair structure" (2.D.1) has had to be included in this element it should be noted separately.

2.C   Roof

2.C.1   *Roof structure*

Construction, including eaves and verges, plates and ceiling joists, gable ends, internal walls and chimneys above plate level, parapet walls, and balustrades.

Notes:

(1) Beams which form an integral part of a roof shall be included with this element.

(2) Roof housings (e.g. lift motor and plant rooms) shall be broken down into the appropriate constituent elements.

2.C.2   *Roof coverings*

Roof screeds and finishings. Battening, felt, slating, tiling, and the like.
Flashings and trims.
Insulation.
Eaves and verge treatment.

2.C.3 *Roof drainage*
Gutters where not integral with roof structure, rainwater heads, and roof outlets. (Rainwater downpipes to be included in "Internal drainage" (5.C.1).)

2.C.4 *Rooflights*
Rooflights, opening gear, frame, kerbs, and glazing.
Pavement lights.

2.D Stairs

2.D.1 *Stair structure*
Construction of ramps, stairs, and landings other than at floor levels.
Ladders.
Escape staircases.
Notes:
   (1) The cost of external escape staircases shall be shown separately.
   (2) If the staircase structure has had to be included in the elements "Frame" (2.A) or "Upper floors " (2.B) this should be stated.

2.D.2 *Stair finishes*
Finishes to treads, risers, landings (other than at floor levels), ramp surfaces, strings and soffits.

2.D.3 *Stair balustrades and handrails*
Balustrades and handrails to stairs, landings, and stairwells.

2.E External walls

External enclosing walls including that to basements but excluding items included with "Roof structure" (2.C.1).
Chimneys forming part of external walls up to plate level.
Curtain walling, sheeting rails, and cladding.
Vertical tanking.
Insulation.
Applied external finishes.
Notes:
   (1) The cost of structural walls which form an integral and important part of the loadbearing framework shall be shown separately.
   (2) Basement walls shall be shown separately and the quantity and cost given for each form of construction.
   (3) If walls are self-finished on internal face, this shall be stated.

2.F Windows and external doors

2.F.1 Windows
Sashes, frames, linings, and trims.
Ironmongery and glazing.
Shop fronts.
Lintels, sills, cavity damp-proof courses and work to reveals of openings.

2.F.2 *External doors*
Doors, fanlights, and sidelights.
Frames, linings, and trims.
Ironmongery and glazing.
Lintels, thresholds, cavity damp-proof courses and work to reveals of
openings.

2.G Internal walls and partitions

Internal walls, partitions and insulation.
Chimneys forming part of internal walls up to plate level.
Screens, borrowed lights and glazing.
Movable space-dividing partitions.
Internal balustrades excluding items included with "Stair balustrades
and handrails" (2.D.3).

Notes:
   (1) The cost of structural walls which form an integral and
       important part of the loadbearing framework shall be shown
       separately.
   (2) The cost of proprietary partitioning shall be shown separately
       stating if self-finished. Doors, etc., provided therein together
       with ironmongery, should be included stating the number of
       units installed.
   (3) The cost of proprietary WC cubicles shall be shown separately
       stating the number provided.
   (4) If design is cross-wall construction, the specification shall be
       stated and the cost shown separately.

2.H Internal doors

Doors, fanlights, and sidelights.
Sliding and folding doors.
Hatches.
Frames, linings, and trims.
Ironmongery and glazing.
Lintels, thresholds and work to reveals of openings.

3.A   Wall finishes

Preparatory work and finishes to surfaces of walls internally.
Picture, dado and similar rails.

Notes:
  (1) Surfaces which are self-finished (e.g. self-finished partitions, fair faced work) shall be included in the appropriate element.
  (2) Insulation which is a wall finishing shall be included here.
  (3) The cost of finishes applied to the inside face of external walls shall be shown separately.

3.B   Floor finishes

Preparatory work, screeds, skirtings, and finishes to floor surfaces excluding items included with "Stair finishes" (2.D.2), and structural screeds included with "Upper floors" (2.B).

Note:
  Where the floor construction does not otherwise provide a platform the flooring surface will be included either in "Sub-structure" (1) or "Upper floors" (2.B) as appropriate.

3.C   Ceiling finishes

3.C.1   *Finishes to ceilings*
Preparatory work and finishes to surfaces of soffits excluding items included with "Stair finishes" (2.D.2) but including sides and soffits of beams not forming part of a wall surface.
Cornices, coves.

3.C.2   *Suspended ceilings*
Construction and finishes of suspended ceilings.

Notes:
  (1) Where ceilings principally provide a source of heat, artificial lighting, or ventilation, they shall be included with the appropriate "Services" element and the cost shall be stated separately.
  (2) The cost of finishes or suspended ceilings to soffits immediately below roofs shall be shown separately.

4.A   Fittings and furnishings

4.A.1   *Fittings, fixtures, and furniture*
Fixed and loose fittings and furniture including shelving, cupboards,

wardrobes, benches, seating, counters, and the like.
Blinds, blind boxes, curtain tracks, and pelmets.
Blackboards, pin-up boards, notice boards, signs, lettering, mirrors, and the like. Ironmongery.

4.A.2 Soft furnishings
Curtains, loose carpets, or similar soft furnishing materials.

4.A.3 Works of art
Works of art if not included in a finishes element or elsewhere.

Note:
Where items in this element have a significant effect on other elements a note should be included in the appropriate element.

4.A.4 Equipment
Non-mechanical and non-electrical equipment related to the function or need of the building (e.g. gymnasia equipment).

5.A Sanitary appliances

Baths, basins, sinks, etc.
WC's, slop sinks, urinals, and the like.
Toilet-roll holders, towel rails, etc.
Traps, waste fittings, overflows, and taps as appropriate.

5.B Services equipment

Kitchen, laundry, hospital and dental equipment, and other specialist mechanical and electrical equipment related to the function of the building.

Note:
Local incinerators shall be included with "Refuse disposal".

5.C Disposal installations

5.C.1 Internal drainage
Waste pipes to "Sanitary appliances" (5.A) and "Services equipment" (5.B).
Soil, anti-syphonage, and ventilation pipes. Rainwater downpipes.
Floor channels and gratings and drains in ground within buildings up to external face of external walls.

Note:
Rainwater gutters are included in "Roof drainage" (2.C.3).

5.C.2 *Refuse disposal*

Refuse ducts, waste disposal (grinding) units, chutes, and bins.
Local incinerators and flues thereto.
Paper shredders and incinerators.

5.D   Water installations

5.D.1 *Mains supply*

Incoming water main from external face of external wall at point of
entry into building including valves, water meters, rising main to (but
excluding) storage tanks, and main taps. Insulation.

5.D.2 *Cold water service*

Storage tanks, pumps, pressure boosters, distribution pipework to
sanitary appliances and to services equipment.
Valves and taps not included with "Sanitary appliances" (5.A) and/or
"Services equipment" (5.B). Insulation.

Note:

> Heater tanks, cold water supplies, etc., for heating systems should
> be included in "Heat source" (5.E).

5.D.3 *Hot water service*

Hot water and/or mixed water services.
Storage cylinders, pumps, calorifiers, instantaneous water heaters,
distribution pipework to sanitary appliances and services equipment.
Valves and taps not included with "Sanitary appliances" (5.A) and/or
"Services equipment" (5.B). Insulation.

5.D.4 *Steam and condensate*

Steam distribution and condensate return pipework to and from
services equipment within the building including all valves, fittings,
etc. Insulation.

Note:

> Steam and condensate pipework installed in connection with space
> heating or the like shall be included as appropriate with "Heat
> source" (5.E) or "Space heating and air treatment" (5.F).

5.E   Heat source

Boilers, mounting, firing equipment, pressurising equipment instrumentation and control, ID and FD fans, gantries, flues and chimneys,
fuel conveyors, and calorifiers. Cold and treated water supplies and

tanks, fuel oil and/or gas supplies, storage tanks, etc., pipework (water or steam mains) pumps, valves, and other equipment. Insulation.

Notes:
(1) Chimneys and flues which are an integral part of the structure shall be included with the appropriate structural element.
(2) Local heat source shall be included with "Local heating" (5.F.4).
(3) Where more than one heat source is provided each shall be analysed separately.

5.F   Space heating and air treatment

(i) Heating only by:

5.F.1   *Water and/or steam*
Heat emission units (radiators, pipe coils, etc.) valves and fittings, instrumentation and control, and distribution pipework from "Heat source" (5.E).

5.F.2   *Ducted warm air*
Ductwork, grilles, fans, filters, etc., instrumentation and control.

5.F.3   *Electricity*
Cable heating systems, off-peak heating systems, including storage radiators.

Note:
Electrically-operated heat emission units other than storage radiators should be included under "Local heating" (5.F.4).

5.F.4   *Local heating*
Fireplaces (except flues), radiant heaters, small electrical or gas appliances, etc.

5.F.5   *Other heating systems*

(ii) Air treatment:

Notes:
(1) System described as having:
"Air treated locally" shall be deemed to include all systems where air treatment (heating or cooling) is performed either in or adjacent to the space to be treated.
"Air treated centrally" shall be deemed to include all systems where air treatment (heating or cooling) is per-

formed at a central point and ducted to the space to being treated.

(2) The combination of treatments used shall be stated, i.e.:

Heating	Dehumidification or drying
Cooling	Filtration
Humidification	Pressurisation

and whether inlet extract or recirculation.

(3) High velocity system shall be identified as:

Fan coil	Induction units 2 pipe
Dual duct	,, ,, 3 ,,
Reheat	,, ,, 4 ,,
Multi-zone	Any other system (state which).

5.F.6 *Heating with ventilation* (air treated locally)
Distribution pipework ducting, grilles, heat emission units including heating calorifiers except those which are part of "Heat source" (5.E) instrumentation and control.

5.F.7 *Heating with ventilation* (air treated centrally)
All work as detailed under (5.F.6) for system where air treated centrally.

5.F.8 *Heating with cooling* (air treated locally)
All work as detailed under (5.F.6) including chilled water systems and/or cold or treated water feeds. The whole of the costs of the cooling plant and distribution pipework to local cooling units shall be shown separately.

5.F.9 *Heating with cooling* (air treated centrally)
All work detailed under (5.F.8) for system where air treated centrally.

Note:
Where more than one system is used, design criteria, specification notes and costs should be given for each.

5.G Ventilating systems

Mechanical ventilating system not incorporating heating or cooling installations including dust and fume extraction and fresh air injection, unit extract fans, rotating ventilators and instrumentation and controls.

5.H Electrical installations

5.H.1 *Electric source and mains*
All work from external face of building up to and including local distribution boards including main switchgear, main and sub-main cables, control gear, power factor correction equipment, stand-by equipment, earthing, etc.

Notes:
(1) Installations for electric heating ("built-in" systems) shall be included with "Space heating and air treatment" (5.F.3).
(2) The cost of stand-by equipment shall be stated separately.

5.H.2 *Electric power supplies*
All wiring, cables, conduits, switches from local distribution boards, etc, to and including outlet points for the following:

General purpose socket outlets.
Services equipment.
Disposal installations.
Water installations.
Heat source.
Space heating and air treatment.
Gas installation.
Lift and conveyor installations.
Protective installations
Communication installations.
Special installations.

Note:
The cost of the power supply to these installations should, where possible, be shown separately.

5.H.3 *Electric lighting*
All wiring, cables, conduits, switches, etc., from local distribution boards and fittings to and including outlet points.

5.H.4 *Electric lighting fittings*
Lighting fittings including fixing.
Where lighting fittings supplied direct by client, this should be stated.

5.I Gas installation

Town and natural gas services from meter or from point of entry where there is no individual meter: distribution pipework to appliances and equipment.

5.J   Lift and conveyor installations

5.J.1   *Lifts and hoists*
The complete installation including gantries, trolleys, blocks, hooks and ropes, downshop leads, pendant controls, and electrical work from and including isolator.

Notes:
   (1) The cost of special structural work, e.g. lift walls, lift motor rooms, etc., shall be included in the appropriate structural elements.
   (2) Remaining electrical work shall be included with "Electric power supplies" (5.H.2).
   (3) The cost of each type of lift or hoist shall be stated separately.

5.J.2   *Escalators*
As detailed under 5.J.1.

5.J.3   *Conveyors*
As detailed under 5.J.1.

5.K   Protective installations

5.K.1   *Sprinkler installations*
The complete sprinkler installation and CO_2 extinguishing system including tanks, control mechanism, etc.

Note:
   Electrical work shall be included with "Electrical power supplies" (5.H.2).

5.K.2   *Fire-fighting installations*
Hosereels, hand extinguishers, asbestos blankets, water and sand buckets, foam inlets, dry risers (and wet risers where only serving fire-fighting equipment).

5.K.3   *Lightning protection*
The complete lightning protection installation from finials conductor tapes, to and including earthing.

Note:
   The cost of lightning protection to boiler and vent stacks shall be stated separately.

5.L Communication installations

The following installations shall be included:

Warning installations (fire and theft)
    Burglar and security alarms.
    Fire alarms.

Visual and audio installations
    Door signals.
    Timed signals.
    Call signals.
    Clocks.
    Telephones.
    Public address.
    Radio.
    Television.
    Pneumatic message systems.

Notes:
(1) The cost of each installation shall be stated separately if possible along with an indication of the specification.
(2) The cost of the work in connection with electrical supply shall be included with"Electric power supplies" (5.H.2).

5.M Special installations

All other mechanical and/or electrical installations (separately identifiable) which have not been included elsewhere, e.g. Chemical gases; Medical gases; Vacuum cleaning; Window cleaning equipment and cradles; Compressed air; Treated water; Refrigerated stores.

Notes:
(1) The cost of each installation shall, where possible, be shown separately along with an indication of the specification.
(2) Items deemed to be included under "Refrigerated stores" comprise all plant required to provide refrigerated conditions (i.e. cooling towers, compressors, instrumentation and controls, cold room thermal insulation and vapour sealing, cold room doors, etc.) for cold rooms, refrigerated stores and the like other than that required for "Space heating and air treatment" (5.F.8 and 5.F.9).

5.N Builder's work in connection with services

Builder's work in connection with mechanical and electrical services.

Notes:
  (1) The cost of builder's work in connection with each of the services elements (5.A to 5.M) shall, where possible, be shown separately.
  (2) Where tank rooms, housings, and the like are included in the gross floor area, their component parts shall be analysed in detail under the appropriate elements. Where this is not the case the cost of such items shall be included here.

5.O   Builder's profit and attendance on services

Builder's profit and attendance in connection with mechanical and electrical services.

Note:
  The cost of profit and attendance in connection with each of the services elements (5.A to 5.M) shall, where possible, be shown separately.

6.A   Site works

6.A.1   *Site preparation*
Clearance and demolitions.
Preparatory earth works to form new contours.

6.A.2   *Surface treatment*
The cost of the following items shall be stated separately if possible:
  Roads and associated footways.
  Vehicle parks.
  Paths and paved areas.
  Playing fields.
  Playgrounds.
  Games courts.
  Retaining walls.
  Land drainage.
  Landscape work.

6.A.3   *Site enclosure and division*
Gates and entrance.
Fencing, walling, and hedges.

6.A.4   *Fittings and furniture*
Notice boards, flag poles, seats, signs.

6.B   Drainage

Surface water drainage.
Foul drainage.
Sewage treatment.

Note:
   To include all drainage works (other than land drainage included
   with "Surface treatment" (6.A.2)) outside the building to and
   including disposal point, connection to sewer or to treatment plant.

6.C   External services

6.C.1   *Water mains*
Main from existing supply up to external face of building.

6.C.2   *Fire mains*
Main from existing supply up to external face of building; fire hydrants.

6.C.3   *Heating mains*
Main from existing supply or heat source up to external face of building.

6.C.4   *Gas mains*
Main from existing supply up to external face of building.

6.C.5   *Electric mains*
Main from existing supply up to external face of building.

6.C.6   *Site lighting*
Distribution, fittings, and equipment.

6.C.7   *Other mains and services*
Mains relating to other service installations (each shown separately).

6.C.8   *Builder's work in connection with external services*
Builder's work in connection with external mechanical and electrical
services: e.g. pits, trenches, ducts, etc.

Note:
   The cost of builder's work shall be stated separately for each of the
   sub-sections (6.C.1) to (6.C.7).

6.C.9   *Builder's profit and attendance on external mechanical and electrical services*

Note:
The cost of profit and attendances shall be stated separately for each of the sub-sections (6.C.1) to (6.C.7).

6.D   Minor building work

6.D.1   *Ancillary buildings*
Separate minor buildings such as sub-stations, bicycle stores, horticultural buildings, and the like, inclusive of local engineering services.

6.D.2   *Alterations to existing buildings*
Alterations and minor additions, shoring, repair, and maintenance to existing buildings.

Preliminaries

Priced items in Preliminaries Bill and Summary but excluding contractors' price adjustments. Individual costs of the main preliminary items should be given.

Notes:
(i) Professional fees will not form part of the cost analysis.
(ii) Lump sum adjustments shall be spread pro rata amongst all elements of the building and external works based on all work excluding Prime Cost and Provisional Sums.

Appendix B
Table of Random Numbers

23	61	75	21	92	45	10	84	83	02	37	63	30	22
63	07	17	94	14	51	06	29	74	37	38	07	70	33
30	00	47	21	50	65	79	34	69	98	85	57	29	33
62	08	86	93	47	31	63	36	73	91	74	24	83	72
58	71	31	21	27	47	67	68	58	44	32	76	42	08
10	95	59	69	21	19	48	35	91	72	71	26	07	96
97	92	03	46	34	51	01	91	77	28	57	61	96	76
55	04	42	32	74	70	00	64	97	01	76	89	43	56
16	33	76	33	61	62	03	89	25	02	63	16	45	56
28	09	81	53	27	74	71	89	20	56	00	68	73	24
73	34	51	61	94	55	44	87	63	00	05	41	40	57
68	14	43	19	08	98	69	19	02	69	46	27	37	99
58	55	54	94	74	50	48	58	95	22	42	81	85	51
42	67	37	72	62	15	60	96	78	60	66	92	12	03
60	86	00	89	92	50	77	65	01	97	59	45	35	30
98	57	04	16	45	85	43	96	86	60	67	45	73	30
70	94	73	75	58	05	21	60	76	31	64	87	75	16
27	14	30	92	14	56	03	23	40	17	36	23	77	01
20	01	18	69	70	75	52	41	73	11	28	56	68	71
47	40	09	73	13	01	33	32	86	82	78	26	79	70
35	98	39	86	77	27	32	07	45	87	80	37	58	64
92	16	16	89	54	10	35	19	35	32	70	48	95	13
86	99	97	52	77	10	86	46	71	34	64	29	70	17
41	77	60	89	81	47	66	18	96	82	93	63	26	07
74	73	29	59	80	96	03	08	04	04	80	31	33	57
27	18	60	83	77	28	85	37	55	75	15	92	44	04
98	99	15	37	28	84	06	98	61	81	68	45	46	06
09	95	85	97	82	98	12	88	63	32	39	63	30	73
20	89	27	55	20	66	67	55	32	18	96	23	59	56
95	43	31	90	54	25	06	28	19	31	82	49	69	80
11	07	21	09	98	61	54	29	96	75	18	59	04	72
60	91	95	50	85	60	12	85	20	27	96	37	93	22
57	80	32	41	10	01	71	92	60	73	50	61	15	43
98	67	62	69	47	71	67	17	48	74	64	64	30	60
13	78	72	88	76	51	89	46	03	93	65	18	69	72
27	97	36	55	67	89	21	39	25	93	99	96	82	18
31	59	28	01	51	40	88	17	31	89	02	62	17	74
90	00	45	19	80	87	58	51	69	08	74	69	53	01
65	09	67	96	52	30	51	97	54	29	16	15	76	40
05	13	79	46	87	08	91	99	16	88	30	53	78	14

Appendix C
Definition of Statistical Terms

Generally

Variable

This is a quantitative measurement to which a numerical value is assigned, e.g. area of a building or number of bed spaces in a building.

Variables can be discrete, i.e. they can only take integer values, or continuous, i.e. they can take any value including fractional values between two limits. In the example above "area" would be a continuous variable and "number of bed spaces" a discrete variable.

Parameter

This is a quantity which is constant in a particular case considered, but which varies in different cases. The parameters of a rectangular building may be length, width and height. Although all rectangular buildings can be described in this manner, for any specific rectangular building these quantities will be fixed.

Abbreviations

Arithmetic mean $= \bar{x} \ or \ \mu$
Standard deviation $= s \ or \ \sigma$
To sum a series $= \Sigma$

Averages

These are measures of location or measures of central tendency and are single figures which sum up certain characteristics of a whole group of figures.

Arithmetic mean

This is the sum (Σ) of all the variables divided by the number of members in the series:

$$\bar{x} = \frac{1}{n} \Sigma x$$

where $\bar{x}$ = arithmetic mean
n = number of members in the sample
x = variable.

Geometric mean

This is the nth root of the product of the values of the variable in question from the 1st to the nth:

Geometric mean = $\sqrt[n]{(X_1 \times X_2 \times X_3 \times X_4 \ldots \times X_n)}$

where n = number of the variables in the sample
X_1 to X_n = the individual values of each variable.

It is preferable to use this mean when *relative* changes in a variable quantity are averaged, e.g. the average annual rate of increase in building costs over the last n years where each year's increase will be relative to the previous year's value.

Median

The median of a data is the value of the middle observation when the items have been arranged in either ascending or descending order. If there are an even number of observations the median is taken as the mean of the middle two observations. The median is only affected by the middle or two observations; the remaining observations do not have any direct influence on its size.

Mode

The mode is the value in the data set that occurs most frequently. Some sets of data have no modal value and others have two or more. By definition there can be no mode in a simple series, where no value occurs more than once.

Measures of dispersion

Averages measure the position or location of a series of observations. They do not give any indication of the total spread of values that go to make up the "average" figure. To help us understand the sample set of data better, some measures of dispersion are available.

Standard deviation

This is sometimes known as the root mean squared deviation and this name is a description of the method of calculation. The deviations (i.e. the difference between *an* observation and the arithmetic

mean calculated for each item of data) is squared to get rid of
negative values. The arithmetic mean of these squared deviations is
then calculated and the square root obtained.

The resultant figure is the standard deviation and it is expressed in
absolute terms and is given in the same unit of measurement as the
variable itself.

The formula is:

$$\text{standard deviation } (s) = \sqrt{\left[\frac{\Sigma(x - \bar{x})^2}{n}\right]}$$

where x = observed value
$\quad\bar{x}$ = arithmetic mean of the data
$\quad n$ = number of observations.

For manual calculation purposes the formula is normally given in
another form:

$$s = \sqrt{\left[\frac{\Sigma x^2}{n} - \left(\frac{\Sigma x}{n}\right)^2\right]}.$$

This formula requires only the aggregate of the series (Σx) and the
aggregate of the squares of the individual values in the series (Σx^2)
for calculation purposes.

The standard deviation is a useful guide to the amount of dispersion
in the data. It can be used with, for example, the arithmetic mean to
describe a complete distribution such as the normal distribution
from which further knowledge of the data set can be obtained.

Coefficient of variation

There are occasions when the standard deviation, being an absolute
measure of dispersion, is inadequate and a relative form becomes
preferable, e.g. if a comparison between the variability of distributions of say, plaster and concrete prices is required, the two distributions will have different arithmetic means. Even if they had the
same amount of variability their standard deviations would therefore be different.

Where a relative measure of variability is required the coefficient of
variation should be used.

$$\text{Coefficient of variation} = \frac{100s}{\bar{x}} \%$$

where s = standard deviation of the data
$\quad\bar{x}$ = arithmetic mean of the data.

The formula simply expresses the standard deviation as a percentage of the arithmetic mean.

Distributions

Frequency distribution
   This is the manner in which the frequency of occurrence of a variable is spread over its range of values.

   It can be expressed in numerical form or by a histogram or curve.

Normal distribution
   This is continuous symmetrical distribution in the form of a bell-shaped curve which slopes downwards on both sides from the maximum value towards the x-axis but never touches the x-axis. A normal distribution is completely specified by two parameters, the mean and the standard deviation.

   It can be shown mathematically that whenever a measurement is affected by a large number of small independent factors, no one of which predominates, the distribution of observations will be "normal".

   Because of its characteristics it is possible, knowing the arithmetic mean and standard deviation, to assess the proportion of a variable under a portion of the curve. This assists in determining the probability of an event occurring.

Skewed distribution
   This is a distribution which is not symmetrical but has its maximum value to one side or other of the arithmetic mean.

Appendix D

Discounting and Interest Formulae and Tables

The interest and discount formulae and tables in this appendix may be used in respect of weekly, monthly or yearly periods.

0.096% per week = 0.417% per month = 5% per annum
0.192% per week = 0.833% per month = 10% per annum
0.289% per week = 1.25% per month = 15% per annum
0.385% per week = 1.667% per month = 20% per annum

In the following formulae n represents the number of periods and i the interest rate expressed as a decimal fraction of the principal, e.g. $5\% = 0.05$.

Formula 1 Compound interest $(1 + i)^n$

Formula 2 Future value of £1 invested at regular intervals $\dfrac{(1 + i)^n - 1}{i}$

Formula 3 Present value of £1 $\dfrac{1}{(1 + i)^n}$

Formula 4 Present value of £1 payable at regular intervals ("years purchase") including a sinking fund at same rate as interest rate

$$\frac{(1 + i)^n - 1}{i(1 + i)^n}$$

Formula 5 Annuity purchased by £1 $\dfrac{i(1 + i)^n}{(1 + i)^n - 1}$

Formula 6 Sinking fund $\dfrac{i}{(1 + i)^n - 1}$

Note: No provision is made in Table 3 and in those that follow for repayment of the original sum by means of a sinking fund. When this is required the relevant value from Table 6 should be added.

Formulae 3, 5 and 6 are the reciprocals of formulae 1, 4 and 2 respectively.

TABLE 1—COMPOUND INTEREST
Value at end of each period of £1 invested at beginning of period 1 and accumulating at compound interest from 1% to 30% per period

Period	1% £	1.5% £	2% £	2.5% £	3% £	4% £	5% £	6% £	7% £	8% £
1	1.01	1.02	1.02	1.03	1.03	1.04	1.05	1.06	1.07	1.08
2	1.02	1.03	1.04	1.05	1.06	1.08	1.10	1.12	1.14	1.17
3	1.03	1.05	1.06	1.08	1.09	1.12	1.16	1.19	1.23	1.26
4	1.04	1.06	1.08	1.10	1.13	1.17	1.22	1.26	1.31	1.36
5	1.05	1.08	1.10	1.13	1.16	1.22	1.28	1.34	1.40	1.47
6	1.06	1.09	1.13	1.16	1.19	1.27	1.34	1.42	1.50	1.59
7	1.07	1.11	1.15	1.19	1.23	1.32	1.41	1.50	1.61	1.71
8	1.08	1.13	1.17	1.22	1.27	1.37	1.48	1.59	1.72	1.85
9	1.09	1.14	1.20	1.25	1.30	1.42	1.55	1.69	1.84	2.00
10	1.10	1.16	1.22	1.28	1.34	1.48	1.63	1.79	1.97	2.16
11	1.12	1.18	1.24	1.31	1.38	1.54	1.71	1.90	2.10	2.33
12	1.13	1.20	1.27	1.34	1.43	1.60	1.80	2.01	2.25	2.52
13	1.14	1.21	1.29	1.38	1.47	1.67	1.89	2.13	2.41	2.72
14	1.15	1.23	1.32	1.41	1.51	1.73	1.98	2.26	2.58	2.94
15	1.16	1.25	1.35	1.45	1.56	1.80	2.08	2.40	2.76	3.17
16	1.17	1.27	1.37	1.48	1.60	1.87	2.18	2.54	2.95	3.43
17	1.18	1.29	1.40	1.52	1.65	1.95	2.29	2.69	3.16	3.70
18	1.20	1.31	1.43	1.56	1.70	2.03	2.41	2.85	3.38	4.00
19	1.21	1.33	1.46	1.60	1.75	2.11	2.53	3.03	3.62	4.32
20	1.22	1.35	1.49	1.64	1.81	2.19	2.65	3.21	3.87	4.66

Period	1% £	1.5% £	2% £	2.5% £	3% £	4% £	5% £	6% £	7% £	8% £
21	1.23	1.37	1.52	1.68	1.86	2.28	2.79	3.40	4.14	5.03
22	1.24	1.39	1.55	1.72	1.92	2.37	2.93	3.60	4.43	5.44
23	1.26	1.41	1.58	1.76	1.97	2.46	3.07	3.82	4.74	5.87
24	1.27	1.43	1.61	1.81	2.03	2.56	3.23	4.05	5.07	6.34
25	1.28	1.45	1.64	1.85	2.09	2.67	3.39	4.29	5.43	6.85
26	1.30	1.47	1.67	1.90	2.16	2.77	3.56	4.55	5.81	7.40
27	1.31	1.49	1.71	1.95	2.22	2.88	3.73	4.82	6.21	7.99
28	1.32	1.52	1.74	2.00	2.29	3.00	3.92	5.11	6.65	8.63
29	1.33	1.54	1.78	2.05	2.36	3.12	4.12	5.42	7.11	9.32
30	1.35	1.56	1.81	2.10	2.43	3.24	4.32	5.74	7.61	10.06
31	1.36	1.59	1.85	2.15	2.50	3.37	4.54	6.09	8.15	10.87
32	1.37	1.61	1.88	2.20	2.58	3.51	4.76	6.45	8.72	11.74
33	1.39	1.63	1.92	2.26	2.65	3.65	5.00	6.84	9.33	12.68
34	1.40	1.66	1.96	2.32	2.73	3.79	5.25	7.25	9.98	13.69
35	1.42	1.68	2.00	2.37	2.81	3.95	5.52	7.69	10.68	14.79
36	1.43	1.71	2.04	2.43	2.90	4.10	5.79	8.15	11.42	15.97
37	1.45	1.73	2.08	2.49	2.99	4.27	6.08	8.64	12.22	17.25
38	1.46	1.76	2.12	2.56	3.07	4.44	6.39	9.15	13.08	18.63
39	1.47	1.79	2.16	2.62	3.17	4.62	6.70	9.70	13.99	20.12
40	1.49	1.81	2.21	2.69	3.26	4.80	7.04	10.29	14.97	21.72

TABLE 1—COMPOUND INTEREST

Value at end of each period of £1 invested at beginning of period 1 and accumulating at compound interest from 1% to 30% per period

Period	9% £	10% £	11% £	12% £	13% £	14% £	15% £	20% £	25% £	30% £
1	1.09	1.10	1.11	1.12	1.13	1.14	1.15	1.20	1.25	1.30
2	1.19	1.21	1.23	1.25	1.28	1.30	1.32	1.44	1.56	1.69
3	1.30	1.33	1.37	1.40	1.44	1.48	1.52	1.73	1.95	2.20
4	1.41	1.46	1.52	1.57	1.63	1.69	1.75	2.07	2.44	2.86
5	1.54	1.61	1.69	1.76	1.84	1.93	2.01	2.49	3.05	3.71
6	1.68	1.77	1.87	1.97	2.08	2.19	2.31	2.99	3.81	4.83
7	1.83	1.95	2.08	2.21	2.35	2.50	2.66	3.58	4.77	6.27
8	1.99	2.14	2.30	2.48	2.66	2.85	3.06	4.30	5.96	8.16
9	2.17	2.36	2.56	2.77	3.00	3.25	3.52	5.16	7.45	10.60
10	2.37	2.59	2.84	3.11	3.39	3.71	4.05	6.19	9.31	13.79
11	2.58	2.85	3.15	3.48	3.84	4.23	4.65	7.43	11.64	17.92
12	2.81	3.14	3.50	3.90	4.33	4.82	5.35	8.92	14.55	23.30
13	3.07	3.45	3.88	4.36	4.90	5.49	6.15	10.70	18.19	30.29
14	3.34	3.80	4.31	4.89	5.53	6.26	7.08	12.84	22.74	39.37
15	3.64	4.18	4.78	5.47	6.25	7.14	8.14	15.41	28.42	51.19
16	3.97	4.59	5.31	6.13	7.07	8.14	9.36	18.49	35.53	66.54
17	4.33	5.05	5.90	6.87	7.99	9.28	10.76	22.19	44.41	86.50
18	4.72	5.56	6.54	7.69	9.02	10.58	12.38	26.62	55.51	112.46
19	5.14	6.12	7.26	8.61	10.20	12.06	14.23	31.95	69.39	146.19
20	5.60	6.73	8.06	9.65	11.52	13.74	16.37	38.34	86.74	190.05

Period	9% £	10% £	11% £	12% £	13% £	14% £	15% £	20% £	25% £	30% £
21	6.11	7.40	8.95	10.80	13.02	15.67	18.82	46.01	108.42	247.06
22	6.66	8.14	9.93	12.10	14.71	17.86	21.64	55.21	135.53	321.18
23	7.26	8.95	11.03	13.55	16.63	20.36	24.89	66.25	169.41	417.54
24	7.91	9.85	12.24	15.18	18.79	23.21	28.63	79.50	211.76	542.80
25	8.62	10.83	13.59	17.00	21.23	26.46	32.92	95.40	264.70	705.64
26	9.40	11.92	15.08	19.04	23.99	30.17	37.86	114.48	330.87	917.33
27	10.25	13.11	16.74	21.32	27.11	34.39	43.54	137.37	413.59	1192.53
28	11.17	14.42	18.58	23.88	30.63	39.20	50.07	164.84	516.99	1550.29
29	12.17	15.86	20.62	26.75	34.62	44.69	57.58	197.81	646.23	2015.38
30	13.27	17.45	22.89	29.86	39.12	50.95	66.21	237.38	807.79	2620.00
31	14.46	19.19	25.41	33.56	44.20	58.08	76.14	284.85	1009.74	3405.99
32	15.76	21.11	28.21	37.58	49.95	66.21	87.57	341.82	1262.18	4427.79
33	17.18	23.23	31.31	42.09	56.44	75.48	100.70	410.19	1577.72	5756.13
34	18.73	25.55	34.75	47.14	63.78	86.05	115.80	492.22	1972.15	7482.97
35	20.41	28.10	38.57	52.80	72.07	98.10	133.18	590.67	2465.19	9727.86
36	22.25	30.91	42.82	59.14	81.44	111.83	153.15	708.80	3081.49	12646.22
37	24.25	34.00	47.53	66.23	92.02	127.49	176.12	850.56	3851.86	16440.08
38	26.44	37.40	52.76	74.18	103.99	145.34	202.54	1020.67	4814.82	21372.11
39	28.82	41.14	58.56	83.08	117.51	165.69	232.92	1224.81	6018.53	27783.74
40	31.41	45.26	65.00	93.05	132.78	188.88	267.86	1469.77	7523.16	36118.86

TABLE 2—FUTURE VALUE OF £1 INVESTED AT REGULAR INTERVALS

Value of £1 invested regularly at end of each period (i.e. weekly, monthly, or yearly) accumulating at compound interest from 1% to 30% per period

Period	1% £	1.5% £	2% £	2.5% £	3% £	4% £	5% £	6% £	7% £	8% £
1	1.00	1.00	1.00	1.00	1.00	1.00	1.00	1.00	1.00	1.00
2	2.01	2.02	2.02	2.03	2.03	2.04	2.05	2.06	2.07	2.08
3	3.03	3.05	3.06	3.08	3.09	3.12	3.15	3.18	3.21	3.25
4	4.06	4.09	4.12	4.15	4.18	4.25	4.31	4.37	4.44	4.51
5	5.10	5.15	5.20	5.26	5.31	5.42	5.53	5.64	5.75	5.87
6	6.15	6.23	6.31	6.39	6.47	6.63	6.80	6.98	7.15	7.34
7	7.21	7.32	7.43	7.55	7.66	7.90	8.14	8.39	8.65	8.92
8	8.29	8.43	8.58	8.74	8.89	9.21	9.55	9.90	10.26	10.64
9	9.37	9.56	9.75	9.95	10.16	10.58	11.03	11.49	11.98	12.49
10	10.46	10.70	10.95	11.20	11.46	12.01	12.58	13.18	13.82	14.49
11	11.57	11.86	12.17	12.48	12.81	13.49	14.21	14.97	15.78	16.65
12	12.68	13.04	13.41	13.80	14.19	15.03	15.92	16.87	17.89	18.98
13	13.81	14.24	14.68	15.14	15.62	16.63	17.71	18.88	20.14	21.50
14	14.95	15.45	15.97	16.52	17.09	18.29	19.60	21.02	22.55	24.21
15	16.10	16.68	17.29	17.93	18.60	20.02	21.58	23.28	25.13	27.15
16	17.26	17.93	18.64	19.38	20.16	21.82	23.66	25.67	27.89	30.32
17	18.43	19.20	20.01	20.86	21.76	23.70	25.84	28.21	30.84	33.75
18	19.61	20.49	21.41	22.39	23.41	25.65	28.13	30.91	34.00	37.45
19	20.81	21.80	22.84	23.95	25.12	27.67	30.54	33.76	37.38	41.45
20	22.02	23.12	24.30	25.54	26.87	29.78	33.07	36.79	41.00	45.76

Period	1% £	1.5% £	2% £	2.5% £	3% £	4% £	5% £	6% £	7% £	8% £
21	23.24	24.47	25.78	27.18	28.68	31.97	35.72	39.99	44.87	50.42
22	24.47	25.84	27.30	28.86	30.54	34.25	38.51	43.39	49.01	55.46
23	25.72	27.23	28.84	30.58	32.45	36.62	41.43	47.00	53.44	60.89
24	26.97	28.63	30.42	32.35	34.43	39.08	44.50	50.82	58.18	66.76
25	28.24	30.06	32.03	34.16	36.46	41.65	47.73	54.86	63.25	73.11
26	29.53	31.51	33.67	36.01	38.55	44.31	51.11	59.16	68.68	79.95
27	30.82	32.99	35.34	37.91	40.71	47.08	54.67	63.71	74.48	87.35
28	32.13	34.48	37.05	39.86	42.93	49.97	58.40	68.53	80.70	95.34
29	33.45	36.00	38.79	41.86	45.22	52.97	62.32	73.64	87.35	103.97
30	34.78	37.54	40.57	43.90	47.58	56.08	66.44	79.06	94.46	113.28
31	36.13	39.10	42.38	46.00	50.00	59.33	70.76	84.80	102.07	123.35
32	37.49	40.69	44.23	48.15	52.50	62.70	75.30	90.89	110.22	134.21
33	38.87	42.30	46.11	50.35	55.08	66.21	80.06	97.34	118.93	145.95
34	40.26	43.93	48.03	52.61	57.73	69.86	85.07	104.18	128.26	158.63
35	41.66	45.59	49.99	54.93	60.46	73.65	90.32	111.43	138.24	172.32
36	43.08	47.28	51.99	57.30	63.28	77.60	95.84	119.12	148.91	187.10
37	44.51	48.99	54.03	59.73	66.17	81.70	101.63	127.27	160.34	203.07
38	45.95	50.72	56.11	62.23	69.16	85.97	107.71	135.90	172.56	220.32
39	47.41	52.48	58.24	64.78	72.23	90.41	114.10	145.06	185.64	238.94
40	48.89	54.27	60.40	67.40	75.40	95.03	120.80	154.76	199.64	259.06

TABLE 2—FUTURE VALUE OF £1 INVESTED AT REGULAR INTERVALS

Value of £1 invested regularly at end of each period (i.e. weekly, monthly, or yearly) accumulating at compound interest from 1% to 30% per period

Period	9% £	10% £	11% £	12% £	13% £	14% £	15% £	20% £	25% £	30% £
1	1.00	1.00	1.00	1.00	1.00	1.00	1.00	1.00	1.00	1.00
2	2.09	2.10	2.11	2.12	2.13	2.14	2.15	2.20	2.25	2.30
3	3.28	3.31	3.34	3.37	3.41	3.44	3.47	3.64	3.81	3.99
4	4.57	4.64	4.71	4.78	4.85	4.92	4.99	5.37	5.77	6.19
5	5.98	6.11	6.23	6.35	6.48	6.61	6.74	7.44	8.21	9.04
6	7.52	7.72	7.91	8.12	8.32	8.54	8.75	9.93	11.26	12.76
7	9.20	9.49	9.78	10.09	10.40	10.73	11.07	12.92	15.07	17.58
8	11.03	11.44	11.86	12.30	12.76	13.23	13.73	16.50	19.84	23.86
9	13.02	13.58	14.16	14.78	15.42	16.09	16.79	20.80	25.80	32.01
10	15.19	15.94	16.72	17.55	18.42	19.34	20.30	25.96	33.25	42.62
11	17.56	18.53	19.56	20.65	21.81	23.04	24.35	32.15	42.57	56.41
12	20.14	21.38	22.71	24.13	25.65	27.27	29.00	39.58	54.21	74.33
13	22.95	24.52	26.21	28.03	29.98	32.09	34.35	48.50	68.76	97.63
14	26.02	27.97	30.09	32.39	34.88	37.58	40.50	59.20	86.95	127.91
15	29.36	31.77	34.41	37.28	40.42	43.84	47.58	72.04	109.69	167.29
16	33.00	35.95	39.19	42.75	46.67	50.98	55.72	87.44	138.11	218.47
17	36.97	40.54	44.50	48.88	53.74	59.12	65.08	105.93	173.64	285.01
18	41.30	45.60	50.40	55.75	61.73	68.39	75.84	128.12	218.04	371.52
19	46.02	51.16	56.94	63.44	70.75	78.97	88.21	154.74	273.56	483.97
20	51.16	57.27	64.20	72.05	80.95	91.02	102.44	186.69	342.94	630.17

Periods	9% £	10% £	11% £	12% £	13% £	14% £	15% £	20% £	25% £	30% £
21	56.76	64.00	72.27	81.70	92.47	104.77	118.81	225.03	429.68	820.22
22	62.87	71.40	81.21	92.50	105.49	120.44	137.63	271.03	538.10	1067.28
23	69.53	79.54	91.15	104.60	120.20	138.30	159.28	326.24	673.63	1388.46
24	76.79	88.50	102.17	118.16	136.83	158.66	184.17	392.48	843.03	1806.00
25	84.70	98.35	114.41	133.33	155.62	181.87	212.79	471.98	1054.79	2348.80
26	93.32	109.18	128.00	150.33	176.85	208.33	245.71	567.38	1319.49	3054.44
27	102.72	121.10	143.08	169.37	200.84	238.50	283.57	681.85	1650.36	3971.78
28	112.97	134.21	159.82	190.70	227.95	272.89	327.10	819.22	2063.95	5164.31
29	124.14	148.63	178.40	214.58	258.58	312.09	377.17	984.07	2580.94	6714.60
30	136.31	164.49	199.02	241.33	293.20	356.79	434.75	1181.88	3227.17	8729.99
31	149.58	181.94	221.91	271.29	332.32	407.74	500.96	1419.26	4034.97	11349.98
32	164.04	201.14	247.32	304.85	376.52	465.82	577.10	1704.11	5044.71	14755.98
33	179.80	222.25	275.53	342.43	426.46	532.04	664.67	2045.93	6306.89	19183.77
34	196.98	245.48	306.84	384.52	482.90	607.52	765.37	2456.12	7884.61	24939.90
35	215.71	271.02	341.59	431.66	546.68	693.57	881.17	2948.34	9856.76	32422.87
36	236.12	299.13	380.16	484.46	618.75	791.67	1014.35	3539.01	12321.95	42150.73
37	258.38	330.04	422.98	543.60	700.19	903.51	1167.50	4247.81	15403.44	54796.95
38	282.63	364.04	470.51	609.83	792.21	1031.00	1343.62	5098.37	19255.30	71237.03
39	309.07	401.45	523.27	684.01	896.20	1176.34	1546.17	6119.05	24070.12	92609.14
40	337.88	442.59	581.83	767.09	1013.70	1342.03	1779.09	7343.86	30088.66	120392.88

TABLE 3—PRESENT VALUE OF £1

Present value of £1 payable (or receivable) at end of any period 1 to 40, discounted at interest rates from 1% to 30% per period. Values shown in pence.

Period	1%	1.5%	2%	2.5%	3%	4%	5%	6%	7%	8%
	p	p	p	p	p	p	p	p	p	p
1	99.0	98.5	98.0	97.6	97.1	96.2	95.2	94.3	93.5	92.6
2	98.0	97.1	96.1	95.2	94.3	92.5	90.7	89.0	87.3	85.7
3	97.1	95.6	94.2	92.9	91.5	88.9	86.4	84.0	81.6	79.4
4	96.1	94.2	92.4	90.6	88.8	85.5	82.3	79.2	76.3	73.5
5	95.1	92.8	90.6	88.4	86.3	82.2	78.4	74.7	71.3	68.1
6	94.2	91.5	88.8	86.2	83.7	79.0	74.6	70.5	66.6	63.0
7	93.3	90.1	87.1	84.1	81.3	76.0	71.1	66.5	62.3	58.3
8	92.3	88.8	85.3	82.1	78.9	73.1	67.7	62.7	58.2	54.0
9	91.4	87.5	83.7	80.1	76.6	70.3	64.5	59.2	54.4	50.0
10	90.5	86.2	82.0	78.1	74.4	67.6	61.4	55.8	50.8	46.3
11	89.6	84.9	80.4	76.2	72.2	65.0	58.5	52.7	47.5	42.9
12	88.7	83.6	78.8	74.4	70.1	62.5	55.7	49.7	44.4	39.7
13	87.9	82.4	77.3	72.5	68.1	60.1	53.0	46.9	41.5	36.8
14	87.0	81.2	75.8	70.8	66.1	57.7	50.5	44.2	38.8	34.0
15	86.1	80.0	74.3	69.0	64.2	55.5	48.1	41.7	36.2	31.5
16	85.3	78.8	72.8	67.4	62.3	53.4	45.8	39.4	33.9	29.2
17	84.4	77.6	71.4	65.7	60.5	51.3	43.6	37.1	31.7	27.0
18	83.6	76.5	70.0	64.1	58.7	49.4	41.6	35.0	29.6	25.0
19	82.8	75.4	68.6	62.6	57.0	47.5	39.6	33.1	27.7	23.2
20	82.0	74.2	67.3	61.0	55.4	45.6	37.7	31.2	25.8	21.5

Period	1%	1.5%	2%	2.5%	3%	4%	5%	6%	7%	8%
	p	*p*	*p*	*p*	*p*	*p*	*p*	*p*	*p*	*p*
21	81.1	73.1	66.0	59.5	53.8	43.9	35.9	29.4	24.2	19.9
22	80.3	72.1	64.7	58.1	52.2	42.2	34.2	27.8	22.6	18.4
23	79.5	71.0	63.4	56.7	50.7	40.6	32.6	26.2	21.1	17.0
24	78.8	70.0	62.2	55.3	49.2	39.0	31.0	24.7	19.7	15.8
25	78.0	68.9	61.0	53.9	47.8	37.5	29.5	23.3	18.4	14.6
26	77.2	67.9	59.8	52.6	46.4	36.1	28.1	22.0	17.2	13.5
27	76.4	66.9	58.6	51.3	45.0	34.7	26.8	20.7	16.1	12.5
28	75.7	65.9	57.4	50.1	43.7	33.3	25.5	19.6	15.0	11.6
29	74.9	64.9	56.3	48.9	42.4	32.1	24.3	18.5	14.1	10.7
30	74.2	64.0	55.2	47.7	41.2	30.8	23.1	17.4	13.1	9.9
31	73.5	63.0	54.1	46.5	40.0	29.6	22.0	16.4	12.3	9.2
32	72.7	62.1	53.1	45.4	38.8	28.5	21.0	15.5	11.5	8.5
33	72.0	61.2	52.0	44.3	37.7	27.4	20.0	14.6	10.7	7.9
34	71.3	60.3	51.0	43.2	36.6	26.4	19.0	13.8	10.0	7.3
35	70.6	59.4	50.0	42.1	35.5	25.3	18.1	13.0	9.4	6.8
36	69.9	58.5	49.0	41.1	34.5	24.4	17.3	12.3	8.8	6.3
37	69.2	57.6	48.1	40.1	33.5	23.4	16.4	11.6	8.2	5.8
38	68.5	56.8	47.1	39.1	32.5	22.5	15.7	10.9	7.6	5.4
39	67.8	56.0	46.2	38.2	31.6	21.7	14.9	10.3	7.1	5.0
40	67.2	55.1	45.3	37.2	30.7	20.8	14.2	9.7	6.7	4.6

TABLE 3—PRESENT VALUE OF £1

Present value of £1 payable (or receivable) at end of any period 1 to 40, discounted at interest rates from 1% to 30% per period. Values shown in pence.

Period	9% p	10% p	11% p	12% p	13% p	14% p	15% p	20% p	25% p	30% p
1	91.7	90.9	90.1	89.3	88.5	87.7	87.0	83.3	80.0	76.9
2	84.2	82.6	81.2	79.7	78.3	76.9	75.6	69.4	64.0	59.2
3	77.2	75.1	73.1	71.2	69.3	67.5	65.8	57.9	51.2	45.5
4	70.8	68.3	65.9	63.6	61.3	59.2	57.2	48.2	41.0	35.0
5	65.0	62.1	59.3	56.7	54.3	51.9	49.7	40.2	32.8	26.9
6	59.6	56.4	53.5	50.7	48.0	45.6	43.2	33.5	26.2	20.7
7	54.7	51.3	48.2	45.2	42.5	40.0	37.6	27.9	21.0	15.9
8	50.2	46.7	43.4	40.4	37.6	35.1	32.7	23.3	16.8	12.3
9	46.0	42.4	39.1	36.1	33.3	30.8	28.4	19.4	13.4	9.4
10	42.2	38.6	35.2	32.2	29.5	27.0	24.7	16.2	10.7	7.3
11	38.8	35.0	31.7	28.7	26.1	23.7	21.5	13.5	8.6	5.6
12	35.6	31.9	28.6	25.7	23.1	20.8	18.7	11.2	6.9	4.3
13	32.6	29.0	25.8	22.9	20.4	18.2	16.3	9.3	5.5	3.3
14	29.9	26.3	23.2	20.5	18.1	16.0	14.1	7.8	4.4	2.5
15	27.5	23.9	20.9	18.3	16.0	14.0	12.3	6.5	3.5	2.0
16	25.2	21.8	18.8	16.3	14.1	12.3	10.7	5.4	2.8	1.5
17	23.1	19.8	17.0	14.6	12.5	10.8	9.3	4.5	2.3	1.2
18	21.2	18.0	15.3	13.0	11.1	9.5	8.1	3.8	1.8	0.9
19	19.4	16.4	13.8	11.6	9.8	8.3	7.0	3.1	1.4	0.7
20	17.8	14.9	12.4	10.4	8.7	7.3	6.1	2.6	1.2	0.5

Period	9% p	10% p	11% p	12% p	13% p	14% p	15% p	20% p	25% p	30% p
21	16.4	13.5	11.2	9.3	7.7	6.4	5.3	2.2	0.9	0.4
22	15.0	12.3	10.1	8.3	6.8	5.6	4.6	1.8	0.7	0.3
23	13.8	11.2	9.1	7.4	6.0	4.9	4.0	1.5	0.6	0.2
24	12.6	10.2	8.2	6.6	5.3	4.3	3.5	1.3	0.5	0.2
25	11.6	9.2	7.4	5.9	4.7	3.8	3.0	1.0	0.4	0.1
26	10.6	8.4	6.6	5.3	4.2	3.3	2.6	0.9	0.3	0.1
27	9.8	7.6	6.0	4.7	3.7	2.9	2.3	0.7	0.2	0.1
28	9.0	6.9	5.4	4.2	3.3	2.6	2.0	0.6	0.2	0.1
29	8.2	6.3	4.8	3.7	2.9	2.2	1.7	0.5	0.2	0.1
30	7.5	5.7	4.4	3.3	2.6	2.0	1.5	0.4	0.1	
31	6.9	5.2	3.9	3.0	2.3	1.7	1.3	0.4	0.1	
32	6.3	4.7	3.5	2.7	2.0	1.5	1.1	0.3	0.1	
33	5.8	4.3	3.2	2.4	1.8	1.3	1.0	0.2	0.1	
34	5.3	3.9	2.9	2.1	1.6	1.2	0.9	0.2	0.1	
35	4.9	3.6	2.6	1.9	1.4	1.0	0.8	0.2	0.1	
36	4.5	3.2	2.3	1.7	1.2	0.9	0.7	0.1		
37	4.1	2.9	2.1	1.5	1.1	0.8	0.6	0.1		
38	3.8	2.7	1.9	1.3	1.0	0.7	0.5	0.1		
39	3.5	2.4	1.7	1.2	0.9	0.6	0.4	0.1		
40	3.2	2.2	1.5	1.1	0.8	0.5	0.4	0.1		

TABLE 4—PRESENT VALUE OF £1 PAYABLE AT REGULAR INTERVALS ("YEARS PURCHASE")

Present value of £1 payable (or receivable) regularly at end of each period (i.e. weekly, monthly, or yearly) discounted at interest rates from 1% to 30% per period.

Period	1% £	1.5% £	2% £	2.5% £	3% £	4% £	5% £	6% £	7% £	8% £
1	0.99	0.99	0.98	0.98	0.97	0.96	0.95	0.94	0.93	0.93
2	1.97	1.96	1.94	1.93	1.91	1.89	1.86	1.83	1.81	1.78
3	2.94	2.91	2.88	2.86	2.83	2.78	2.72	2.67	2.62	2.58
4	3.90	3.85	3.81	3.76	3.72	3.63	3.55	3.47	3.39	3.31
5	4.85	4.78	4.71	4.65	4.58	4.45	4.33	4.21	4.10	3.99
6	5.80	5.70	5.60	5.51	5.42	5.24	5.08	4.92	4.77	4.62
7	6.73	6.60	6.47	6.35	6.23	6.00	5.79	5.58	5.39	5.21
8	7.65	7.49	7.33	7.17	7.02	6.73	6.46	6.21	5.97	5.75
9	8.57	8.36	8.16	7.97	7.79	7.44	7.11	6.80	6.52	6.25
10	9.47	9.22	8.98	8.75	8.53	8.11	7.72	7.36	7.02	6.71
11	10.37	10.07	9.79	9.51	9.25	8.76	8.31	7.89	7.50	7.14
12	11.26	10.91	10.58	10.26	9.95	9.39	8.86	8.38	7.94	7.54
13	12.13	11.73	11.35	10.98	10.63	9.99	9.39	8.85	8.36	7.90
14	13.00	12.54	12.11	11.69	11.30	10.56	9.90	9.29	8.75	8.24
15	13.87	13.34	12.85	12.38	11.94	11.12	10.38	9.71	9.11	8.56
16	14.72	14.13	13.58	13.06	12.56	11.65	10.84	10.11	9.45	8.85
17	15.56	14.91	14.29	13.71	13.17	12.17	11.27	10.48	9.76	9.12
18	16.40	15.67	14.99	14.35	13.75	12.66	11.69	10.83	10.06	9.37
19	17.23	16.43	15.68	14.98	14.32	13.13	12.09	11.16	10.34	9.60
20	18.05	17.17	16.35	15.59	14.88	13.59	12.46	11.47	10.59	9.82

Period	1% £	1.5% £	2% £	2.5% £	3% £	4% £	5% £	6% £	7% £	8% £
21	18.86	17.90	17.01	16.18	15.42	14.03	12.82	11.76	10.84	10.02
22	19.66	18.62	17.66	16.77	15.94	14.45	13.16	12.04	11.06	10.20
23	20.46	19.33	18.29	17.33	16.44	14.86	13.49	12.30	11.27	10.37
24	21.24	20.03	18.91	17.88	16.94	15.25	13.80	12.55	11.47	10.53
25	22.02	20.72	19.52	18.42	17.41	15.62	14.09	12.78	11.65	10.67
26	22.80	21.40	20.12	18.95	17.88	15.98	14.38	13.00	11.83	10.81
27	23.56	22.07	20.71	19.46	18.33	16.33	14.64	13.21	11.99	10.94
28	24.32	22.73	21.28	19.96	18.76	16.66	14.90	13.41	12.14	11.05
29	25.07	23.38	21.84	20.45	19.19	16.98	15.14	13.59	12.28	11.16
30	25.81	24.02	22.40	20.93	19.60	17.29	15.37	13.76	12.41	11.26
31	26.54	24.65	22.94	21.40	20.00	17.59	15.59	13.93	12.53	11.35
32	27.27	25.27	23.47	21.85	20.39	17.87	15.80	14.08	12.65	11.43
33	27.99	25.88	23.99	22.29	20.77	18.15	16.00	14.23	12.75	11.51
34	28.70	26.48	24.50	22.72	21.13	18.41	16.19	14.37	12.85	11.59
35	29.41	27.08	25.00	23.15	21.49	18.66	16.37	14.50	12.95	11.65
36	30.11	27.66	25.49	23.56	21.83	18.91	16.55	14.62	13.04	11.72
37	30.80	28.24	25.97	23.96	22.17	19.14	16.71	14.74	13.12	11.78
38	31.48	28.81	26.44	24.35	22.49	19.37	16.87	14.85	13.19	11.83
39	32.16	29.36	26.90	24.73	22.81	19.58	17.02	14.95	13.26	11.88
40	32.83	29.92	27.36	25.10	23.11	19.79	17.16	15.05	13.33	11.92

TABLE 4—PRESENT VALUE OF £1 PAYABLE AT REGULAR INTERVALS ("YEARS PURCHASE")

Present value of £1 payable (or receivable) regularly at end of each period (i.e. weekly, monthly, or yearly) discounted at interest rates from 1% to 30% per period.

Period	9% £	10% £	11% £	12% £	13% £	14% £	15% £	20% £	25% £	30% £
1	0.92	0.91	0.90	0.89	0.88	0.88	0.87	0.83	0.80	0.77
2	1.76	1.74	1.71	1.69	1.67	1.65	1.63	1.53	1.44	1.36
3	2.53	2.49	2.44	2.40	2.36	2.32	2.28	2.11	1.95	1.82
4	3.24	3.17	3.10	3.04	2.97	2.91	2.85	2.59	2.36	2.17
5	3.89	3.79	3.70	3.60	3.52	3.43	3.35	2.99	2.69	2.44
6	4.49	4.36	4.23	4.11	4.00	3.89	3.78	3.33	2.95	2.64
7	5.03	4.87	4.71	4.56	4.42	4.29	4.16	3.60	3.16	2.80
8	5.53	5.33	5.15	4.97	4.80	4.64	4.49	3.84	3.33	2.92
9	6.00	5.76	5.54	5.33	5.13	4.95	4.77	4.03	3.46	3.02
10	6.42	6.14	5.89	5.65	5.43	5.22	5.02	4.19	3.57	3.09
11	6.81	6.50	6.21	5.94	5.69	5.45	5.23	4.33	3.66	3.15
12	7.16	6.81	6.49	6.19	5.92	5.66	5.42	4.44	3.73	3.19
13	7.49	7.10	6.75	6.42	6.12	5.84	5.58	4.53	3.78	3.22
14	7.79	7.37	6.98	6.63	6.30	6.00	5.72	4.61	3.82	3.25
15	8.06	7.61	7.19	6.81	6.46	6.14	5.85	4.68	3.86	3.27
16	8.31	7.82	7.38	6.97	6.60	6.27	5.95	4.73	3.89	3.28
17	8.54	8.02	7.55	7.12	6.73	6.37	6.05	4.77	3.91	3.29
18	8.76	8.20	7.70	7.25	6.84	6.47	6.13	4.81	3.93	3.30
19	8.95	8.36	7.84	7.37	6.94	6.55	6.20	4.84	3.94	3.31
20	9.13	8.51	7.96	7.47	7.02	6.62	6.26	4.87	3.95	3.32

Period	9% £	10% £	11% £	12% £	13% £	14% £	15% £	20% £	25% £	30% £
21	9.29	8.65	8.08	7.56	7.10	6.69	6.31	4.89	3.96	3.32
22	9.44	8.77	8.18	7.64	7.17	6.74	6.36	4.91	3.97	3.32
23	9.58	8.88	8.27	7.72	7.23	6.79	6.40	4.92	3.98	3.33
24	9.71	8.98	8.35	7.78	7.28	6.84	6.43	4.94	3.98	3.33
25	9.82	9.08	8.42	7.84	7.33	6.87	6.46	4.95	3.98	3.33
26	9.93	9.16	8.49	7.90	7.37	6.91	6.49	4.96	3.99	3.33
27	10.03	9.24	8.55	7.94	7.41	6.94	6.51	4.96	3.99	3.33
28	10.12	9.31	8.60	7.98	7.44	6.96	6.53	4.97	3.99	3.33
29	10.20	9.37	8.65	8.02	7.47	6.98	6.55	4.97	3.99	3.33
30	10.27	9.43	8.69	8.06	7.50	7.00	6.57	4.98	4.00	3.33
31	10.34	9.48	8.73	8.08	7.52	7.02	6.58	4.98	4.00	3.33
32	10.41	9.53	8.77	8.11	7.54	7.03	6.59	4.99	4.00	3.33
33	10.46	9.57	8.80	8.14	7.56	7.05	6.60	4.99	4.00	
34	10.52	9.61	8.83	8.16	7.57	7.06	6.61	4.99	4.00	
35	10.57	9.64	8.86	8.18	7.59	7.07	6.62	4.99	4.00	
36	10.61	9.68	8.88	8.19	7.60	7.08	6.62	4.99	4.00	
37	10.65	9.71	8.90	8.21	7.61	7.09	6.63	4.99	4.00	
38	10.69	9.73	8.92	8.22	7.62	7.09	6.63	5.00	4.00	
39	10.73	9.76	8.94	8.23	7.63	7.10	6.64	5.00		
40	10.76	9.78	8.95	8.24	7.63	7.11	6.64	5.00		

TABLE 5—ANNUITY £1 WILL PURCHASE (ANNUAL EQUIVALENT)

Annual equivalent of £1 invested at the beginning of the period or the annuity purchased by a lump sum payment of £1 at rates of interest from 1% to 30% per period.

Period	1% £	1.5% £	2% £	2.5% £	3% £	4% £	5% £	6% £	7% £	8% £
1	1.010	1.015	1.020	1.025	1.030	1.040	1.050	1.060	1.070	1.080
2	0.508	0.511	0.515	0.519	0.523	0.530	0.538	0.545	0.553	0.561
3	0.340	0.343	0.347	0.350	0.354	0.360	0.367	0.374	0.381	0.388
4	0.256	0.259	0.263	0.266	0.269	0.275	0.282	0.289	0.295	0.302
5	0.206	0.209	0.212	0.215	0.218	0.225	0.231	0.237	0.244	0.250
6	0.173	0.176	0.179	0.182	0.185	0.191	0.197	0.203	0.210	0.216
7	0.149	0.152	0.155	0.157	0.161	0.167	0.173	0.179	0.186	0.192
8	0.131	0.134	0.137	0.139	0.142	0.149	0.155	0.161	0.167	0.174
9	0.117	0.120	0.123	0.125	0.128	0.134	0.141	0.147	0.153	0.160
10	0.106	0.108	0.111	0.114	0.117	0.123	0.130	0.136	0.142	0.149
11	0.096	0.099	0.102	0.105	0.108	0.114	0.120	0.127	0.133	0.140
12	0.089	0.092	0.095	0.097	0.100	0.107	0.113	0.119	0.126	0.133
13	0.082	0.085	0.088	0.091	0.094	0.100	0.106	0.113	0.120	0.127
14	0.077	0.080	0.083	0.086	0.089	0.095	0.101	0.108	0.114	0.121
15	0.072	0.075	0.078	0.081	0.084	0.090	0.096	0.103	0.110	0.117
16	0.068	0.071	0.074	0.077	0.080	0.086	0.092	0.099	0.106	0.113
17	0.064	0.067	0.070	0.073	0.076	0.082	0.089	0.095	0.102	0.110
18	0.061	0.064	0.067	0.070	0.073	0.079	0.086	0.092	0.099	0.107
19	0.058	0.061	0.064	0.067	0.070	0.076	0.083	0.090	0.097	0.104
20	0.055	0.058	0.061	0.064	0.067	0.074	0.080	0.087	0.094	0.102

Period	1% £	1.5% £	2% £	2.5% £	3% £	4% £	5% £	6% £	7% £	8% £
21	0.053	0.056	0.059	0.062	0.065	0.071	0.078	0.085	0.092	0.100
22	0.051	0.054	0.057	0.060	0.063	0.069	0.076	0.083	0.090	0.098
23	0.049	0.052	0.055	0.058	0.061	0.067	0.074	0.081	0.089	0.096
24	0.047	0.050	0.053	0.056	0.059	0.066	0.072	0.080	0.087	0.095
25	0.045	0.048	0.051	0.054	0.057	0.064	0.071	0.078	0.086	0.094
26	0.044	0.047	0.050	0.053	0.056	0.063	0.070	0.077	0.085	0.093
27	0.042	0.045	0.048	0.051	0.055	0.061	0.068	0.076	0.083	0.091
28	0.041	0.044	0.047	0.050	0.053	0.060	0.067	0.075	0.082	0.090
29	0.040	0.043	0.046	0.049	0.052	0.059	0.066	0.074	0.081	0.090
30	0.039	0.042	0.045	0.048	0.051	0.058	0.065	0.073	0.081	0.089
31	0.038	0.041	0.044	0.047	0.050	0.057	0.064	0.072	0.080	0.088
32	0.037	0.040	0.043	0.046	0.049	0.056	0.063	0.071	0.079	0.087
33	0.036	0.039	0.042	0.045	0.048	0.055	0.062	0.070	0.078	0.087
34	0.035	0.038	0.041	0.044	0.047	0.054	0.062	0.070	0.078	0.086
35	0.034	0.037	0.040	0.043	0.047	0.054	0.061	0.069	0.077	0.086
36	0.033	0.036	0.039	0.042	0.046	0.053	0.060	0.068	0.077	0.085
37	0.032	0.035	0.039	0.042	0.045	0.052	0.060	0.068	0.076	0.085
38	0.032	0.035	0.038	0.041	0.044	0.052	0.059	0.067	0.076	0.085
39	0.031	0.034	0.037	0.040	0.044	0.051	0.059	0.067	0.075	0.084
40	0.030	0.033	0.037	0.040	0.043	0.051	0.058	0.066	0.075	0.084

TABLE 5—ANNUITY £1 WILL PURCHASE (ANNUAL EQUIVALENT)

Annual equivalent of £1 invested at the beginning of the period or the annuity purchased by a lump sum payment of £1 at rates of interest from 1% to 30% per period.

Period	9% £	10% £	11% £	12% £	13% £	14% £	15% £	20% £	25% £	30% £
1	1.090	1.100	1.110	1.120	1.130	1.140	1.150	1.200	1.250	1.300
2	0.568	0.576	0.584	0.592	0.599	0.607	0.615	0.655	0.694	0.735
3	0.395	0.402	0.409	0.416	0.424	0.431	0.438	0.475	0.512	0.551
4	0.309	0.315	0.322	0.329	0.336	0.343	0.350	0.386	0.423	0.462
5	0.257	0.264	0.271	0.277	0.284	0.291	0.298	0.334	0.372	0.411
6	0.233	0.230	0.236	0.243	0.250	0.257	0.264	0.301	0.339	0.378
7	0.199	0.205	0.212	0.219	0.226	0.233	0.240	0.277	0.316	0.357
8	0.181	0.187	0.194	0.201	0.208	0.216	0.223	0.261	0.300	0.342
9	0.167	0.174	0.181	0.188	0.195	0.202	0.210	0.248	0.289	0.331
10	0.156	0.163	0.170	0.177	0.184	0.192	0.199	0.239	0.280	0.323
11	0.147	0.154	0.161	0.168	0.176	0.183	0.191	0.231	0.273	0.318
12	0.140	0.147	0.154	0.161	0.169	0.177	0.184	0.225	0.268	0.313
13	0.134	0.141	0.148	0.156	0.163	0.171	0.179	0.221	0.265	0.310
14	0.128	0.136	0.143	0.151	0.159	0.167	0.175	0.217	0.262	0.308
15	0.124	0.131	0.139	0.147	0.155	0.163	0.171	0.214	0.259	0.306
16	0.120	0.128	0.136	0.143	0.151	0.160	0.168	0.211	0.257	0.305
17	0.117	0.125	0.132	0.140	0.149	0.157	0.165	0.209	0.256	0.304
18	0.114	0.122	0.130	0.138	0.146	0.155	0.163	0.208	0.255	0.303
19	0.112	0.120	0.128	0.136	0.144	0.153	0.161	0.206	0.254	0.302
20	0.110	0.117	0.126	0.134	0.142	0.151	0.160	0.205	0.253	0.302

Period	9% £	10% £	11% £	12% £	13% £	14% £	15% £	20% £	25% £	30% £
21	0.108	0.116	0.124	0.132	0.141	0.150	0.158	0.204	0.252	0.301
22	0.106	0.114	0.122	0.131	0.139	0.148	0.157	0.204	0.252	0.301
23	0.104	0.113	0.121	0.130	0.138	0.147	0.156	0.203	0.251	0.301
24	0.103	0.111	0.128	0.128	0.137	0.146	0.155	0.203	0.251	0.301
25	0.102	0.110	0.119	0.127	0.136	0.145	0.155	0.202	0.251	0.300
26	0.101	0.109	0.118	0.127	0.136	0.145	0.154	0.202	0.251	0.300
27	0.100	0.108	0.117	0.126	0.135	0.144	0.154	0.201	0.251	0.300
28	0.099	0.107	0.116	0.125	0.134	0.144	0.153	0.201	0.250	0.300
29	0.098	0.107	0.116	0.125	0.134	0.143	0.153	0.201	0.250	0.300
30	0.097	0.106	0.115	0.124	0.133	0.143	0.152	0.201	0.250	0.300
31	0.097	0.105	0.115	0.124	0.133	0.142	0.152	0.201	0.250	0.300
32	0.096	0.105	0.114	0.123	0.133	0.142	0.152	0.201	0.250	0.300
33	0.096	0.104	0.114	0.123	0.132	0.142	0.152	0.200	0.250	0.300
34	0.095	0.104	0.113	0.123	0.132	0.142	0.151	0.200	0.250	0.300
35	0.095	0.104	0.113	0.122	0.132	0.141	0.151	0.200	0.250	0.300
36	0.094	0.103	0.113	0.122	0.132	0.141	0.151	0.200	0.250	0.300
37	0.094	0.103	0.112	0.122	0.131	0.141	0.151	0.200	0.250	0.300
38	0.094	0.103	0.112	0.122	0.131	0.141	0.151	0.200	0.250	0.300
39	0.093	0.102	0.112	0.121	0.131	0.141	0.151	0.200	0.250	0.300
40	0.093	0.102	0.112	0.121	0.131	0.141	0.151	0.200	0.250	0.300

TABLE 6—SINKING FUND

Amount (in pence) which has to be invested regularly at the end of each period (i.e. weekly, monthly, or yearly) in order to accumulate to £1 by the end of the chosen term; at compound interest of from 0.096% to 12% per period.

Period	1%	1.5%	2%	3%	4%	5%	6%	8%	10%	12%
	p	p	p	p	p	p	p	p	p	p
2	49.8	49.6	49.5	49.3	49.0	48.8	48.5	48.1	47.6	47.2
3	33.0	32.8	32.7	32.4	32.0	31.7	31.4	30.8	30.2	29.6
4	24.6	24.4	24.3	23.9	23.5	23.2	22.9	22.2	21.5	20.9
5	19.6	19.4	19.2	18.8	18.5	18.1	17.7	17.0	16.4	15.7
6	16.3	16.1	15.9	15.5	15.1	14.7	14.3	13.6	13.0	12.3
7	13.9	13.7	13.5	13.1	12.7	12.3	11.9	11.2	10.5	9.9
8	12.1	11.9	11.7	11.2	10.9	10.5	10.1	9.4	8.7	8.1
9	10.7	10.5	10.3	9.8	9.4	9.1	8.7	8.0	7.4	6.8
10	9.6	9.3	9.1	8.7	8.3	8.0	7.6	6.9	6.3	5.7
11	8.6	8.4	8.2	7.8	7.4	7.0	6.7	6.0	5.4	4.8
12	7.9	7.7	7.5	7.0	6.7	6.3	5.9	5.3	4.7	4.1
13	7.2	7.0	6.8	6.4	6.0	5.6	5.3	4.7	4.1	3.6
14	6.7	6.5	6.3	5.9	5.5	5.1	4.8	4.1	3.6	3.1
15	6.2	6.0	5.8	5.4	5.0	4.6	4.3	3.7	3.1	2.7
16	5.8	5.6	5.4	5.0	4.6	4.2	3.9	3.3	2.8	2.3
17	5.4	5.2	5.0	4.6	4.2	3.9	3.5	3.0	2.5	2.0
18	5.1	4.9	4.7	4.3	3.9	3.6	3.2	2.7	2.2	1.8
19	4.8	4.6	4.4	4.0	3.6	3.3	3.0	2.4	2.0	1.6
20	4.5	4.3	4.1	3.7	3.4	3.0	2.7	2.2	1.7	1.4

Period	1%	1.5%	2%	3%	4%	5%	6%	8%	10%	12%
	p	p	p	p	p	p	p	p	p	p
21	4.3	4.1	3.9	3.5	3.1	2.8	2.5	2.0	1.6	1.2
22	4.1	3.9	3.7	3.3	2.9	2.6	2.3	1.8	1.4	1.1
23	3.9	3.7	3.5	3.1	2.7	2.4	2.1	1.6	1.3	1.0
24	3.7	3.5	3.3	2.9	2.6	2.2	2.0	1.5	1.1	0.8
25	3.5	3.3	3.1	2.7	2.4	2.1	1.8	1.4	1.0	0.7
26	3.4	3.2	3.0	2.6	2.3	2.0	1.7	1.3	0.9	0.7
27	3.2	3.0	2.8	2.5	2.1	1.8	1.6	1.1	0.8	0.6
28	3.1	2.9	2.7	2.3	2.0	1.7	1.5	1.0	0.7	0.5
29	3.0	2.8	2.6	2.2	1.9	1.6	1.4	1.0	0.7	0.5
30	2.9	2.7	2.5	2.1	1.8	1.5	1.3	0.9	0.6	0.4
31	2.8	2.6	2.4	2.0	1.7	1.4	1.2	0.8	0.5	0.4
32	2.7	2.5	2.3	1.9	1.6	1.3	1.1	0.7	0.5	0.3
33	2.6	2.4	2.2	1.8	1.5	1.2	1.0	0.7	0.4	0.3
34	2.5	2.3	2.1	1.7	1.4	1.2	1.0	0.6	0.4	0.3
35	2.4	2.2	2.0	1.7	1.4	1.1	0.9	0.6	0.4	0.2
36	2.3	2.1	1.9	1.6	1.3	1.0	0.8	0.5	0.3	0.2
37	2.2	2.0	1.9	1.5	1.2	1.0	0.8	0.5	0.3	0.2
38	2.2	2.0	1.8	1.4	1.2	0.9	0.7	0.5	0.3	0.2
39	2.1	1.9	1.7	1.4	1.1	0.9	0.7	0.4	0.2	0.1
40	2.0	1.8	1.7	1.3	1.1	0.8	0.6	0.4	0.2	0.1

Index